COUNSELS ON
Diet & Foods

A Compilation From the Writings of

ELLEN G. WHITE

*"Blessed art thou, O land, when . . . thy
princes eat in due season, for strength,
and not for drunkenness!"*
Eccl. 10:17

REVIEW AND HERALD® PUBLISHING ASSOCIATION
Since 1861 | www.reviewandherald.com

Printed in U.S.A.

ISBN 978-0-8280-2060-2

YOU SHOULD READ THIS
How This Book Came to Be

Decades before many physiologists were concerned with the close relationship between diet and health, Ellen G. White in her writings clearly pointed out the connection between the food we eat and our physical and spiritual welfare. In her discourses and writings from 1863 onward, she discussed frequently the importance of diet and adequate nutrition. Her counsels, as preserved in pamphlets and books, in the journals of the denomination, and in personal testimonies, have exerted a strong influence on the dietetic habits of Seventh-day Adventists, and indirectly have left their impress upon the general public.

Mrs. White's writings regarding foods and a healthful diet were drawn together in 1926 in a topically arranged work designed to serve primarily as a textbook for students of dietetics at the College of Medical Evangelists at Loma Linda. This initial printing, titled *Testimony Studies on Diet and Foods,* was soon exhausted.

A new and enlarged volume, titled *Counsels on Diet and Foods,* appeared in 1938. It was referred to as a "second edition," and was prepared under the direction of the Board of Trustees of the Ellen G. White Estate. A third edition, printed in a smaller page size to conform to the requirements of the Christian Home Library series, was published in 1946. The present edition is the fourth, and involves no change in text or pagination.

This Is a Unique Compilation

In assembling the materials comprising *Counsels on Diet and Foods,* an effort was made to include the full range of instruction on the subject from Mrs. White's pen. The resulting compilation is unique among the Ellen G. White books, for it presents the counsels clustered topically under a general heading, with no attempt to provide a continuity in reading.

Each section contains the E. G. White materials that, assembled, make a representative presentation of the topic dealt with. Nothing that would make a substantial contribution has been ignored. Often in the original sources many phases of health instruction are treated together in one paragraph. To give all the context in such cases would have involved considerable repetition. Through the use of cross references such repetition is minimized.

While the limitations of space and the effort to avoid repetition have made it inadvisable to include every statement on the more general phases of the diet question, a complete and comprehensive presentation of the E. G. White teachings has been given.

Peril of Taking a Part for the Whole

The fact that this volume is constructed somewhat like an encyclopedia, isolating the major presentations and grouping them by topic, makes it a convenient reference work. But the encyclopedia design also makes the book one that may easily be misused. To gain the author's intent and the full impact of all her teachings, it is imperative that the book be studied as a whole.

The reader should bear in mind that a single Ellen White statement on some phase of the subject of nutrition may come far short of expressing her full intent and understanding of the nutritional needs of the body. For example, in a sentence appearing on page 314 of this book, taken from *Testimonies,* volume 2, page 352, she says: "Grains and fruits prepared free from grease, and in as natural a condition as possible, should be the food for the tables of all who claim to be preparing for translation." In the light of other of her statements, clearly it was not Mrs. White's intent to teach that those preparing for translation should reduce their diet to simply "grains and fruits." Penned in 1869 in the setting of counsel against the use of meat, this statement seems to make "grains and fruits" stand for the nonmeat diet. The statement does not mention nuts, vegetables, or dairy products, all of which Ellen White recognized as important to a balanced nutritional program.

Another statement on the same page (314), written some twenty years later, in delineating a diet intended to impart nourishment and give endurance and vigor of intellect, mentions "fruit, grains, and vegetables" prepared with "milk or cream." Nuts are not mentioned. Across the page in another paragraph written in 1905, "grains, nuts, vegetables, and fruits" are listed as taking the place of meat. In this statement milk is not mentioned. Yet milk is included in her 1909 statement that appears on page 355: "Vegetables should be made palatable with a little milk or cream, or something equivalent. . . . Some, in abstaining from milk, eggs, and butter, have failed to supply the system with proper nourishment, and as a consequence have become weak and unable to work. Thus health reform is brought into disrepute."

There are a number of other instances similar to those cited above where Ellen White does not in a given statement enumerate all the elements of an adequate diet. Care must be exercised to get her complete thought on each subject. An isolated statement should not be used by itself, lest the part be taken for the whole.

A Call for Everyone to Study

Ellen White did not intend that her writings along nutritional lines should exclude the need for earnest study to find the best and most agreeable diet, taking advantage of a growing knowledge, and the experience and investigation of others. She wrote:

"To keep the body in a healthy condition, in order that all parts of the living machinery may act harmoniously, should be the study of our life."—Page 18.

"It is plainly our duty to give these [nature's] laws careful study. We should study their requirements in regard to our own bodies, and conform to them. Ignorance in these things is sin."—*Ibid.*

Clearly Mrs. White felt that each person should become well informed, taking advantage of the advancements of science in nutritional investigations, so long as the conclusions harmonize with the counsels given through inspiration.

The Hazards of Extremes

Ellen White was not slow to point out the hazards of extremes, or inattention, or laxity in providing an adequate diet for the family. This fact is illustrated by the statement that the mother "by ill-prepared, unwholesome food" might actually "hinder and even ruin both the adult's usefulness and the child's development" (p. 476). In the same statement she called for "providing food adapted to the needs of the body, and at the same time inviting and palatable."

While the reasons for including some dairy products in a balanced, adequate diet were not fully understood, Ellen White spoke in favor of them, and even cautioned against eliminating them. Today in the light of the knowledge that certain minute nutrients are vital to body functions, we have a better understanding. Some of these nutrients, while apparently not present in an all-vegetable diet, are available in adequate amounts in a lacto-ovo-vegetarian diet. This is particularly important to children whose proper development Ellen White stated might be hindered by "ill-prepared unwholesome food."

Near the turn of the century Ellen White began to write that because of accumulating disease in the animal kingdom all animal foods, including milk, will in time have to be given up (see pp. 356, 357); yet at the same time she repeatedly cautioned against premature steps in this direction and in 1909 declared that the time will come when such *may* be necessary, but urged against creating perplexity by "premature and extreme restrictions." She counseled that we "wait until the circumstances demand it, and the Lord prepares the way for it" (pp. 355-359).

It was the lacto-ovo-vegetarian diet that sustained Ellen White in active service well into her eighty-eighth year.

Employ Sound Principles in Study

Certain sound principles must ever be applied in the study of the dietary counsels found in this book. All the instruction, as a broad, consistent, well-balanced whole, should be studied with an open mind. Care should be taken to read the entire statement on a given topic. Then, to gain the full intent of the author, statement should be put with statement. If one statement does not seem to accord with another, the student would do well to trace one, or both, to the original settings.

The student should also follow Ellen White's example in recognizing three basic principles as enumerated on page 481:

1. "The diet reform should be progressive."—MH 320.

2. "We do not mark out any precise line to be followed in diet."—9T 159.

3. "I make myself a criterion for no one else."—Letter 45, 1903.

A Recommendation for Health Reform

True diet reform will recommend itself because of its good sense. Its fruitage will be seen in good health, strength, a sweet breath, and a sense of well-being. Even the spiritual life may be aided by good health habits. It has been gratifying to witness, through the onward march of scientific study, a full substantiation of many great principles and even minute points of instruction revealed to Seventh-day Adventists through Ellen White's inspired pen.

That this volume may aid its readers in obtaining better health, both physical and spiritual, is our sincere wish.

THE TRUSTEES OF THE ELLEN G. WHITE ESTATE
Washington, D.C.
September 17, 1976

Contents by Sections

Dates of Writing or First Publication

As an aid to the student, the date of writing or of first publication of each selection is indicated in connection with the source reference. Where articles have been drawn from published volumes, the date of publication appears preceding the reference. In the case of the matter drawn from the periodical articles and the manuscript files, the year of writing or of first publication forms a part of the source reference.

In a number of instances the articles drawn from later books, such as "Counsels on Health," appeared first in works now out of print. The reference to the current work is given, but the information as to the first publication of the article is noted in parentheses in connection with the source reference. COMPILERS.

Key to Credits and Abbreviations

THE articles comprising this book have been gathered from the Ellen G. White writings as they appear in current books, books now out of print, periodical articles, pamphlets, and the E. G. White manuscript files. In each case the source of the selection is given. The following abbreviations to sources have been used:

C.O.L.—"Christ's Object Lessons"
C.T.B.H.—"Christian Temperance and Bible Hygiene"*
C.H.—"Counsels on Health"
C.T.—"Counsels to Teachers"
D.A.—"The Desire of Ages"
Ed.—"Education"
E. from U.T.—Extracts from Unpublished Testimonies in Regard to Flesh Foods*
F.E.—"Fundamentals of Christian Education"
G.W.—"Gospel Workers"
H. to L.—"How to Live"* (Six Pamphlets)
Letter—Statement from E. G. White manuscript files †
L. & T.—"Life and Teachings of Ellen G. White"
MS.—Statement from the E. G. White manuscript files †
M.H.—"Ministry of Healing"
M.M.—"Medical Ministry"
R. & H.—*Review and Herald**
Sp. Gifts IV—"Spiritual Gifts," Vol. IV*
        (Also referred to as "Facts of Faith," Vol. II)
1T—"Testimonies for the Church," Vol. 1
Y.I.—*Youth's Instructor**

————————
* Out of print.
† The source of articles selected from the manuscript files is indicated by the use of the file number of the original manuscripts as they appear in the Ellen G. White files in the White Estate Office, such as *Letter 3, 1884,* and *MS 49, 1908.*

SECTION I

Reasons for Reform

Quotations in Section I

Reasons for Reform

For the Glory of God

[C.T.B.H. 41, 42] (1890) C.H. 107, 108

1. ONLY one lease of life is granted us; and the inquiry with every one should be, "How can I invest my powers so that they may yield the greatest profit? How can I do most for the glory of God and the benefit of my fellow men?" For life is valuable only as it is used for the attainment of these ends.

Our first duty toward God and our fellow beings is that of self-development. Every faculty with which the Creator has endowed us should be cultivated to the highest degree of perfection, that we may be able to do the greatest amount of good of which we are capable. Hence that time is spent to good account which is used in the establishment and preservation of physical and mental health. We cannot afford to dwarf or cripple any function of body or mind. As surely as we do this, we must suffer the consequences.

CHOICE OF LIFE OR DEATH

Every man has the opportunity, to a great extent, of making himself whatever he chooses to be. The blessings of this life, and also of the immortal state, are within his reach. He may build up a character of solid worth, gaining new strength at every step. He may advance daily in knowledge and wisdom, conscious of new delights as he progresses, adding virtue to virtue, grace to grace. His faculties will improve by use; the more wisdom he gains, the greater will be his capacity for acquiring. His intelligence, knowledge, and virtue will thus develop into greater strength and more perfect symmetry.

On the other hand, he may allow his powers to rust out for want of use, or to be perverted through evil habits, lack of self-control, or moral and religious stamina. His course then tends downward; he is disobedient to the law of God and

15

to the laws of health. Appetite conquers him; inclination carries him away. It is easier for him to allow the powers of evil, which are always active, to drag him backward, than to struggle against them, and go forward. Dissipation, disease, and death follow. This is the history of many lives that might have been useful in the cause of God and humanity.

Seek for Perfection

(1905) M.H. 114, 115

2. God desires us to reach the standard of perfection made possible for us by the gift of Christ. He calls upon us to make our choice on the right side, to connect with heavenly agencies, to adopt principles that will restore in us the divine image. In His written word and in the great book of nature He has revealed the principles of life. It is our work to obtain a knowledge of these principles, and by obedience to cooperate with Him in restoring health to the body as well as to the soul.

Letter 73a, 1896

3. The living organism is God's property. It belongs to Him by creation and by redemption; and by a misuse of any of our powers we rob God of the honor due to Him.

A Question of Obedience

MS 49, 1897

4. The obligations we owe to God in presenting to Him clean, pure, healthy bodies are not comprehended.

Letter 120, 1901

5. A failure to care for the living machinery is an insult to the Creator. There are divinely appointed rules which if observed will keep human beings from disease and premature death.

R. & H., May 8, 1883

6. One reason why we do not enjoy more of the blessing of the Lord is, we do not heed the light which He has been pleased to give us in regard to the laws of life and health.

(1900) C.O.L. 347, 348

7. God is as truly the author of physical laws as He is author of the moral law. His law is written with His own finger upon every nerve, every muscle, every faculty, which has been entrusted to man.

MS 3, 1897

8. The Creator of man has arranged the living machinery of our bodies. Every function is wonderfully and wisely made. And God pledged Himself to keep this human machinery in healthful action if the human agent will obey His laws and cooperate with God. Every law governing the human machinery is to be considered just as truly divine in origin, in character, and in importance as the word of God. Every careless, inattentive action, any abuse put upon the Lord's wonderful mechanism, by disregarding His specified laws in the human habitation, is a violation of God's law. We may behold and admire the work of God in the natural world, but the human habitation is the most wonderful.

[Sin of taking a course which needlessly expends vitality or beclouds the brain—194]

(1890) C.T.B.H. 53

9. It is as truly a sin to violate the laws of our being as it is to break the ten commandments. To do either is to break God's laws. Those who transgress the law of God in their physical organism, will be inclined to violate the law of God spoken from Sinai.

[See also 63]

Our Saviour warned His disciples that just prior to His second coming a state of things would exist very similar to that which preceded the flood. Eating and drinking would be carried to excess, and the world would be given up to pleasure. This state of things does exist at the present time. The world is largely given up to the indulgence of appetite; and the disposition to follow worldly customs will bring us into bondage to perverted habits,—habits that will make us more and more like the doomed inhabitants of Sodom. I have wondered that the inhabitants of the earth were not destroyed, like the people of Sodom and Gomorrah. I see reason enough for the present state of degeneracy and mortality in the world. Blind passion controls reason, and every high consideration is, with many, sacrificed to lust.

To keep the body in a healthy condition, in order that all parts of the living machinery may act harmoniously, should be a study of our life. The children of God cannot glorify Him with sickly bodies or dwarfed minds. Those who indulge in any species of intemperance, either in eating or drinking, waste their physical energies and weaken moral power.

(1900) 6T 369, 370

10. Since the laws of nature are the laws of God, it is plainly our duty to give these laws careful study. We should study their requirements in regard to our own bodies, and conform to them. Ignorance in these things is sin.

[Willful ignorance increases sin—53]

"Know ye not that your bodies are the members of Christ?" "What! know ye not that your body is the temple of the Holy Ghost which is in you, which ye have of God, and ye are not your own? For ye are bought with a price; therefore glorify God in your body and in your spirit, which are God's." 1 Cor. 6:15, 19, 20. Our bodies are Christ's purchased property, and we are not at liberty to do with them as we please. Man has done this. He has treated his body as if its laws had no penalty. Through perverted appetite its organs and powers have become enfeebled, diseased, and crippled. And these results which Satan has brought about by his own specious temptations, he uses to taunt God with. He presents before God the human body that Christ has purchased as His property; and what an unsightly representation of his Maker man is! Because man has sinned against his body, and has corrupted his ways, God is dishonored.

When men and women are truly converted, they will conscientiously regard the laws of life that God has established in their being, thus seeking to avoid physical, mental, and moral feebleness. Obedience to these laws must be made a matter of personal duty. We ourselves must suffer the ills of violated law. We must answer to God for our habits and practices. Therefore, the question for us is not, "What will the world say?" but, "How shall I, claiming to be a Christian, treat the habitation God has given me? Shall I work for my highest temporal and spiritual good by keeping my body as a temple for the indwelling of the Holy Spirit, or shall I sacrifice myself to the world's ideas and practices?"

Penalty for Ignorance

Health Reformer, October, 1866

11. God has formed laws which govern our constitutions, and these laws which He has placed in our being are divine, and for every transgression there is affixed a penalty, which must sooner or later be realized. The majority of diseases which the human family have been and still are suffering under, they have created by ignorance of their own organic laws. They seem indifferent in regard to the matter of health, and work perseveringly to tear themselves to pieces, and when broken down and debilitated in body and mind, send for the doctor and drug themselves to death.

Not Always Ignorant

(1900) 6T 372

12. When persons are spoken to on the subject of health, they often say, "We know a great deal better than we do." They do not realize that they are accountable for every ray of light in regard to their physical well-being, and that their every habit is open to the inspection of God. Physical life is not to be treated in a haphazard manner. Every organ, every fiber of the being, is to be sacredly guarded from harmful practices.

Responsibility for Light

Good Health, November, 1880

13. At the time the light of health reform dawned upon us, and since that time, the questions have come home every day, "Am I practicing true temperance in all things?" "Is my diet such as will bring me in a position where I can accomplish the greatest amount of good?" If we cannot

answer these questions in the affirmative, we stand condemned before God, for He will hold us all responsible for the light which has shone upon our path. The time of ignorance God winked at, but as fast as light shines upon us, He requires us to change our health-destroying habits, and place ourselves in a right relation to physical laws.

(1890) C.T.B.H. 150

14. Health is a treasure. Of all temporal possessions it is the most precious. Wealth, learning, and honor are dearly purchased at the loss of the vigor of health. None of these can secure happiness, if health is lacking. It is a terrible sin to abuse the health that God has given us; such abuses enfeeble us for life, and make us losers, even if we gain by such means any amount of education.

[Examples of suffering due to disregarding light—119, 204]

(1890) C.T.B.H. 151

15. God has bountifully provided for the sustenance and happiness of all His creatures; if His laws were never violated, if all acted in harmony with the divine will, health, peace, and happiness, instead of misery and continual evil, would be the result.

Health Reformer, August, 1866

16. A careful conformity to the laws God has implanted in our being, will ensure health, and there will not be a breaking down of the constitution.

[Health reform the Lord's means of lessening suffering—788]

An Offering Without Blemish

(1890) C.T.B.H. 15

17. In the ancient Jewish service it was required that every sacrifice should be without blemish. In the text we are told to present our bodies a living sacrifice, holy, acceptable unto God, which is our reasonable service. We are God's workmanship. The psalmist, meditating upon the marvelous work of God in the human frame, exclaimed, "I am fearfully and wonderfully made." There are many who are educated in the sciences and are familiar with the theory of the truth, who do not understand the laws that govern their

own being. God has given us faculties and talents; and it is our duty, as His sons and daughters, to make the best use of them. If we weaken these powers of mind or body by wrong habits or indulgence of perverted appetite, it will be impossible for us to honor God as we should.

[C.T.B.H. 52, 53] (1890) C.H. 121

18. God requires the body to be rendered a living sacrifice to Him, not a dead or a dying sacrifice. The offerings of the ancient Hebrews were to be without blemish, and will it be pleasing to God to accept a human offering that is filled with disease and corruption? He tells us that our body is the temple of the Holy Ghost; and He requires us to take care of this temple, that it may be a fit habitation for His Spirit. The apostle Paul gives us this admonition: "Ye are not your own; for ye are bought with a price; therefore, glorify God in your body and in your spirit, which are God's." All should be very careful to preserve the body in the best condition of health, that they may render to God perfect service, and do their duty in the family and in society.

A Pitiful Offering

(1872) 3T 164, 165

19. Knowledge must be gained in regard to how to eat, and drink, and dress so as to preserve health. Sickness is caused by violating the laws of health; it is the result of violating nature's law. Our first duty, one which we owe to God, to ourselves, and to our fellow men, is to obey the laws of God, which include the laws of health. If we are sick, we impose a weary tax upon our friends, and unfit ourselves for discharging our duties to our families and to our neighbors. And when premature death is the result of our violation of nature's law, we bring sorrow and suffering to others; we deprive our neighbors of the help we ought to render them in living; we rob our families of the comfort and help we might render them, and rob God of the service He claims of us to advance His glory. Then, are we not, in the worst sense, transgressors of God's law?

But God is all-pitiful, gracious, and tender, and when light comes to those who have injured their health by sinful indulgences, and they are convinced of sin, and repent and seek pardon, He accepts the poor offering rendered to Him, and receives them. Oh, what tender mercy that He does not refuse the remnant of the abused life of the suffering, repenting sinner! In His gracious mercy, He saves these souls as by fire. But what an inferior, pitiful sacrifice at best, to offer to a pure and holy God! Noble faculties have been paralyzed by wrong habits of sinful indulgence. The aspirations are perverted, and the soul and body defaced.

Why the Light on Health Reform

(1870) 2T 399, 400

20. The Lord has let His light shine upon us in these last days, that the gloom and darkness which have been gathering in past generations because of sinful indulgence, might in some degree be dispelled, and that the train of evils which have resulted because of intemperate eating and drinking, might be lessened.

The Lord in wisdom designed to bring His people into a position where they would be separate from the world in spirit and practice, that their children might not so readily be led into idolatry, and become tainted with the prevailing corruptions of this age. It is God's design that believing parents and their children should stand forth as living representatives of Christ, candidates for everlasting life. All who are partakers of the divine nature will escape the corruption that is in the world through lust. It is impossible for those who indulge the appetite to attain to Christian perfection.

(1890) C.T.B.H. 75

21. God has permitted the light of health reform to shine upon us in these last days, that by walking in the light we may escape many of the dangers to which we shall be exposed. Satan is working with great power to lead men to indulge appetite, gratify inclination, and spend their days in heedless folly. He presents attractions in a life of selfish enjoyment and of sensual indulgence. Intemperance saps

the energies of both mind and body. He who is thus over-come, has placed himself upon Satan's ground, where he will be tempted and annoyed, and finally controlled at pleasure by the enemy of all righteousness.

[C.T.B.H. 52] (1890) C.H. 120, 121

22. In order to preserve health, temperance in all things is necessary,—temperance in labor, temperance in eating and drinking. Our heavenly Father sent the light of health re-form to guard against the evils resulting from a debased appetite, that those who love purity and holiness may know how to use with discretion the good things He has provided for them, and that by exercising temperance in daily life, they may be sanctified through the truth.

(1890) C.T.B.H. 120

23. Let it ever be kept before the mind that the great object of hygienic reform is to secure the highest possible development of mind and soul and body. All the laws of nature—which are the laws of God—are designed for our good. Obedience to them will promote our happiness in this life, and will aid us in a preparation for the life to come.

Importance of Health Principles

(1909) 9T 158-160

24. I have been shown that the principles that were given us in the early days of the message are as important and should be regarded just as conscientiously today as they were then. There are some who have never followed the light given on the question of diet. It is now time to take the light from under the bushel, and let it shine forth in clear, bright rays.

The principles of healthful living mean a great deal to us individually and as a people. . . .

All are now being tested and proved. We have been baptized into Christ, and if we will act our part by separat-ing from everything that would drag us down and make us what we ought not to be, there will be given us strength to grow up into Christ, who is our living head, and we shall see the salvation of God.

Only when we are intelligent in regard to the principles of healthful living, can we be fully aroused to see the evils resulting from improper diet. Those who, after seeing their mistakes, have courage to change their habits will find that the reformatory process requires a struggle and much perseverance; but when correct tastes are once formed, they will realize that the use of the food which they formerly regarded as harmless, was slowly but surely laying the foundation for dyspepsia and other diseases.

In the Front Ranks of Reformers

(1909) 9T 158

25. Seventh-day Adventists are handling momentous truths. More than forty years ago the Lord gave us special light on health reform, but how are we walking in that light? How many have refused to live in harmony with the counsels of God! As a people, we should make advancement proportionate to the light received. It is our duty to understand and respect the principles of health reform. On the subject of temperance we should be in advance of all other people; and yet there are among us well-instructed members of the church, and even ministers of the gospel, who have little respect for the light that God has given upon this subject. They eat as they please, and work as they please.

Let those who are teachers and leaders in our cause take their stand firmly on Bible ground in regard to health reform and give a straight testimony to those who believe we are living in the last days of this earth's history. A line of distinction must be drawn between those who serve God, and those who serve themselves.

(1867) 1T 487

26. Shall those who are "looking for that blessed hope, and the glorious appearing of the great God and our Saviour Jesus Christ, who gave Himself for us, that He might redeem us from all iniquity, and purify unto Himself a peculiar people, zealous of good works," be behind the religionists of the day who have no faith in the soon appearing of our Saviour? The peculiar people whom He is purifying unto Him-

self, to be translated to heaven without seeing death, should not be behind others in good works. In their efforts to cleanse themselves from all filthiness of the flesh and spirit, perfecting holiness in the fear of God, they should be as far ahead of any other class of people on the earth, as their profession is more exalted than that of others.

Health Reform and Prayer for the Sick

(1909) 9T 164, 165

27. In order to be purified and to remain pure, Seventh-day Adventists must have the Holy Spirit in their hearts and in their homes. The Lord has given me light that when the Israel of today humble themselves before Him, and cleanse the soul temple from all defilement, He will hear their prayers in behalf of the sick, and will bless in the use of His remedies for disease. When in faith the human agent does all he can to combat disease, using the simple methods of treatment that God has provided, his efforts will be blessed of God.

If, after so much light has been given, God's people will cherish wrong habits, indulging self and refusing to reform, they will suffer the sure consequences of transgression. If they are determined to gratify perverted appetite at any cost, God will not miraculously save them from the consequences of their indulgence. They "shall lie down in sorrow." Isa. 50:11.

Those who choose to be presumptuous, saying, "The Lord has healed me, and I need not restrict my diet; I can eat and drink as I please," will erelong need, in body and soul, the restoring power of God. Because the Lord has graciously healed you, you must not think you can link yourselves up with the self-indulgent practices of the world. Do as Christ commanded after His work of healing,—"go, and sin no more." John 8:11. Appetite must not be your god.

(1867) 1T 560, 561

28. The health reform is a branch of the special work of God for the benefit of His people. . . .

I saw that the reason why God did not hear the prayers of His servants for the sick among us more fully was, that

He could not be glorified in so doing while they were violating the laws of health. And I also saw that He designed the health reform and Health Institute to prepare the way for the prayer of faith to be fully answered. Faith and good works should go hand in hand in relieving the afflicted among us, and in fitting them to glorify God here, and to be saved at the coming of Christ.

(1864) Sp. Gifts IV, 144, 145

29. Many have expected that God would keep them from sickness merely because they have asked Him to do so. But God did not regard their prayers, because their faith was not made perfect by works. God will not work a miracle to keep those from sickness who have no care for themselves, but are continually violating the laws of health, and make no efforts to prevent disease. When we do all we can on our part to have health, then may we expect that the blessed results will follow, and we can ask God in faith to bless our efforts for the preservation of health. He will then answer our prayer, if His name can be glorified thereby. But let all understand that they have a work to do. God will not work in a miraculous manner to preserve the health of persons who are taking a sure course to make themselves sick, by their careless inattention to the laws of health.

Those who will gratify their appetite, and then suffer because of their intemperance, and take drugs to relieve them, may be assured that God will not interpose to save health and life which is so recklessly periled. The cause has produced the effect. Many, as their last resort, follow the directions in the word of God, and request the prayers of the elders of the church for their restoration to health. God does not see fit to answer prayers offered in behalf of such, for He knows that if they should be restored to health, they would again sacrifice it upon the altar of unhealthy appetite.

[See also 713]

A Lesson From Israel's Failure

(1909) 9T 165

30. The Lord gave His word to ancient Israel, that if they would cleave strictly to Him, and do all His requirements,

He would keep them from all the diseases such as He had brought upon the Egyptians; but this promise was given on the condition of obedience. Had the Israelites obeyed the instruction they received, and profited by their advantages, they would have been the world's object lesson of health and prosperity. The Israelites failed of fulfilling God's purpose, and thus failed of receiving the blessings that might have been theirs. But in Joseph and Daniel, in Moses and Elijah, and many others, we have noble examples of the results of the true plan of living. Like faithfulness today will produce like results. To us it is written, "Ye are a chosen generation, a royal priesthood, a holy nation, a peculiar people; that we should show forth the praises of Him who hath called you out of darkness into His marvelous light." 1 Peter 2:9.

(1905) M.H. 283

31. Had the Israelites obeyed the instruction they received, and profited by their advantages, they would have been the world's object lesson of health and prosperity. If as a people they had lived according to God's plan, they would have been preserved from the diseases that afflicted other nations. Above any other people they would have possessed physical strength and vigor of intellect.

[See also 641-644]

The Christian Race

(1890) C.T.B.H. 25

32. "Know ye not that they which run in a race run all, but one receiveth the prize? So run, that ye may obtain. And every man that striveth for the mastery is temperate in all things. Now they do it to obtain a corruptible crown; but we an incorruptible."

Here the good results of self-control and temperate habits are set forth. The various games instituted among the ancient Greeks in honor of their gods, are presented before us by the apostle Paul to illustrate the spiritual warfare and its reward. Those who were to participate in these games were trained by the most severe discipline. Every indulgence that would tend to weaken the physical powers was forbidden. Luxurious food and wine were prohibited, in order to promote physical vigor, fortitude, and firmness.

To win the prize for which they strove,—a chaplet of perishable flowers, bestowed amid the applause of the multitude,—was considered the highest honor. If so much could be endured, so much self-denial practiced, in the hope of gaining so worthless a prize, which only one at best could obtain, how much greater should be the sacrifice, how much more willing the self-denial, for an incorruptible crown, and for everlasting life!

There is work for us to do—stern, earnest work. All our habits, tastes, and inclinations must be educated in harmony with the laws of life and health. By this means we may secure the very best physical conditions, and have mental clearness to discern between the evil and the good.

Daniel's Example

(1890) C.T.B.H. 25-28

33. In order rightly to understand the subject of temperance, we must consider it from a Bible standpoint; and nowhere can we find a more comprehensive and forcible illustration of true temperance and its attendant blessings, than is afforded by the history of the prophet Daniel and his Hebrew associates in the court of Babylon. . . .

God always honors the right. The most promising youth from all the lands subdued by the great conqueror had been gathered at Babylon, yet amid them all, the Hebrew captives were without a rival. The erect form, the firm, elastic step, the fair countenance, the undimmed senses, the untainted breath,—all were so many certificates of good habits,—insignia of the nobility with which nature honors those who are obedient to her laws.

The history of Daniel and his companions has been recorded on the pages of the Inspired Word for the benefit of the youth of all succeeding ages. What men have done, men may do. Did those youthful Hebrews stand firm amid great temptations, and bear a noble testimony in favor of true temperance? The youth of today may bear a similar testimony.

The lesson here presented is one which we would do well to ponder. Our danger is not from scarcity, but from abundance. We are constantly tempted to excess. Those who would preserve their powers unimpaired for the service of God, must observe strict temperance in the use of His bounties, as well as total abstinence from every injurious or debasing indulgence.

The rising generation are surrounded with allurements calculated to tempt the appetite. Especially in our large cities, every form of indulgence is made easy and inviting. Those who, like Daniel, refuse to defile themselves, will reap the reward of their temperate habits. With their greater physical stamina and increased power of endurance, they have a bank of deposit upon which to draw in case of emergency.

Right physical habits promote mental superiority. Intellectual power, physical strength, and longevity depend upon immutable laws. There is no happen-so, no chance, about this matter. Nature's God will not interfere to preserve men from the consequences of violating nature's laws. There is much sterling truth in the adage, "Every man is the architect of his own fortune." While parents are responsible for the stamp of character, as well as for the education and training, of their sons and daughters, it is still true that our position and usefulness in the world depend, to a great degree, upon our own course of action. Daniel and his companions enjoyed the benefits of correct training and education in early life, but these advantages alone would not have made them what they were. The time came when they must act for themselves—when their future depended upon their own course. Then they decided to be true to the lessons given them in childhood. The fear of God, which is the beginning of wisdom, was the foundation of their greatness. His Spirit strengthened every true purpose, every noble resolution.

R. & H., Jan. 25, 1881

34. The youth [Daniel, Hananiah, Mishael, and Azariah] in this school of training were not only to be admitted to the royal palace, but it was provided that they should eat of the meat, and drink of the wine, which came from the king's

table. In all this the king considered that he was not only bestowing great honor upon them, but securing for them the best physical and mental development that could be attained.

Among the viands placed before the king were swine's flesh and other meats which were declared unclean by the law of Moses, and which the Hebrews had been expressly forbidden to eat. Here Daniel was brought to a severe test. Should he adhere to the teachings of his fathers concerning meats and drinks, and offend the king, probably losing not only his position but his life, or should he disregard the commandment of the Lord, and retain the favor of the king, thus securing great intellectual advantages and the most flattering worldly prospects?

Daniel did not long hesitate. He decided to stand firmly for his integrity, let the result be what it might. He "purposed in his heart that he would not defile himself with the portion of the king's meat, nor with the wine which he drank."

There are many among professed Christians today who would decide that Daniel was too particular, and would pronounce him narrow and bigoted. They consider the matter of eating and drinking of too little consequence to require such a decided stand,—one involving the probable sacrifice of every earthly advantage. But those who reason thus will find in the day of judgment that they turned from God's express requirements, and set up their own opinion as a standard of right and wrong. They will find that what seemed to them unimportant was not so regarded of God. His requirements should be sacredly obeyed. Those who accept and obey one of His precepts because it is convenient to do so, while they reject another because its observance would require a sacrifice, lower the standard of right, and by their example lead others to lightly regard the holy law of God. "Thus saith the Lord" is to be our rule in all things. . . .

The character of Daniel is presented to the world as a striking example of what God's grace can make of men fallen by nature and corrupted by sin. The record of his noble, self-denying life is an encouragement to our common humanity. From it we may gather strength to nobly resist temptation, and firmly, and in the grace of meekness, stand for the right under the severest trial.

Daniel might have found a plausible excuse to depart from his strictly temperate habits; but the approbation of God was dearer to him than the favor of the most powerful earthly potentate,—dearer even than life itself. Having by his courteous conduct obtained favor with Melzar, the officer in charge of the Hebrew youth, Daniel made a request that they might not eat of the king's meat, or drink of his wine Melzar feared that should he comply with this request, he might incur the displeasure of the king, and thus endanger his own life. Like many at the present day, he thought that an abstemious diet would render these youth pale and sickly in appearance and deficient in muscular strength, while the luxurious food from the king's table would make them ruddy and beautiful, and would impart superior physical activity.

Daniel requested that the matter be decided by a ten days' trial,—the Hebrew youth during this brief period being permitted to eat of simple food, while their companions partook of the king's dainties. The request was finally granted, and then Daniel felt assured that he had gained his case. Although but a youth, he had seen the injurious effects of wine and luxurious living upon physical and mental health.

At the end of the ten days the result was found to be quite the opposite of Melzar's expectations. Not only in personal appearance, but in physical activity and mental vigor, those who had been temperate in their habits exhibited a marked superiority over their companions who had indulged appetite. As a result of this trial, Daniel and his associates were permitted to continue their simple diet during the whole course of their training for the duties of the kingdom.

GOD'S APPROVAL WON

The Lord regarded with approval the firmness and self-denial of these Hebrew youth, and His blessing attended them. He "gave them knowledge and skill in all learning and wisdom; and Daniel had understanding in all visions and dreams." At the expiration of the three years of training, when their ability and acquirements were tested by the king, he "found none like Daniel, Hananiah, Mishael, and Azariah; therefore stood they before the king. And in all matters of wisdom and understanding that the king required of them he found them ten times better than all the magicians and astrologers that were in all his realm."

Here is a lesson for all, but especially for the young. A strict compliance with the requirements of God is beneficial to the health of body and mind. In order to reach the highest standard of moral and intellectual attainments, it is necessary to seek wisdom and strength from God, and to observe strict temperance in all the habits of life. In the experience of Daniel and his companions we have an instance of the triumph of principle over temptation to indulge the appetite. It shows us that through religious principle young men may triumph over the lusts of the flesh, and remain true to God's requirements, even though it cost them a great sacrifice.

[Daniel's diet—117, 241, 242]

Unready for the Loud Cry

(1867) 1T 486, 487

35. The health reform, I was shown, is a part of the third angel's message, and is just as closely connected with it as are the arm and hand with the human body. I saw that we as a people must make an advance move in this great work. Ministers and people must act in concert. God's people are not prepared for the loud cry of the third angel. They have a work to do for themselves which they should not leave for God to do for them. He has left this work for them to do. It is an individual work; one cannot do it for another. "Having therefore these promises, dearly beloved, let us cleanse ourselves from all filthiness of the flesh and spirit, perfecting holiness in the fear of God." Gluttony is the prevailing sin of this age. Lustful appetite makes slaves of men and women, and beclouds their intellects and stupefies their moral sensibilities to such a degree that the sacred, elevated truths of God's word are not appreciated. The lower propensities have ruled men and women.

In order to be fitted for translation, the people of God must know themselves. They must understand in regard to their own physical frames, that they may be able with the psalmist to exclaim, "I will praise Thee, for I am fearfully and wonderfully made." They should ever have the appetite in subjection to the moral and intellectual organs. The body should be servant to the mind, and not the mind to the body.

Preparation for the Refreshing

(1867) 1T 619

36. God requires His people to cleanse themselves from all filthiness of the flesh and spirit, perfecting holiness in the fear of the Lord. All those who are indifferent and excuse themselves from this work, waiting for the Lord to do for them that which He requires them to do for themselves, will be found wanting when the meek of the earth, who have wrought His judgments, are hid in the day of the Lord's anger.

I was shown that if God's people make no efforts on their part, but wait for the refreshing to come upon them and remove their wrongs and correct their errors; if they depend upon that to cleanse them from filthiness of the flesh and spirit, and fit them to engage in the loud cry of the third angel, they will be found wanting. The refreshing or power of God comes only on those who have prepared themselves for it by doing the work which God bids them, namely, cleansing themselves from all filthiness of the flesh and spirit, perfecting holiness in the fear of God.

Appeals to the Hesitant

(R. & H., May 27, 1902) C.H. 578, 579

37. The failure to follow sound principles has marred the history of God's people. There has been a continual backsliding in health reform, and as a result God is dishonored by a great lack of spirituality. Barriers have been erected which would never have been seen had God's people walked in the light.

Shall we who have had such great opportunities allow the people of the world to go in advance of us in health reform? Shall we cheapen our minds and abuse our talents by wrong eating? Shall we transgress God's holy law by following selfish practices? Shall our inconsistency become a byword? Shall we live such unchristianlike lives that the Saviour will be ashamed to call us brethren?

Shall we not rather do that medical missionary work which is the gospel in practice, living in such a way that the peace of God can rule in our hearts? Shall we not remove every stumbling block from the feet of unbelievers, ever remembering what is due to a profession of Christianity? Far better give up the name of Christian than make a profession and at the same time indulge appetites which strengthen unholy passions.

God calls upon every church member to dedicate his life unreservedly to the Lord's service. He calls for decided reformation. All creation is groaning under the curse. God's people should place themselves where they will grow in grace, being sanctified, body, soul, and spirit, by the truth. When they break away from all health-destroying indulgences, they will have a clearer perception of what constitutes true godliness. A wonderful change will be seen in the religious experience.

All Being Proved

R. & H., Feb. 10, 1910

38. It is of great importance that individually we act well our part, and have an intelligent understanding of what we should eat and drink, and how we should live to preserve health. All are being proved to see whether they will accept the principles of health reform or follow a course of self-indulgence.

Let no one think that he can do as he pleases in the matter of diet. But before all who sit at the table with you, let it appear that you follow principle in the matter of eating, as in all other matters, that the glory of God may be revealed. You cannot afford to do otherwise; for you have a character to form for the future immortal life. Great responsibilities rest upon every human soul. Let us comprehend these responsibilities, and bear them nobly in the name of the Lord.

To every one who is tempted to indulge appetite I would say, Yield not to temptation, but confine yourself to the use of wholesome foods. You can train yourself to enjoy a healthful diet. The Lord helps those who seek to help themselves; but when men will not take special pains to follow out the mind and will of God, how can He work with them? Let us act our part, working out our salvation with fear and trembling,—with fear and trembling lest we make mistakes in the treatment of our bodies, which, before God, we are under obligation to keep in the most healthy condition possible.

True Reform Is Heart Reform

(1896) Special Testimonies, Series A, No. 9, p. 54

39. Those who would work in God's service must not be seeking worldly gratification and selfish indulgence. The physicians in our institutions must be imbued with the living principles of health reform. Men will never be truly temperate until the grace of Christ is an abiding principle in the heart. All the pledges in the world will not make you or your wife health reformers. No mere restriction of your diet will cure your diseased appetite. Brother and Sister ——— will not practice temperance in all things until their hearts are transformed by the grace of God.

Circumstances cannot work reforms. Christianity proposes a reformation in the heart. What Christ works within, will be worked out under the dictation of a converted intellect. The plan of beginning outside and trying to work inward has always failed, and always will fail. God's plan with you is to begin at the very seat of all difficulties, the heart, and then from out of the heart will issue the principles of righteousness; the reformation will be outward as well as inward.

Letter 3, 1884

40. Those who elevate the standard as nearly as they can to the order of God, according to the light God has given them through His word and the testimonies of His Spirit, will not change their course of action to meet the wishes of their friends or relatives, be they one or two or a host, who

are living contrary to God's wise arrangement. If we move from principle in these things, if we observe strict rules of diet, if as Christians we educate our tastes after God's plan, we shall exert an influence which will meet the mind of God. The question is, "Are we willing to be true health reformers?"

[For context see 720]

A Question of Primary Importance

(1909) 9T 153-156

41. I am instructed to bear a message to all our people on the subject of health reform; for many have backslidden from their former loyalty to health reform principles.

God's purpose for His children is that they shall grow up to the full stature of men and women in Christ. In order to do this, they must use aright every power of mind, soul, and body. They cannot afford to waste any mental or physical strength.

The question of how to preserve the health is one of primary importance. When we study this question in the fear of God, we shall learn that it is best, for both our physical and our spiritual advancement, to observe simplicity in diet. Let us patiently study this question. We need knowledge and judgment in order to move wisely in this matter. Nature's laws are not to be resisted, but obeyed.

Those who have received instruction regarding the evils of the use of flesh foods, tea and coffee, and rich and unhealthful food preparations, and who are determined to make a covenant with God by sacrifice, will not continue to indulge their appetite for food that they know to be unhealthful. God demands that the appetites be cleansed, and that self-denial be practiced in regard to those things which are not good. This is a work that will have to be done before His people can stand before Him a perfected people.

The remnant people of God must be a converted people. The presentation of this message is to result in the conversion and sanctification of souls. We are to feel the power of the Spirit of God in this movement. This is a wonderful, definite message; it means everything to the receiver, and it is to be proclaimed with a loud cry. We must have a true, abiding faith that this message will go forth with increasing importance till the close of time.

There are some professed believers who accept certain portions of the Testimonies as the message of God, while they reject those portions that condemn their favorite indulgences. Such persons are working contrary to their own welfare, and the welfare of the church. It is essential that we walk in the light while we have the light. Those who claim to believe in health reform, and yet work counter to its principles in the daily life practice, are hurting their own souls and are leaving wrong impressions upon the minds of believers and unbelievers.

A solemn responsibility rests upon those who know the truth that all their works shall correspond with their faith, and that their lives shall be refined and sanctified, and they be prepared for the work that must rapidly be done in these closing days of the message. They have no time or strength to spend in the indulgence of appetite. The words should come to us now with impelling earnestness, "Repent ye therefore, and be converted, that your sins may be blotted out, when the times of refreshing shall come from the presence of the Lord." Acts 3:19. There are many among us who are deficient in spirituality, and who, unless they are wholly converted, will certainly be lost. Can you afford to run the risk? . . .

The power of Christ alone can work the transformation in heart and mind that all must experience who would partake with Him of the new life in the kingdom of heaven. "Except a man be born again," the Saviour has said, "he cannot see the kingdom of God." John 3:3. The religion that comes from God is the only religion that can lead to God. In order to serve Him aright, we must be born of the Divine Spirit. This will lead to watchfulness. It will purify the heart and renew the mind, and give us a new capacity for knowing and loving God. It will give us willing obedience to all His requirements. This is true worship.

A United Front

Letter 48, 1902

42. We have been given the work of advancing health reform. The Lord desires His people to be in harmony with one another. As you must know, we shall not leave the position in which, for the last thirty-five years,* the Lord has been bidding us stand. Beware how you place yourself in opposition to the work of health reform. It will go forward; for it is the Lord's means of lessening the suffering in our world, and of purifying His people.

Be careful what attitude you assume, lest you be found causing division. My brother, even while you fail to bring into your life and into your family the blessing that comes from following the principles of health reform, do not harm others by opposing the light God has given on this subject.

[Special Testimonies, Series A, No. 7, p. 40] C.H. 561, 562

43. The Lord has given His people a message in regard to health reform. This light has been shining upon their pathway for thirty years; and the Lord cannot sustain His servants in a course which will counteract it. He is displeased when His servants act in opposition to the message upon this point, which He has given them to give to others. Can He be pleased when half the workers laboring in a place, teach that the principles of health reform are as closely allied with the third angel's message as the arm is to the body, while their co-workers, by their practice, teach principles that are entirely opposite? This is regarded as a sin in the sight of God. . . .

Nothing brings such discouragement upon the Lord's watchmen as to be connected with those who have mental capacity, and who understand the reasons of our faith, but by precept and example manifest indifference to moral obligations.

The light which God has given upon health reform cannot be trifled with without injury to those who attempt it; and no man can hope to succeed in the work of God while, by precept and example, he acts in opposition to the light which God has sent.

---

* Written in 1902.

(1867) 1T 618

44. It is important that instructions should be given by ministers in regard to living temperately. They should show the relation which eating, working, resting, and dressing, sustain to health. All who believe the truth for these last days, have something to do in this matter. It concerns them, and God requires them to arouse and interest themselves in this reform. He will not be pleased with their course if they regard this question with indifference.

Stumbling Over the Blessing

(1867) 1T 546

45. Said the angel, "Abstain from fleshly lusts which war against the soul." You have stumbled at the health reform. It appears to you to be a needless appendix to the truth. It is not so; it is a part of the truth. Here is a work before you which will come closer and be more trying than anything which has yet been brought to bear upon you. While you hesitate and stand back, failing to lay hold upon the blessing which it is your privilege to receive, you suffer loss. You are stumbling over the very blessing which heaven has placed in your path to make progress less difficult. Satan presents this before you in the most objectionable light, that you may combat that which would prove the greatest benefit to you, which would be for your physical and spiritual health.

[Excuses for wrongdoing framed under satanic influences—710]

Consider the Judgment

Letter 135, 1902

46. The Lord calls for volunteers to enter His army. Sickly men and women need to become health reformers. God will cooperate with His children in preserving their health, if they eat with care, refusing to put unnecessary burdens on the stomach. He has graciously made the path of nature sure and safe, wide enough for all who walk in it. He has given for our sustenance the wholesome and health-giving productions of the earth.

He who does not heed the instruction God has given in His word and in His works, he who does not obey the divine commands, has a defective experience. He is a sickly Christian. His spiritual life is feeble. He lives, but his life is devoid of fragrance. He fritters away precious moments of grace.

Many have done the body much injury by a disregard of the laws of life, and they may never recover from the effects of their neglect; but even now they may repent and be converted. Man has tried to be wiser than God. He has become a law unto himself. God calls upon us to give attention to His requirements, no longer to dishonor Him by dwarfing the physical, mental, and spiritual capabilities. Premature decay and death are the result of walking away from God to follow the ways of the world. He who indulges self must bear the penalty. In the judgment we shall see how seriously God regards the violation of the laws of health. Then, as we take a retrospective view of our course of action, we shall see what knowledge of God we might have gained, what noble characters we might have formed, if we had taken the Bible as our counselor.

The Lord is waiting for His people to become wise in understanding. As we see the wretchedness, deformity, and disease that have come into the world as the result of ignorance in regard to the proper care of the body, how can we refrain from giving the warning? Christ has declared that as it was in the days of Noah, when the earth was filled with violence and corrupted by crime, so shall it be when the Son of man is revealed. God has given us great light, and if we walk in this light, we shall see His salvation.

There is need of decided changes. It is time for us to humble our proud, self-willed hearts, and seek the Lord while He may be found. As a people we need to humble our hearts before God; for the scars of inconsistency are on our practice.

The Lord is calling upon us to come into line. The day is far spent. The night is at hand. The judgments of God are already seen, both on land and on sea. No second probation will be granted us. This is no time for making false moves. Let every one thank God that we still have an opportunity to form characters for the future eternal life.

SECTION II

Diet and Spirituality

Quotations in Section II

Diet and Spirituality

Intemperance a Sin

[R. & H., Jan. 25, 1881] C.H. 67

47. LET none who profess godliness regard with indifference the health of the body, and flatter themselves that intemperance is no sin, and will not affect their spirituality. A close sympathy exists between the physical and the moral nature.

(1905) M.H. 129

48. With our first parents, intemperate desire resulted in the loss of Eden. Temperance in all things has more to do with our restoration to Eden than men realize.

MS 49, 1897

49. The transgression of physical law is the transgression of God's law. Our Creator is Jesus Christ. He is the author of our being. He has created the human structure. He is the author of physical laws, as He is the author of the moral law. And the human being who is careless and reckless of the habits and practices that concern his physical life and health, sins against God. Many who profess to love Jesus Christ do not show proper reverence and respect for Him who gave His life to save them from eternal death. He is not reverenced, or respected, or recognized. This is shown by the injury done to their own bodies in violation of the laws of their being.

(1876) 4T 30

50. A continual transgression of nature's laws is a continual transgression of the law of God. The present weight of suffering and anguish which we see everywhere, the present deformity, decrepitude, disease, and imbecility now flooding the world, make it, in comparison to what it might be and what God designed it should be, a lazar house; and the present generation are feeble in mental, moral, and physical power. All this misery has accumulated from generation to generation because fallen man will break the

law of God. Sins of the greatest magnitude are committed through the indulgence of perverted appetite.

(1880) 4T 417

51. Excessive indulgence in eating, drinking, sleeping, or seeing, is sin. The harmonious healthy action of all the powers of body and mind results in happiness; and the more elevated and refined the powers, the more pure and unalloyed the happiness.

[God marks the sin of indulgence—246]

When Sanctification Is Impossible

Health Reformer, March, 1878

52. A large proportion of all the infirmities that afflict the human family, are the results of their own wrong habits, because of their willing ignorance, or of their disregard of the light which God has given in relation to the laws of their being. It is not possible for us to glorify God while living in violation of the laws of life. The heart cannot possibly maintain consecration to God while lustful appetite is indulged. A diseased body and disordered intellect, because of continual indulgence in hurtful lust, make sanctification of the body and spirit impossible. The apostle understood the importance of the healthful conditions of the body for the successful perfection of Christian character. He says, "I keep under my body, and bring it into subjection: lest that by any means, when I have preached to others, I myself should be a castaway." He mentions the fruit of the Spirit, among which is temperance. "They that are Christ's have crucified the flesh with the affections and lusts."

[Impossibility of attaining Christian perfection while giving reins to appetite—356]

Willing Ignorance Increases Sin

(1868) 2T 70, 71

53. It is a duty to know how to preserve the body in the very best condition of health, and it is a sacred duty to live up to the light which God has graciously given. If we close our eyes to the light for fear we shall see our wrongs, which we are unwilling to forsake, our sins are not lessened, but

increased. If light is turned from in one case, it will be disregarded in another. It is just as much sin to violate the laws of our being as to break one of the ten commandments, for we cannot do either without breaking God's law. We cannot love the Lord with all our heart, mind, soul, and strength while we are loving our appetites, our tastes, a great deal better than we love the Lord. We are daily lessening our strength to glorify God, when He requires all our strength, all our mind. By our wrong habits we are lessening our hold on life, and yet professing to be Christ's followers, preparing for the finishing touch of immortality.

My brother and sister, you have a work to do which no one can do for you. Awake from your lethargy, and Christ shall give you life. Change your course of living, your eating, your drinking, and your working. While you pursue the course you have been following for years, you cannot clearly discern sacred and eternal things. Your sensibilities are blunted, and your intellect beclouded. You have not been growing in grace and in the knowledge of the truth as was your privilege. You have not been increasing in spirituality, but growing more and more darkened.

R. & H., June 18, 1895

54. Man was the crowning act of the creation of God, made in the image of God, and designed to be a counterpart of God. . . . Man is very dear to God, because he was formed in His own image. This fact should impress us with the importance of teaching by precept and example the sin of defiling, by the indulgence of appetite or by any other sinful practice, the body which is designed to represent God to the world.

[Natural law proclaimed distinctly—97]

Mental Effects of Disobedience to Physical Law

(1909) 9T 156

55. God requires of His people continual advancement. We need to learn that indulged appetite is the greatest hindrance to mental improvement and soul sanctification. With all our profession of health reform, many of us eat improperly.

(1905) M.H. 307

56. We should not provide for the Sabbath a more liberal supply or a greater variety of food than for other days. Instead of this, the food should be more simple, and less should be eaten, in order that the mind may be clear and vigorous to comprehend spiritual things. A clogged stomach means a clogged brain. The most precious words may be heard and not appreciated, because the mind is confused by an improper diet. By overeating on the Sabbath, many do more than they think, to unfit themselves for receiving the benefit of its sacred opportunities.

(1882) 5T 162-164

57. I have been shown that some of our camp meetings are far from being what the Lord designed they should be. The people come unprepared for the visitation of God's Holy Spirit. Generally the sisters devote considerable time before the meeting to the preparation of garments for the outward adorning, while they entirely forget the inward adorning, which is in the sight of God of great price. There is also much time spent in needless cooking, in the preparation of rich pies and cakes and other articles of food that do positive injury to those who partake of them. Should our sisters provide good bread and some other healthful kinds of food, both they and their families would be better prepared to appreciate the words of life, and far more susceptible to the influence of the Holy Spirit.

Often the stomach is overburdened with food which is seldom as plain and simple as that eaten at home, where the amount of exercise taken is double or treble. This causes the mind to be in such a lethargy that it is difficult to appreciate eternal things, and the meeting closes, and they are disappointed in not having enjoyed more of the Spirit of God. . . . Let the preparation for eating and dressing be a secondary matter, but let deep heart searching commence at home.

[Indulged appetite prevents one from understanding present truth—72]

[Indulged appetite paralyzes the senses—227]

[Indulged appetite causes dullness in brain—209, 226]

[Indulged appetite disqualifies one in laying plans and counseling—71]

[Indulged appetite weakens spiritual, mental, and physical powers of children—346]

[Sleeping under burning truths of the word—222]

[Mental and moral vigor increased by abstemious diet—85, 117, 206]

[Effect of flesh diet on mental vigor—678, 680, 682, 686]

[More about camp meeting dietary—124]

Effect on Appreciation of Truth

(1868) 2T 66

58. You need clear, energetic minds, in order to appreciate the exalted character of the truth, to value the atonement, and to place the right estimate upon eternal things. If you pursue a wrong course, and indulge in wrong habits of eating, and thereby weaken the intellectual powers, you will not place that high estimate upon salvation and eternal life which will inspire you to conform your life to the life of Christ; you will not make those earnest, self-sacrificing efforts for entire conformity to the will of God, which His word requires and which are necessary to give you a moral fitness for the finishing touch of immortality.

(1870) 2T 364

59. Even if you are strict in the quality of your food, do you glorify God in your bodies and spirits which are His, by partaking of such a quantity of food? Those who place so much food upon the stomach, and thus load down nature, could not appreciate the truth should they hear it dwelt upon. They could not arouse the benumbed sensibilities of the brain to realize the value of the atonement, and the great sacrifice that has been made for fallen man. It is impossible for such to appreciate the great, the precious, and the exceedingly rich reward that is in reserve for the faithful overcomers. The animal part of our nature should never be left to govern the moral and intellectual.

(1867) 1T 548, 549

60. Some are indulging lustful appetite, which wars against the soul, and is a constant hindrance to their spiritual advancement. They constantly bear an accusing conscience, and if straight truths are talked, they are prepared to be offended. They are self-condemned, and feel that subjects

have been purposely selected to touch their case. They feel grieved and injured, and withdraw themselves from the assemblies of the saints. They forsake the assembling of themselves together, for then their consciences are not so disturbed. They soon lose their interest in the meetings and their love for the truth, and, unless they entirely reform, will go back and take their position with the rebel host, who stand under the black banner of Satan. If these will crucify fleshly lusts which war against the soul, they will get out of the way, where the arrows of truth will pass harmlessly by them. But while they indulge lustful appetite, and thus cherish their idols, they make themselves a mark for the arrows of truth to hit, and if truth is spoken at all, they must be wounded. . . .

The use of unnatural stimulants is destructive to health and has a benumbing influence upon the brain, making it impossible to appreciate eternal things. Those who cherish these idols cannot rightly value the salvation which Christ has wrought out for them by a life of self-denial, continual suffering and reproach, and by finally yielding His own sinless life to save perishing man from death.

(1870) 2T 486

61. Butter and meat stimulate. These have injured the stomach and perverted the taste. The sensitive nerves of the brain have been benumbed, and the animal appetite strengthened at the expense of the moral and intellectual faculties. These higher powers, which should control, have been growing weaker, so that eternal things have not been discerned. Paralysis has benumbed the spiritual and devotional. Satan has triumphed to see how easily he can come in through the appetite and control men and women of intelligence, calculated by the Creator to do a good and great work.

[Impossible for the intemperate to value the atonement—119]
[The intemperate cannot be susceptible to sanctifying influence of the truth—780]

Effect Upon Discernment and Decision

(1900) C.O.L. 346

62. Anything that lessens physical strength enfeebles the mind, and makes it less capable of discriminating between

right and wrong. We become less capable of choosing the good, and have less strength of will to do that which we know to be right.

The misuse of our physical powers shortens the period of time in which our lives can be used for the glory of God. And it unfits us to accomplish the work God has given us to do.

(1890) **C.T.B.H. 159**

63. Those who, having had the light upon the subject of eating and dressing with simplicity, in obedience to moral and physical laws, still turn from the light which points out their duty, will shun duty in other things. By shunning the cross which they would have to take up in order to be in harmony with natural law, they blunt the conscience; and they will, to avoid reproach, violate the ten commandments. There is with some a decided unwillingness to endure the cross and despise the shame.

(1864) **Sp. Gifts IV, 148, 149**

64. Those who bring disease upon themselves, by self-gratification, have not healthy bodies and minds. They cannot weigh the evidences of truth, and comprehend the requirements of God. Our Saviour will not reach His arm low enough to raise such from their degraded state, while they persist in pursuing a course to sink themselves still lower.

All are required to do what they can to preserve healthy bodies and sound minds. If they will gratify a gross appetite, and by so doing blunt their sensibilities, and becloud their perceptive faculties so that they cannot appreciate the exalted character of God, or delight in the study of His word, they may be assured that God will not accept their unworthy offering any sooner than that of Cain. God requires them to cleanse themselves from all filthiness of the flesh and spirit, perfecting holiness in the fear of the Lord. After man has done all in his power to ensure health, by the denying of appetite and gross passions, that he may possess a healthy mind, and a sanctified imagination, that he may render to God an offering in righteousness, then he is saved alone by a miracle of God's mercy, as was the ark upon the stormy billows. Noah had done all that God required of him in making the ark secure; then God performed that which man could not do, and preserved the ark by His miraculous power.

(1867) 1T 618, 619

65. The abuses of the stomach by the gratification of appetite, are the fruitful source of most church trials. Those who eat and work intemperately and irrationally, talk and act irrationally. An intemperate man cannot be a patient man. It is not necessary to drink alcoholic liquors in order to be intemperate. The sin of intemperate eating, eating too frequently, too much, and of rich, unwholesome food, destroys the healthy action of the digestive organs, affects the brain, and perverts the judgment, preventing rational, calm, healthy thinking and acting. And this is a fruitful source of church trials. Therefore, in order for the people of God to be in an acceptable state with Him, where they can glorify Him in their bodies and spirits, which are His, they must with interest and zeal deny the gratification of their appetites, and exercise temperance in all things. Then may they comprehend the truth in its beauty and clearness, and carry it out in their lives, and by a judicious, wise, straightforward course, give the enemies of our faith no occasion to reproach the cause of truth.

(1870) 2T 404

66. Brother and Sister G, arouse yourselves, I beg of you. You have not received the light of health reform and acted upon it. If you had restricted your appetites, you would have been saved much extra labor and expense; and what is of vastly more consequence, you would have preserved to yourselves a better condition of physical health, and a greater degree of intellectual strength to appreciate eternal truths; you would have a clearer brain to weigh the evidences of truth, and would be better prepared to give to others a reason of the hope that is in you.

(1867) 1T 487-489

67. Some have sneered at this work of reform, and have said it was all unnecessary; that it was an excitement to divert minds from present truth. They have said that matters were being carried to extremes. Such do not know what

they are talking about. While men and women professing godliness are diseased from the crown of their head to the soles of their feet, while their physical, mental, and moral energies are enfeebled through gratification of depraved appetite and excessive labor, how can they weigh the evidences of truth, and comprehend the requirements of God? If their moral and intellectual faculties are beclouded, they cannot appreciate the value of the atonement or the exalted character of the work of God, nor delight in the study of His word. How can a nervous dyspeptic be ready always to give an answer to every man that asketh him a reason of the hope that is in him, with meekness and fear? How soon would such a one become confused and agitated, and by his diseased imagination be led to view matters in altogether a wrong light, and by a lack of that meekness and calmness which characterized the life of Christ, be caused to dishonor his profession while contending with unreasonable men? Viewing matters from a high religious standpoint, we must be thorough reformers in order to be Christlike.

I saw that our heavenly Father has bestowed upon us the great blessing of light upon the health reform, that we may obey the claims which He has upon us, and glorify Him in our bodies and spirits, which are His, and finally stand without fault before the throne of God. Our faith requires us to elevate the standard, and take advance steps. While many question the course pursued by other health reformers, they, as reasonable men, should do something themselves. Our race is in a deplorable condition, suffering from disease of every description. Many have inherited disease, and are great sufferers because of the wrong habits of their parents; and yet they pursue the same wrong course in regard to themselves and their children which was pursued toward them. They are ignorant in regard to themselves. They are sick and do not know that their own wrong habits are causing them immense suffering.

There are but few as yet who are aroused sufficiently to understand how much their habits of diet have to do with their health, their characters, their usefulness in this world, and their eternal destiny. I saw that it is the duty of those who have received the light from heaven, and have realized the benefit of walking in it, to manifest a greater interest for those who are still suffering for want of knowledge. Sabbathkeepers who are looking for the soon appearing of their Saviour should be the last to manifest a lack of interest in this great work of reform. Men and women must be instructed, and ministers and people should feel that the burden of the work rests upon them to agitate the subject, and urge it home upon others.

Letter 93, 1898

68. Physical habits have a great deal to do with the success of every individual. The more careful you are in your diet, the more simple and unstimulating the food that sustains the body in its harmonious action, the more clear will be your conception of duty. There needs to be a careful review of every habit, every practice, lest a morbid condition of the body shall cast a cloud upon everything.

MS 129, 1901

69. Our physical health is maintained by that which we eat; if our appetites are not under the control of a sanctified mind, if we are not temperate in all our eating and drinking, we shall not be in a state of mental and physical soundness to study the word with a purpose to learn what saith the Scripture—what shall I do to inherit eternal life? Any unhealthful habit will produce an unhealthful condition in the system, and the delicate, living machinery of the stomach will be injured, and will not be able to do its work properly. The diet has much to do with the disposition to enter into temptation and commit sin.

(1869) 2T 202, 203

70. If the Saviour of men, with His divine strength, felt the need of prayer, how much more should feeble, sinful mortals feel the necessity of prayer—fervent, constant prayer! When Christ was the most fiercely beset by temptation, He ate nothing. He committed Himself to God, and through earnest prayer, and perfect submission to the will of His Father, came off conqueror. Those who profess the

truth for these last days, above every other class of professed Christians, should imitate the great Exemplar in prayer.

"It is enough for the disciple that he be as his Master, and the servant as his Lord." Our tables are frequently spread with luxuries neither healthful nor necessary, because we love these things more than we love self-denial, freedom from disease, and soundness of mind. Jesus sought earnestly for strength from His Father. This the divine Son of God considered of more value, even for Himself, than to sit at the most luxurious table. He has given us evidence that prayer is essential in order to receive strength to contend with the powers of darkness, and to do the work allotted us. Our own strength is weakness, but that which God gives is mighty, and will make every one who obtains it more than conqueror.

[Indulged appetite unbalances the mind—237]
[Indulged appetite blunts the conscience—72]

Effect Upon Influence and Usefulness

MS 93, 1901

71. What a pity it is that often, when the greatest self-denial should be exercised, the stomach is crowded with a mass of unhealthful food, which lies there to decompose. The affliction of the stomach affects the brain. The imprudent eater does not realize that he is disqualifying himself for giving wise counsel, disqualifying himself for laying plans for the best advancement of the work of God. But this is so. He cannot discern spiritual things, and in council meetings, when he should say Yea and Amen, he says Nay. He makes propositions that are wide of the mark. The food he has eaten has benumbed his brain power.

Self-indulgence debars the human agent from witnessing for the truth. The gratitude we offer to God for His blessings is greatly affected by the food placed in the stomach. Indulgence of appetite is the cause of dissension, strife, discord, and many other evils. Impatient words are spoken and unkind deeds are done, dishonest practices are followed and passion is manifested, and all because the nerves of the brain are diseased by the abuse heaped upon the stomach.

(1870) 2T 368

72. Some cannot be impressed with the necessity of eating and drinking to the glory of God. The indulgence of appetite affects them in all the relations of life. It is seen in their family, in their church, in the prayer meeting, and in the conduct of their children. It has been the curse of their lives. You cannot make them understand the truths for these last days. God has bountifully provided for the sustenance and happiness of all His creatures; and if His laws were never violated, and all acted in harmony with the divine will, health, peace, and happiness, instead of misery and continual evil, would be experienced.

(1875) 3T 486, 487

73. The Redeemer of the world knew that the indulgence of appetite would bring physical debility, and so deaden the perceptive organs that sacred and eternal things would not be discerned. Christ knew that the world was given up to gluttony, and that this indulgence would pervert the moral powers. If the indulgence of appetite was so strong upon the race that, in order to break its power, the divine Son of God, in behalf of man, was required to fast nearly six weeks, what a work is before the Christian in order that he may overcome even as Christ overcame! The strength of the temptation to indulge perverted appetite can be measured only by the inexpressible anguish of Christ in that long fast in the wilderness.

Christ knew that in order to successfully carry forward the plan of salvation He must commence the work of redeeming man just where the ruin began. Adam fell by the indulgence of appetite. In order to impress upon man his obligations to obey the law of God, Christ began His work of redemption by reforming the physical habits of man. The declension in virtue and the degeneracy of the race are chiefly attributable to the indulgence of perverted appetite.

SPECIAL RESPONSIBILITIES AND TEMPTATIONS OF MINISTERS

There is a solemn responsibility upon all, especially upon ministers who teach the truth, to overcome upon the point of appetite. Their usefulness would be much greater if they had control of their appetites and passions; and their mental and moral powers would be stronger if they combined physical labor with mental exertion. With strictly temperate habits, and with mental and physical labor combined, they could accomplish a far greater amount of labor and preserve clearness of mind. If they would pursue such a course, their thoughts and words would flow more freely, their religious exercises would be more energized, and the impressions made upon their hearers would be more marked.

Intemperance in eating, even of food of the right quality, will have a prostrating influence upon the system, and will blunt the keener and holier emotions.

Undated MS 88

74. Some persons bring upon the campground food that is entirely unsuitable to such occasions, rich cakes and pies, and a variety of dishes that would derange the digestion of a healthy laboring man. Of course, the best is thought none too good for the minister. The people send these things to his table, and invite him to their tables. In this way ministers are tempted to eat too much, and food that is injurious. Not only is their efficiency at the camp meeting lessened; but many become dyspeptics.

The minister should decline this well-meant but unwise hospitality, even at the risk of seeming discourteous. And the people should have too much true kindness to press such an alternative upon him. They err when they tempt the minister with unhealthful food. Precious talent has thus been lost to the cause of God; and many, while they do live, are deprived of half the vigor and strength of their faculties. Ministers, above all others, should economize the strength of brain and nerve. They should avoid all food or drink that has a tendency to irritate or excite the nerves. Excitement will be followed by depression; overindulgence will cloud the mind, and render thought difficult and confused. No man can become a successful workman in spiritual things until he observes strict temperance in his dietetic habits. God cannot let His Holy Spirit rest upon those who, while they know how they should eat for health, persist in a course that will enfeeble mind and body.

"Do All to the Glory of God"

(1896) Special Testimonies, Series A, No. 9, p. 58

75. By the inspiration of the Spirit of God, Paul the apostle writes that "whatsoever ye do," even the natural act of eating or drinking, should be done, not to gratify a perverted appetite, but under a sense of responsibility,—"do all to the glory of God." Every part of the man is to be guarded; we are to beware lest that which is taken into the stomach shall banish from the mind high and holy thoughts. May I not do as I please with myself? ask some, as if we were seeking to deprive them of a great good, when we present before them the necessity of eating intelligently, and conforming all their habits to the laws God has established.

There are rights which belong to every individual. We have an individuality and an identity that is our own. No one can submerge his identity in that of any other. All must act for themselves, according to the dictates of their own conscience. As regards our responsibility and influence, we are amenable to God as deriving our life from Him. This we do not obtain from humanity, but from God only. We are His by creation and by redemption. Our very bodies are not our own, to treat as we please, to cripple by habits that lead to decay, making it impossible to render to God perfect service. Our lives and all our faculties belong to Him. He is caring for us every moment; He keeps the living machinery in action; if we were left to run it for one moment, we should die. We are absolutely dependent upon God.

A great lesson is learned when we understand our relation to God, and His relation to us. The words, "Ye are not your own, ye are bought with a price," should be hung in memory's hall, that we may ever recognize God's rights to our talents, our property, our influence, our individual selves. We are to learn how to treat this gift of God, in mind, in soul, in body, that as Christ's purchased possession, we may do Him healthful, savory service.

(1868) 2T 60

76. The light has been shining upon your pathway in regard to health reform, and the duty resting upon God's people in these last days to exercise temperance in all things. You, I saw, were among the number who would be backward to see the light, and correct your manner of eating, and drinking, and working. As the light of truth is received and followed out, it will work an entire reformation in the life and character of all those who are sanctified through it.

Relation to the Victorious Life

Y.I., May 31, 1894

77. Eating, drinking, and dressing all have a direct bearing upon our spiritual advancement.

(1905) M.H. 280

78. Many articles of food eaten freely by the heathen about them were forbidden to the Israelites. It was no arbitrary distinction that was made. The things prohibited were unwholesome. And the fact that they were pronounced unclean taught the lesson that the use of injurious foods is defiling. That which corrupts the body tends to corrupt the soul. It unfits the user for communion with God, unfits him for high and holy service.

Health Reformer, September, 1871

79. The Spirit of God cannot come to our help, and assist us in perfecting Christian characters, while we are indulging our appetites to the injury of health, and while the pride of life controls.

(1870) 2T 400

80. All who are partakers of the divine nature will escape the corruption that is in the world through lust. It is impossible for those who indulge the appetite to attain to Christian perfection.

R. & H., Jan. 25, 1881

81. This is true sanctification. It is not merely a theory, an emotion, or a form of words, but a living, active principle, entering into the everyday life. It requires that our habits of eating, drinking, and dressing be such as to secure the preservation of physical, mental, and moral health, that we may

present to the Lord our bodies,—not an offering corrupted
by wrong habits, but "a living sacrifice, holy, acceptable
unto God."

[For context see 254]

(1900) 6T 372

82. Our habits of eating and drinking show whether we
are of the world or among the number whom the Lord by
His mighty cleaver of truth has separated from the world

Letter 135, 1902

83. It is intemperance in eating that causes so much in-
validism, and robs the Lord of the glory due Him. Because
of a failure to deny self, many of God's people are unable
to reach the high standard of spirituality He has set for them
and though they repent and are converted, all eternity will
testify to the loss they have sustained by yielding to selfishness.

(1909) 9T 165, 166

84. O how many lose the richest blessings that God has
in store for them in health and spiritual endowments! There
are many souls who wrestle for special victories and special
blessings that they may do some great thing. To this end
they are always feeling that they must make an agonizing
struggle in prayer and tears. When these persons search the
Scripture with prayer to know the expressed will of God
and then do His will from the heart without one reservation
or self-indulgence, they will find rest. All the agonizing, all
the tears and struggles, will not bring them the blessing they
long for. Self must be entirely surrendered. They must do
the work that presents itself, appropriating the abundance of
the grace of God which is promised to all who ask in faith

"If any man will come after Me," said Jesus, "let him deny
himself, and take up his cross daily, and follow Me." Luke
9:23. Let us follow the Saviour in His simplicity and self-
denial. Let us lift up the Man of Calvary by word and by
holy living. The Saviour comes very near to those who con-
secrate themselves to God. If ever there was a time when
we needed the working of the Spirit of God upon our hearts
and lives, it is now. Let us lay hold of this divine power
for strength to live a life of holiness and self-surrender

(1875) **3T** 491, 492

85. As our first parents lost Eden through the indulgence of appetite, our only hope of regaining Eden is through the firm denial of appetite and passion. Abstemiousness in diet, and control of all the passions, will preserve the intellect and give mental and moral vigor, enabling men to bring all their propensities under the control of the higher powers, and to discern between right and wrong, the sacred and the common. All who have a true sense of the sacrifice made by Christ in leaving His home in heaven to come to this world that He might by His own life show man how to resist temptation, will cheerfully deny itself and choose to be partakers with Christ of His sufferings.

The fear of the Lord is the beginning of wisdom. Those who overcome as Christ overcame will need to constantly guard themselves against the temptations of Satan. The appetite and passions should be restricted and under the control of enlightened conscience, that the intellect may be unimpaired, the perceptive powers clear, so that the workings of Satan and his snares may not be interpreted to be the providence of God. Many desire the final reward and victory which are to be given to overcomers, but are not willing to endure toil, privation, and denial of self, as did their Redeemer. It is only through obedience and continual effort that we shall overcome as Christ overcame.

The controlling power of appetite will prove the ruin of thousands, when, if they had conquered on this point, they would have had moral power to gain the victory over every other temptation of Satan. But those who are slaves to appetite will fail in perfecting Christian character. The continual transgression of man for six thousand years has brought sickness, pain, and death as its fruits. And as we near the close of time, Satan's temptation to indulge appetite will be more powerful and more difficult to overcome.

[C.T.B.H. 10] (1890) **C.H.** 22

86. He who cherishes the light which God has given him upon health reform has an important aid in the work of

becoming sanctified through the truth, and fitted for immor
tality.

[Relation of simple diet to spiritual discernment—119]
[Failure to control appetite weakens resistance to temptation
—237]
[Walls of self-control not to be broken down—260]
[Flesh diet a hindrance to spiritual advancement—655, 656
657, 660, 682, 683, 684, 688]
[Power for victory over other temptations given to those who
overcome on appetite—253]
[Character formation hindered by improper care of stomach
—719]

THE RELATION OF DIET TO MORALS
Moral Pollution in Early Times

(1864) Sp. Gifts IV, 121

87. The people who lived before the flood ate anima
food, and gratified their lusts until their cup of iniquity wa
full, and God cleansed the earth of its moral pollution by
a flood. . . .

Sin has prevailed since the fall. While a few have re
mained faithful to God, the great majority have corrupted
their ways before Him. The destruction of Sodom and
Gomorrah was on account of their great wickedness. They
gave loose rein to their intemperate appetites, then to their
corrupt passions, until they were so debased, and their sins
were so abominable, that their cup of iniquity was full
and they were consumed with fire from heaven.

(1873) 3T 163, 164

88. The same sins exist in our day which brought the
wrath of God upon the world in the days of Noah. Men and
women now carry their eating and drinking to gluttony and
drunkenness. This prevailing sin, the indulgence of per
verted appetite, inflamed the passions of men in the days of
Noah, and led to general corruption, until their violence
and crimes reached to heaven, and God washed the earth
of its moral pollution by a flood.

The same sins of gluttony and drunkenness benumbed
the moral sensibilities of the inhabitants of Sodom, so that
crimes seemed to be the delight of the men and women of

that wicked city. Christ thus warns the world: "Likewise also as it was in the days of Lot; they did eat, they drank, they bought, they sold, they planted, they builded; but the same day that Lot went out of Sodom, it rained fire and brimstone from heaven, and destroyed them all. Even thus shall it be in the day when the Son of man is revealed."

Christ has here left us a most important lesson. He does not in His teaching encourage indolence. His example was the opposite of this. Christ was an earnest worker. His life was one of self-denial, diligence, perseverance, industry, and economy. He would lay before us the danger of making eating and drinking paramount. He reveals the result of giving up to indulgence of appetite. The moral powers are enfeebled, so that sin does not appear sinful. Crimes are winked at, and base passions control the mind, until general corruption roots out good principles and impulses, and God is blasphemed. All this is the result of eating and drinking to excess. This is the very condition of things which He declares will exist at His second coming.

Will men and women be warned? Will they cherish the light, or will they become slaves to appetite and base passions? Christ presents to us something higher to toil for than merely what we shall eat, and what we shall drink, and wherewithal we shall be clothed. Eating, drinking, and dressing are carried to such excess that they become crimes, and are among the marked sins of the last days, and constitute a sign of Christ's soon coming. Time, money, and strength, which are the Lord's, but which He has entrusted to us, are wasted in needless superfluities of dress, and luxuries for the perverted appetite, which lessen vitality and bring suffering and decay. It is impossible to present our bodies a living sacrifice to God, when they are filled with corruption and disease by our own sinful indulgence.

Prevailing Corruptions Due to Unrestrained Appetite

(1864) Sp. Gifts IV, 124

89. Many marvel that the human race have so degenerated, physically, mentally, and morally. They do not under-

stand that it is the violation of God's constitution and laws, and the violation of the laws of health, that has produced this sad degeneracy. The transgression of God's commandments has caused His prospering hand to be removed.

Intemperance in eating and in drinking, and the indulgence of base passions, have benumbed the fine sensibilities, so that sacred things have been placed upon a level with common things.

(1864) Sp. Gifts IV, 131

90. Those who permit themselves to become slaves to a gluttonous appetite, often go still farther, and debase themselves by indulging their corrupt passions, which have become excited by intemperance in eating and in drinking. They give loose rein to their debasing passions, until health and intellect greatly suffer. The reasoning faculties are, in a great measure, destroyed by evil habits.

Health Reformer, October, 1871

91. Irregularity in eating and drinking, and improper dressing, deprave the mind and corrupt the heart, and bring the noble attributes of the soul in slavery to the animal passions.

R. & H., Jan. 25, 1881

92. Let none who profess godliness regard with indifference the health of the body, and flatter themselves that intemperance is no sin, and will not affect their spirituality. A close sympathy exists between the physical and the moral nature. The standard of virtue is elevated or degraded by the physical habits. Excessive eating of the best of food will produce a morbid condition of the moral feelings. And if the food is not the most healthful, the effects will be still more injurious. Any habit which does not promote healthful action in the human system, degrades the higher and nobler faculties. Wrong habits of eating and drinking lead to errors in thought and action. Indulgence of appetite strengthens the animal propensities, giving them the ascendancy over the mental and spiritual powers.

"Abstain from fleshly lusts, which war against the soul," is the language of the apostle Peter. Many regard this warning as applicable only to the licentious; but it has a broader meaning. It guards against every injurious gratification of appetite or passion. It is a most forcible warning against the use of such stimulants and narcotics as tea, coffee, tobacco, alcohol, and morphine. These indulgences may well be classed among the lusts that exert a pernicious influence upon moral character. The earlier these hurtful habits are formed, the more firmly will they hold their victim in slavery to lust, and the more certainly will they lower the standard of spirituality.

(1870) 2T 413, 414

93. You need to exercise temperance in all things. Cultivate the higher powers of the mind, and there will be less strength of growth of the animal. It is impossible for you to increase in spiritual strength while your appetite and passions are not under perfect control. Says the inspired apostle, "I keep under my body, and bring it into subjection; lest that by any means, when I have preached to others, I myself should be a castaway."

My brother, arouse yourself, I pray you, and let the work of the Spirit of God reach deeper than the external; let it reach down to the deep springs of every action. It is principle that is wanted, firm principle, and vigor of action in spiritual as well as temporal things. Your efforts lack earnestness. Oh, how many are low in the scale of spirituality, because they will not deny their appetite! The brain nerve energy is benumbed and almost paralyzed by overeating. When such go to the house of God upon the Sabbath, they cannot hold their eyes open. The most earnest appeals fail to arouse their leaden, insensible intellects. The truth may be presented with deep feeling; but it does not awaken the moral sensibilities, or enlighten the understanding. Have such studied to glorify God in all things?

Influence of a Simple Diet

(1869) 2T 352

94. If all who profess to obey the law of God were free from iniquity, my soul would be relieved; but they are not. Even some who profess to keep all the commandments of

God are guilty of the sin of adultery. What can I say to arouse their benumbed sensibilities? Moral principle, strictly carried out, becomes the only safeguard of the soul. If ever there was a time when the diet should be of the most simple kind, it is now. Meat should not be placed before our children. Its influence is to excite and strengthen the lower passions, and has a tendency to deaden the moral powers. Grains and fruits prepared free from grease, and in as natural a condition as possible, should be the food for the tables of all who claim to be preparing for translation to heaven. The less feverish the diet, the more easily can the passions be controlled. Gratification of taste should not be consulted irrespective of physical, intellectual, or moral health.

Indulgence of the baser passions will lead very many to shut their eyes to the light; for they fear that they will see sins which they are unwilling to forsake. All may see if they will. If they choose darkness rather than light, their criminality will be none the less. Why do not men and women read, and become intelligent upon these things, which so decidedly affect their physical, intellectual, and moral strength? God has given you a habitation to care for, and preserve in the best condition for His service and glory.

Temperance an Aid to Moral Control

(1870) 2T 404, 405

95. Your food is not of that simple, healthful quality which will make the best kind of blood. Foul blood will surely becloud the moral and intellectual powers, and arouse and strengthen the baser passions of your nature. Neither of you can afford a feverish diet; for it is at the expense of the health of the body, and the prosperity of your own souls and the souls of your children.

You place upon your table food which taxes the digestive organs, excites the animal passions, and weakens the moral and intellectual faculties. Rich food and flesh meats are no benefit to you. . . .

I entreat you, for Christ's sake, to set your house and hearts in order. Let the truth of heavenly origin elevate and sanctify you, soul, body, and spirit. "Abstain from fleshly lusts, which war against the soul." Brother G, your eating has a tendency to strengthen the baser passions. You do not control your body as it is your duty to do in order to perfect holiness in the fear of God. Temperance in eating must be practiced before you can be a patient man.

(1876) 4T 35, 36

96. The world should be no criterion for us. It is fashionable to indulge the appetite in luxurious food and unnatural stimulus, thus strengthening the animal propensities, and crippling the growth and development of the moral faculties. There is no encouragement given to any of the sons or daughters of Adam that they may become victorious overcomers in the Christian warfare unless they decide to practice temperance in all things. If they do this, they will not fight as one that beateth the air.

If Christians will keep the body in subjection, and bring all their appetites and passions under the control of enlightened conscience, feeling it a duty that they owe to God and to their neighbors to obey the laws which govern health and life, they will have the blessing of physical and mental vigor. They will have moral power to engage in the warfare against Satan; and in the name of Him who conquered appetite in their behalf, they may be more than conquerors on their own account. This warfare is open to all who will engage in it.

[Effect of flesh diet on moral power—658, 683, 684, 685, 686, 687]

[The country home—its relation to diet and morals—711]

[Lack of moral power due to indulgence of children in eating and drinking—347]

[Foods that cause irritability and nervousness—556, 558, 562, 574]

[Indulged appetite enfeebles moral powers—231]

Health Reform and the Third Angel's Message

Quotations in Section III

Health Reform and the Third Angel's Message

As the Hand to the Body

(1873) 3T 161, 162

97. December 10, 1871, I was again shown that the health reform is one branch of the great work which is to fit a people for the coming of the Lord. It is as closely connected with the third angel's message as the hand is with the body. The law of ten commandments has been lightly regarded by man; but the Lord would not come to punish the transgressors of that law without first sending them a message of warning. The third angel proclaims that message. Had men ever been obedient to the law of ten commandments, carrying out in their lives the principles of those precepts, the curse of disease now flooding the world would not be.

TO PREPARE A PEOPLE

Men and women cannot violate natural law by indulging depraved appetite and lustful passions, and not violate the law of God. Therefore He has permitted the light of health reform to shine upon us, that we may see our sin in violating the laws which He has established in our being. All our enjoyment or suffering may be traced to obedience or transgression of natural law. Our gracious heavenly Father sees the deplorable condition of men, who, some knowingly but many ignorantly, are living in violation of the laws that He has established. And in love and pity to the race, He causes the light to shine upon health reform. He publishes His law, and the penalty that will follow the transgression of it, that all may learn, and be careful to live in harmony with natural law. He proclaims His law so distinctly, and makes it so prominent, that it is like a city set on a hill. All accountable beings can understand it if they will. Idiots will not be responsible. To make plain natural law, and urge the obedience of it, is the work that accompanies the third angel's message, to prepare a people for the coming of the Lord.

ADAM'S DEFEAT—CHRIST'S VICTORY

Adam and Eve fell through intemperate appetite. Christ came and withstood the fiercest temptation of Satan, and, in behalf of the race, overcame appetite, showing that man may overcome. As Adam fell through appetite, and lost blissful Eden, the children of Adam may, through Christ, overcome appetite, and through temperance in all things regain Eden.

AIDS IN DISCERNING TRUTH

Ignorance is no excuse now for the transgression of law. The light shines clearly, and none need be ignorant, for the great God Himself is man's instructor. All are bound by the most sacred obligations to God to heed the sound philosophy and genuine experience which He is now giving them in reference to health reform. He designs that the great subject of health reform shall be agitated, and the public mind deeply stirred to investigate; for it is impossible for men and women, with all their sinful, health-destroying, brain-enervating habits, to discern sacred truth, through which they are to be sanctified, refined, elevated, and made fit for the society of heavenly angels in the kingdom of glory. . . .

SANCTIFIED OR PUNISHED

The apostle Paul exhorts the church, "I beseech you therefore, brethren, by the mercies of God, that ye present your bodies a living sacrifice, holy, acceptable unto God, which is your reasonable service." Men, then, can make their bodies unholy by sinful indulgences. If unholy, they are unfitted to be spiritual worshipers, and are not worthy of heaven. If man will cherish the light that God in mercy gives him upon health reform, he may be sanctified through the truth, and fitted for immortality. But if he disregards that light, and lives in violation of natural law, he must pay the penalty.

Work of Elijah and John a Type

(1872) 3T 61-64

98. For years the Lord has been calling the attention of His people to health reform. This is one of the great branches of the work of preparation for the coming of the

Son of man. John the Baptist went forth in the spirit and power of Elijah, to prepare the way of the Lord, and to turn the people to the wisdom of the just. He was a representative of those living in these last days, to whom God has entrusted sacred truths to present before the people, to prepare the way for the second appearing of Christ. John was a reformer. The angel Gabriel, direct from heaven, gave a discourse upon health reform to the father and mother of John. He said that he should not drink wine or strong drink, and that he should be filled with the Holy Ghost from his birth.

John separated himself from friends, and from the luxuries of life. The simplicity of his dress, a garment woven of camel's hair, was a standing rebuke to the extravagance and display of the Jewish priests, and of the people generally. His diet, purely vegetable, of locusts and wild honey, was a rebuke to the indulgence of appetite, and the gluttony that everywhere prevailed. The prophet Malachi declares, "Behold, I will send you Elijah the prophet before the coming of the great and dreadful day of the Lord; and he shall turn the heart of the fathers to the children, and the heart of the children to their fathers." Here the prophet describes the character of the work. Those who are to prepare the way for the second coming of Christ, are represented by faithful Elijah, as John came in the spirit of Elijah to prepare the way for Christ's first advent.

The great subject of reform is to be agitated, and the public mind is to be stirred. Temperance in all things is to be connected with the message, to turn the people of God from their idolatry, their gluttony, and their extravagance in dress and other things.

A MARKED CONTRAST

The self-denial, humility, and temperance required of the righteous, whom God especially leads and blesses, is to be presented to the people in contrast to the extravagant, health-destroying habits of those who live in this degenerate age. God has shown that health reform is as closely connected with the third angel's message as the hand is with the body. There is nowhere to be found so great a cause of physical and moral degeneracy as a neglect of this important subject. Those who indulge appetite and passion, and close their eyes to the light for fear they will see sinful indulgences which they are unwilling to forsake, are guilty before God.

Whoever turns from the light in one instance hardens his heart to disregard the light upon other matters. Whoever violates moral obligations in the matter of eating and dressing, prepares the way to violate the claims of God in regard to eternal interests. . . .

The people whom God is leading will be peculiar. They will not be like the world. But if they follow the leadings of God, they will accomplish His purposes, and will yield their will to His will. Christ will dwell in the heart. The temple of God will be holy. Your body, says the apostle, is the temple of the Holy Ghost.

God does not require His children to deny themselves to the injury of physical strength. He requires them to obey natural law, to preserve physical health. Nature's path is the road He marks out, and it is broad enough for any Christian. God has, with a lavish hand, provided us with rich and varied bounties for our sustenance and enjoyment. But in order for us to enjoy the natural appetite, which will preserve health and prolong life, He restricts the appetite. He says, Beware; restrain, deny, unnatural appetite. If we create a perverted appetite, we violate the laws of our being, and assume the responsibility of abusing our bodies and of bringing disease upon ourselves.

Give the Health Work Its Place

(1900) 6T 327

99. The indifference with which the health books have been treated by many is an offense to God. To separate the health work from the great body of the work is not in His order. Present truth lies in the work of health reform as verily as in other features of gospel work. No one branch, when separated from others, can be a perfect whole.

The gospel of health has able advocates, but their work has been made very hard because so many ministers, presidents of conferences, and others in positions of influence, have failed to give the question of health reform its proper attention. They have not recognized it in its relation to the work of the message as the right arm of the body. While very little respect has been shown to this department by many of the people, and by some of the ministers, the Lord has shown His regard for it by giving it abundant prosperity.

When properly conducted, the health work is an entering wedge, making a way for other truths to reach the heart. When the third angel's message is received in its fullness, health reform will be given its place in the councils of the conference, in the work of the church, in the home, at the table, and in all the household arrangements. Then the right arm will serve and protect the body.

But while the health work has its place in the promulgation of the third angel's message, its advocates must not in any way strive to make it take the place of the message.

Need for Self-Mastery

(1905) M.H. 129, 130

100. One of the most deplorable effects of the original apostasy was the loss of man's power of self-control. Only as this power is regained, can there be real progress.

The body is the only medium through which the mind and the soul are developed for the upbuilding of character. Hence it is that the adversary of souls directs his temptations to the enfeebling and degrading of the physical powers. His success here means the surrender to evil of the whole being. The tendencies of our physical nature, unless under the dominion of a higher power, will surely work ruin and death.

The body is to be brought into subjection. The higher powers of the being are to rule. The passions are to be controlled by the will, which is itself to be under the control of God. The kingly power of reason, sanctified by divine grace, is to bear sway in our lives.

The requirements of God must be brought home to the conscience. Men and women must be awakened to the duty of self-mastery, the need of purity, freedom from every depraving appetite and defiling habit. They need to be impressed with the fact that all their powers of mind and body are the gift of God, and are to be preserved in the best possible condition for His service.

Ministers and People to Act in Concert

(1867) 1T 469, 470

101. One important part of the work of the ministry is to faithfully present to the people the health reform, as it stands connected with the third angel's message, as a part and parcel of the same work. They should not fail to adopt it themselves, and should urge it upon all who profess to believe the truth.

(1867) 1T 486

102. The health reform, I was shown, is a part of the third angel's message, and is just as closely connected with it as are the arm and hand with the human body. I saw that we as a people must make an advance move in this great work. Ministers and people must act in concert. God's people are not prepared for the loud cry of the third angel. They have a work to do for themselves which they should not leave for God to do for them. He has left this work for them to do. It is an individual work; one cannot do it for another.

A Part of, but Not the Whole Message

(1867) 1T 559

103. The health reform is closely connected with the work of the third message, yet it is not the message. Our preachers should teach the health reform, yet they should not make this the leading theme in the place of the message. Its place is among those subjects which set forth the preparatory work to meet the events brought to view by the message; among these it is prominent. We should take hold of every reform with zeal, yet should avoid giving the impression that we are vacillating, and subject to fanaticism.

Letter 57, 1896

104. The health reform is as closely related to the third angel's message as the arm to the body; but the arm cannot take the place of the body. The proclamation of the third angel's message, the commandments of God and the testimony of Jesus, is the burden of our work. The message is to be proclaimed with a loud cry, and is to go to the whole world. The presentation of health principles must be united with this message, but must not in any case be independent of it, or in any way take the place of it.

Its Relation to Medical Institutions

MS 23, 1901

105. The sanitariums which are established are to be closely and inseparably bound up with the gospel. The Lord has given instruction that the gospel is to be carried forward; and the gospel includes health reform in all its phases. Our work is to enlighten the world; for it is blind to the movements which are taking place, preparing the way for the plagues which God will permit to come upon the world. God's faithful watchmen must give the warning. . . .

Health reform is to stand out more prominently in the proclamation of the third angel's message. The principles of health reform are found in the word of God. The gospel of health is to be firmly linked with the ministry of the word. It is the Lord's design that the restoring influence of health reform shall be a part of the last great effort to proclaim the gospel message.

Our physicians are to be God's workers. They are to be men whose powers have been sanctified and transformed by the grace of Christ. Their influence is to be knit up with the truth that is to be given to the world. In perfect and complete unity with the gospel ministry, the work of health reform will reveal its God-given power. Under the influence of the gospel, great reforms will be made by medical missionary work. But separate medical missionary work from the gospel, and the work will be crippled.

Letter 146, 1909

106. Our sanitariums and our churches may reach a higher, holier standard. Health reform is to be taught and practiced by our people. The Lord is calling for a revival of the principles of health reform. Seventh-day Adventists have a special work to do as messengers to labor for the souls and bodies of men.

Christ has said of His people, "Ye are the light of the world." We are the Lord's denominated people, to proclaim the truths of heavenly origin. The most solemn, sacred work ever given to mortals is the proclamation of the first, second, and third angels' messages to our world. In our large cities there should be health institutes to care for the sick, and to teach the grand principles of health reform.

An Entering Wedge

Letter 203, 1905

107. I have been instructed that we are not to delay to do the work that needs to be done in health reform lines. Through this work we are to reach souls in the highways and the byways.

[Tract] (1893) C.H. 535

108. I can see in the Lord's providence that the medical missionary work is to be a great entering wedge, whereby the diseased soul may be reached.

To Remove Prejudice—Increase Influence

(1890) C.T.B.H. 121, 122

109. Much of the prejudice that prevents the truth of the third angel's message from reaching the hearts of the people, might be removed if more attention were given to health reform. When people become interested in this subject, the way is often prepared for the entrance of other truths. If they see that we are intelligent with regard to health, they will be more ready to believe that we are sound in Bible doctrines.

This branch of the Lord's work has not received due attention, and through this neglect much has been lost. If the church would manifest a greater interest in the reforms through which God Himself is seeking to fit them for His coming, their influence would be far greater than it now is. God has spoken to His people, and He designs that they shall hear and obey His voice. Although the health reform is not the third angel's message, it is closely connected with it. Those who proclaim the message should teach health reform also. It is a subject that we must understand, in order to be prepared for the events that are close upon us, and it should have a prominent place. Satan and his agents are seeking to hinder this work of reform, and will do all they can to perplex and burden those who heartily engage in it. Yet none should be discouraged at this, or cease their efforts because of it. The prophet Isaiah speaks thus of one characteristic of Christ, "He shall not fail nor be discouraged, till He have set judgment in the earth." Then let not His followers talk of failure or discouragement, but remember the price paid to rescue man that he might not perish, but have eternal life.

(1909) 9T 112, 113

110. The work of health reform is the Lord's means for lessening suffering in our world and for purifying His church. Teach the people that they can act as God's helping hand, by cooperating with the Master Worker in restoring physical and spiritual health. This work bears the signature of heaven, and will open doors for the entrance of other precious truths. There is room for all to labor who will take hold of this work intelligently.

[See *Medical Ministry*, Section 2, "The Divine Plan in the Medical Missionary Work," and Section 13, "Medical Missionary Work and the Gospel Ministry"]

SECTION IV

The Proper Dietary

Quotations in Section IV

The Proper Dietary

PART I—THE ORIGINAL DIET

Chosen by the Creator

(1905) M.H. 295, 296

111. In order to know what are the best foods, we must study God's original plan for man's diet. He who created man and who understands his needs appointed Adam his food. "Behold," He said, "I have given you every herb yielding seed, . . . and every tree, in which is the fruit of a tree yielding seed; to you it shall be for food." Upon leaving Eden to gain his livelihood by tilling the earth under the curse of sin, man received permission to eat also "the herb of the field."

Grains, fruits, nuts, and vegetables constitute the diet chosen for us by our Creator. These foods, prepared in as simple and natural a manner as possible, are the most healthful and nourishing. They impart a strength, a power of endurance, and a vigor of intellect, that are not afforded by a more complex and stimulating diet.

(1864) Sp. Gifts IV, 120

112. God gave our first parents the food He designed that the race should eat. It was contrary to His plan to have the life of any creature taken. There was to be no death in Eden. The fruit of the trees in the garden, was the food man's wants required.

[For context see 639]

A Call to Return

(Written 1890) E. from U.T. 5, 6

113. The Lord intends to bring His people back to live upon simple fruits, vegetables, and grains. . . . God provided fruit in its natural state for our first parents.

(1902) 7T 125, 126

114. God is working in behalf of His people. He does not desire them to be without resources. He is bringing them back to the diet originally given to man. Their diet is

to consist of the foods made from the materials He has provided. The materials principally used in these foods will be fruits and grains and nuts, but various roots will also be used.

Letter 3, 1884

115. Again and again I have been shown that God is bringing His people back to His original design, that is, not to subsist upon the flesh of dead animals. He would have us teach people a better way. . . .

If meat is discarded, if the taste is not educated in that direction, if a liking for fruits and grains is encouraged, it will soon be as God in the beginning designed it should be. No meat will be used by His people.

[Israel brought back to the original diet—644]
[God's purpose in restricting Israel's diet—641, 643, 644]

PART II—THE SIMPLE DIET
An Aid to Quick Perception

(1869) 2T 352

116. If ever there was a time when the diet should be of the most simple kind, it is now.

(1880) 4T 515, 516

117. God wants men to cultivate force of character. Those who are merely timeservers are not the ones who will receive a rich reward by and by. He wants those who labor in His cause to be men of keen feeling and quick perception. They should be temperate in eating; rich and luxurious food should find no place upon their tables; and when the brain is constantly taxed, and there is a lack of physical exercise, they should eat sparingly, even of plain food. Daniel's clearness of mind and firmness of purpose, his strength of intellect in acquiring knowledge, were due in a great degree to the plainness of his diet, in connection with his life of prayer

[Simple diet chosen by Daniel—33, 34, 241, 242]

(1885) 5T 311

118. My dear friends, instead of taking a course to baffle disease, you are petting it and yielding to its power. You should avoid the use of drugs, and carefully observe the laws

Letter 309, 1905

122. We are all to consider that there is to be no extravagance in any line. We must be satisfied with pure, simple food, prepared in a simple manner. This should be the diet of high and low. Adulterated substances are to be avoided. We are preparing for the future, immortal life in the kingdom of heaven. We expect to do our work in the light and in the power of the great, mighty Healer. All are to act the self-sacrificing part.

Health Reformer, August, 1866

123. Many have inquired of me, What course shall I take best to preserve my health? My answer is, Cease to transgress the laws of your being; cease to gratify a depraved appetite, eat simple food, dress healthfully, which will require modest simplicity, work healthfully, and you will not be sick.

Camp Meeting Diet

(1870) 2T 602, 603

124. Nothing should be taken to camp meeting except the most healthful articles, cooked in a simple manner, free from all spices and grease.

I am convinced that none need to make themselves sick preparing for camp meeting, if they observe the laws of health in their cooking. If they make no cake or pies, but cook simple graham bread, and depend on fruit, canned or dried, they need not get sick in preparing for the meeting, and they need not be sick while at the meeting. None should go through the entire meeting without some warm food. There are always cookstoves upon the ground, where this may be obtained.

Brethren and sisters must not be sick upon the encampment. If they clothe themselves properly in the chill of morning and night, and are particular to vary their clothing according to the changing weather, so as to preserve proper circulation, and strictly observe regularity in sleeping and in eating of simple food, taking nothing between meals, they need not be sick. They may be well during the meeting, their minds may be clear, and able to appreciate the truth, and they may return to their homes refreshed in body and spirit. Those who have been engaged in hard labor from day to day now cease their exercise; therefore they should not eat their average amount of food. If they do, their stomachs will be overtaxed.

We wish to have the brain power especially vigorous at these meetings, and in the most healthy condition to hear the truth, appreciate it, and retain it, that all may practice it after their return from the meeting. If the stomach is burdened with too much food, even of a simple character, the brain force is called to the aid of the digestive organs. There is a benumbed sensation upon the brain. It is almost impossible to keep the eyes open. The very truths which should be heard, understood, and practiced, are entirely lost through indisposition, or because the brain is almost paralyzed in consequence of the amount of food eaten.

I would advise all to take something warm into the stomach, every morning at least. You can do this without much labor. You can make graham gruel. If the graham flour is too coarse, sift it, and while the gruel is hot, add milk. This will make a most palatable and healthful dish for the campground. And if your bread is dry, crumb it into the gruel, and it will be enjoyed. I do not approve of eating much cold food, for the reason that the vitality must be drawn from the system to warm the food until it becomes of the same temperature as the stomach before the work of digestion can be carried on. Another very simple yet wholesome dish, is beans boiled or baked. Dilute a portion of them with water, add milk or cream, and make a broth; the bread can be used as in graham gruel.

[Selling candies, ice cream, etc., on campground—529, 530]
[Needless cooking in preparing for camp meeting—57]

The Picnic Lunch

(1867) 1T 514

125. Let several families living in a city or village unite and leave the occupations which have taxed them physically and mentally, and make an excursion into the country, to the side of a fine lake, or to a nice grove, where the scenery of nature is beautiful. They should provide themselves with

plain, hygienic food, the very best fruits and grains, and spread their table under the shade of some tree or under the canopy of heaven. The ride, the exercise, and the scenery will quicken the appetite, and they can enjoy a repast which kings might envy.

[Avoid excess in cooking—793]
[Advice to sedentary workers—225]
[Simplicity in Sabbath dietary—56]

Letter 135, 1902

126. Let those who advocate health reform strive earnestly to make it all that they claim it is. Let them discard everything detrimental to health. Use simple, wholesome food. Fruit is excellent, and saves much cooking. Discard rich pastries, cakes, desserts, and the other dishes prepared to tempt the appetite. Eat fewer kinds of food at one meal, and eat with thanksgiving.

Simplicity in Entertaining

(1900) 6T 345

127. Christ has given in His own life a lesson of hospitality. When surrounded by the hungry multitude beside the sea, He did not send them unrefreshed to their homes. He said to His disciples, "Give ye them to eat." Matt. 14:16. And by an act of creative power He supplied food sufficient to satisfy their need. Yet how simple was the food provided! There were no luxuries. He who had all the resources of heaven at His command could have spread for the people a rich repast. But He supplied only that which would suffice for their need, that which was the daily food of the fisherfolk about the sea.

If men were today simple in their habits, living in harmony with nature's laws, there would be an abundant supply for all the needs of the human family. There would be fewer imaginary wants, and more opportunity to work in God's ways. Christ did not seek to attract men to Him by gratifying the desire for luxury. The simple fare He provided was an assurance not only of His power but of His love, of His tender care for them in the common needs of life.

(1865) H. to L., ch. 1, 54, 55

128. Men and women who profess to be followers of Christ, are often slaves to fashion, and to a gluttonous appetite. Preparatory to fashionable gatherings, time and strength, which should be devoted to higher and nobler purposes, are expended in cooking a variety of unwholesome dishes. Because it is fashion, many who are poor and dependent upon their daily labor, will be to the expense of preparing different kinds of rich cakes, preserves, pies, and a variety of fashionable food for visitors, which only injure those who partake of them; when, at the same time they need the amount thus expended, to purchase clothing for themselves and children. This time occupied in cooking food to gratify the taste at the expense of the stomach should be devoted to the moral and religious instruction of their children.

Fashionable visiting is made an occasion of gluttony. Hurtful food and drinks are partaken of in such a measure as to greatly tax the organs of digestion. The vital forces are called into unnecessary action in the disposal of it, which produces exhaustion, and greatly disturbs the circulation of the blood, and, as a result, want of vital energy is felt throughout the system. The blessings which might result from social visiting, are often lost for the reason that your entertainer, instead of being profited by your conversation, is toiling over the cookstove, preparing a variety of dishes for you to feast upon. Christian men and women should never permit their influence to countenance such a course by eating of the dainties thus prepared. Let them understand that your object in visiting them is not to indulge the appetite, but that your associating together, and interchange of thoughts and feelings, might be a mutual blessing. The conversation should be of that elevated, ennobling character which could afterward be called to remembrance with feelings of the highest pleasure.

(1865) H. to L., ch. 1, 55, 56

129. Those who entertain visitors, should have wholesome, nutritious food, from fruits, grains, and vegetables, prepared in a simple, tasteful manner. Such cooking will require but little extra labor or expense, and, partaken of in

moderate quantities, will not injure any one. If worldlings choose to sacrifice time, money, and health, to gratify the appetite, let them do so, and pay the penalty of the violation of the laws of health; but Christians should take their position in regard to these things, and exert their influence in the right direction. They can do much in reforming these fashionable, health and soul destroying customs.

[Example of Christians at their table a help to those weak in self-control—354]

[Elaborate feasts a burden and an injury—214]

[Effect of elaborate entertaining upon one's own children and family—348]

[Sin of spare diet for family, and excess for visitors—284]

[A simple diet best for children—349, 356, 357, 360, 365]

[Simplicity in preparation of health foods—399, 400, 401, 402, 403, 404, 405, 407, 410]

Ready for the Unexpected Guest

(1905) M.H. 322

130. Some householders stint the family table in order to provide expensive entertainment for visitors. This is unwise. In the entertainment of guests there should be greater simplicity. Let the needs of the family have first attention.

Unwise economy and artificial customs often prevent the exercise of hospitality where it is needed and would be a blessing. The regular supply of food for our tables should be such that the unexpected guest can be made welcome without burdening the housewife to make extra preparation.

[E. G. White's practice—no extra cooking for visitors—Appendix I:8]

[Simple food served in the White home—Appendix I:1, 13, 14, 15]

[The menu to be varied from meal to meal and prepared with nicety—320]

Think Less About Temporal Food

Letter 73, 1896

131. We must be constantly meditating upon the word, eating it, digesting it, and by practice, assimilating it, so that it is taken into the life current. He who feeds on Christ daily will by his example teach others to think less of that

which they eat, and to feel much greater anxiety for the food
they give to the soul.

The true fasting which should be recommended to all, is
abstinence from every stimulating kind of food, and the
proper use of wholesome, simple food, which God has provided in abundance. Men need to think less about what
they shall eat and drink, of temporal food, and much more
in regard to the food from heaven, that will give tone and
vitality to the whole religious experience.

Reforming Influence of the Simple Life

(1882) 5T 206

132. Should we dress in plain, modest apparel without
reference to the fashions; should our tables at all times be
set with simple, healthful food, avoiding all luxuries, all
extravagance; should our houses be built with becoming
plainness, and furnished in the same manner, it would show
the sanctifying power of the truth, and would have a telling
influence upon unbelievers. But while we conform to the
world in these matters, in some cases apparently seeking to
excel worldlings in fanciful arrangement, the preaching of
the truth will have but little or no effect. Who will believe
the solemn truth for this time, when those who already profess to believe it contradict their faith by their works? It is
not God who has closed the windows of heaven to us, but
it is our own conformity to the customs and practices of the
world.

(1905) M.H. 47

133. It was by a miracle of divine power that Christ fed
the multitude; yet how humble was the fare provided,—
only the fishes and barley loaves that were the daily fare of
the fisherfolk of Galilee.

Christ could have spread for the people a rich repast, but
food prepared merely for the gratification of appetite would
have conveyed no lesson for their good. Through this miracle Christ desired to teach a lesson of simplicity. If men
today were simple in their habits, living in harmony with
nature's laws, as did Adam and Eve in the beginning, there

would be an abundant supply for the needs of the human family. But selfishness and the indulgence of appetite have brought sin and misery, from excess on the one hand, and from want on the other.

(1875) 3T 401

134. If professed Christians would use less of their wealth in adorning the body and in beautifying their own houses, and would consume less in extravagant health-destroying luxuries upon their tables, they could place much larger sums in the treasury of God. They would thus imitate their Redeemer, who left heaven, His riches, and His glory, and for our sakes became poor, that we might have eternal riches.

PART III—AN ADEQUATE DIET

Not a Matter of Indifference

[C.T.B.H. 49, 50] (1890) C.H. 118

135. Because it is wrong to eat merely to gratify perverted taste, it does not follow that we should be indifferent in regard to our food. It is a matter of the highest importance. No one should adopt an impoverished diet. Many are debilitated from disease, and need nourishing, well-cooked food. Health reformers, above all others, should be careful to avoid extremes. The body must have sufficient nourishment. The God who gives His beloved sleep has furnished them also suitable food to sustain the physical system in a healthy condition.

(1905) M.H. 271

136. In order to have good health, we must have good blood; for the blood is the current of life. It repairs waste, and nourishes the body. When supplied with the proper food elements and when cleansed and vitalized by contact with pure air, it carries life and vigor to every part of the system. The more perfect the circulation, the better will his work be accomplished.

[Relation of adequate diet to soundness of mind—314]
[Relation of adequate diet to sound spiritual experience—24, par. 4]

God's Bountiful Provision

[C.T.B.H. 47] (1890) C.H. 114, 115

137. God has furnished man with abundant means for the gratification of an unperverted appetite. He has spread before him the products of the earth,—a bountiful variety of food that is palatable to the taste and nutritious to the system. Of these our benevolent heavenly Father says we may freely eat. Fruits, grains, and vegetables, prepared in a simple way, free from spice and grease of all kinds, make with milk or cream, the most healthful diet. They impart nourishment to the body, and give a power of endurance and a vigor of intellect that are not produced by a stimulating diet.

MS 27, 1906

138. In grains, fruits, vegetables, and nuts are to be found all the food elements that we need. If we will come to the Lord in simplicity of mind, He will teach us how to prepare wholesome food free from the taint of flesh meat.

An Impoverished Diet Discredits Health Reform

Letter 135, 1902

139. Some of our people conscientiously abstain from eating improper food, and at the same time neglect to eat the food that would supply the elements necessary for the proper sustenance of the body. Let us never bear testimony against health reform by failing to use wholesome, palatable food in place of the harmful articles of diet that we have discarded. Much tact and discretion should be employed in preparing nourishing food to take the place of that which has constituted the diet of many families. This effort requires faith in God, earnestness of purpose, and a willingness to help one another. A diet lacking in the proper elements of nutrition brings reproach upon the cause of health reform. We are mortal, and must supply ourselves with food that will give proper sustenance to the body.

[An impoverished diet not recommended—315, 317, 318, 388]
[An impoverished diet the result of extreme views—316]
[Guarding against impoverished diet when discarding flesh meat—320, 816]

[Spiritual experience not deepened by impoverished diet—323]
[Instance of members of a family perishing for lack of simple, nourishing food—329]

[C.T.B.H. 58] (1890) C.H. 155, 156

140. Investigate your habits of diet. Study from cause to effect, but do not bear false witness against health reform by ignorantly pursuing a course which militates against it. Do not neglect or abuse the body, and thus unfit it to render to God that service which is His due. To my certain knowledge, some of the most useful workers in our cause have died through such neglect. To care for the body by providing for it food which is relishable and strengthening, is one of the first duties of the householder. Better by far have less expensive clothing and furniture, than to scrimp the supply of necessary articles for the table.

Adjusting the Diet to Individual Needs

(1902) 7T 133, 134

141. In the use of foods, we should exercise good, sound common sense. When we find that a certain food does not agree with us, we need not write letters of inquiry to learn the cause of the disturbance. Change the diet; use less of some foods; try other preparations. Soon we shall know the effect that certain combinations have on us. As intelligent human beings, let us individually study the principles, and use our experience and judgment in deciding what foods are best for us.

[Not all can subsist on the same diet—322]

(1905) M.H. 297

142. God has given us an ample variety of healthful foods, and each person should choose from it the things that experience and sound judgment prove to be best suited to his own necessities.

Nature's abundant supply of fruits, nuts, and grains is ample, and year by year the products of all lands are more generally distributed to all, by the increased facilities for transportation. As a result, many articles of food which a few years ago were regarded as expensive luxuries, are now within the reach of all as foods for everyday use. This is especially the case with dried and canned fruits.

[Not to limit diet in anticipation of time of trouble—323]
[Variety and nicety in preparation—320]
[Adequate diet in our sanitariums—426, 427, 428, 429, 430]
[No impoverished diet in the White home—Appendix I:8, 17]

PART IV—DIET IN VARIOUS COUNTRIES

Suited to Season and Climate

Letter 14, 1901

143. The foods used should correspond to the climate. Some foods suitable for one country would not do at all in another place.

(1905) M.H. 296, 297

144. Not all foods wholesome in themselves are equally suited to our needs under all circumstances. Care should be taken in the selection of food. Our diet should be suited to the season, to the climate in which we live, and to the occupation we follow. Some foods that are adapted for use at one season or in one climate are not suited to another. So there are different foods best suited for persons in different occupations. Often food that can be used with benefit by those engaged in hard physical labor is unsuitable for persons of sedentary pursuits or intense mental application. God has given us an ample variety of healthful foods, and each person should choose from it the things that experience and sound judgment prove to be best suited to his own necessities.

Nourishing Foods Found in Every Land

Letter 135, 1902

145. Let us make intelligent advancement in simplifying our diet. In the providence of God, every country produces articles of food containing the nourishment necessary for the upbuilding of the system. These may be made into healthful, appetizing dishes.

(1905) M.H. 299

146. If we plan wisely, that which is most conducive to health can be secured in almost every land. The various

preparations of rice, wheat, corn, and oats are sent abroad everywhere, also beans, peas, and lentils. These, with native or imported fruits, and the variety of vegetables that grow in each locality, give an opportunity to select a dietary that is complete without the use of flesh meats. . . . Wherever dried fruits, such as raisins, prunes, apples, pears, peaches, and apricots, are obtainable at moderate prices, it will be found that they can be used as staple articles of diet much more freely than is customary, with the best results to the health and vigor of all classes of workers.

A Suggestion for the Tropics

Letter 91, 1898

147. In warm, heating climates, there should be given to the worker, in whatever line of work he is to do, less work than in a more bracing climate. The Lord remembers that we are but dust. . . .

The less sugar introduced into the food in its preparation, the less difficulty will be experienced because of the heat of the climate.

Tact Needed in Teaching Health Reform

Letter 37, 1901

148. In order to do our work in straight, simple lines, we must recognize the conditions to which the human family are subjected. God has made provisions for those who live in the different countries of the world. Those who desire to be co-workers with God must consider carefully how they teach health reform in God's great vineyard. They must move carefully in specifying just what food should and should not be eaten. The human messenger must unite with the divine Helper in presenting the message of mercy to the multitudes God would save.

[For context see 324]
[Especial care needed in new countries and poverty-stricken districts regarding meat, milk, and eggs—324]

(1909) 9T 159

149. We do not mark out any precise line to be followed in diet; but we do say that in countries where there are

fruits, grain, and nuts in abundance, flesh food is not the right food for God's people.

(1902) 7T 126

150. The Lord desires those living in countries where fresh fruit can be obtained during a large part of the year, to awake to the blessing they have in this fruit. The more we depend upon the fresh fruit just as it is plucked from the tree, the greater will be the blessing.

[For context see 397]

An Assurance of Divine Guidance

(1902) 7T 124, 125

151. The Lord will teach many in all parts of the world to combine fruits, grains, and vegetables into foods that will sustain life and will not bring disease. Those who have never seen the recipes for making the health foods now on the market, will work intelligently, experimenting with the food productions of the earth, and will be given light regarding the use of these productions. The Lord will show them what to do. He who gives skill and understanding to His people in one part of the world will give skill and understanding to His people in other parts of the world. It is His design that the food treasures of each country shall be so prepared that they can be used in the countries for which they are suited. As God gave manna from heaven to sustain the children of Israel, so He will now give His people in different places skill and wisdom to use the productions of these countries in preparing foods to take the place of meat.

(1902) 7T 133

152. It is the Lord's design that in every place men and women shall be encouraged to develop their talents by preparing healthful foods from the natural products of their own section of the country. If they look to God, exercising their skill and ingenuity under the guidance of His Spirit, they will learn how to prepare natural products into healthful foods. Thus they will be able to teach the poor how to provide themselves with foods that will take the place of flesh meats. Those thus helped can in turn instruct others.

Such a work will yet be done with consecrated zeal and energy. If it had been done before, there would today be many more people in the truth, and many more who could give instruction. Let us learn what our duty is, and then do it. We are not to be dependent and helpless, waiting for others to do the work that God has committed to us.

[See also 401, 407]

SECTION V

Physiology of Digestion

Quotations in Section V

Physiology of Digestion

The Reward of Respecting Nature's Laws

Letter 274, 1908

153. Respect paid to the proper treatment of the stomach will be rewarded in clearness of thought and strength of mind. Your digestive organs will not be prematurely worn out to testify against you. We are to show that we appreciate our God-given intelligence by eating and studying and working wisely. A sacred duty devolves upon us to keep the body in such a state that we shall have a sweet, clean breath. We are to appreciate the light God has given on health reform, by word and practice reflecting clear light to others upon this subject.

Physical Effects of Overeating

(1870) 2T 364

154. What influence does overeating have upon the stomach? It becomes debilitated, the digestive organs are weakened, and disease, with all its train of evils, is brought on as the result. If persons were diseased before, they thus increase the difficulties upon them, and lessen their vitality every day they live. They call their vital powers into unnecessary action to take care of the food that they place in their stomachs.

Letter 73a, 1896

155. Often this intemperance is felt at once in the form of headache, indigestion, and colic. A load has been placed upon the stomach that it cannot care for, and a feeling of oppression comes. The head is confused, the stomach is in rebellion. But these results do not always follow overeating. In some cases the stomach is paralyzed. No sensation of pain is felt, but the digestive organs lose their vital force. The foundation of the human machinery is gradually undermined, and life is rendered very unpleasant.

Letter 142, 1900

156. I advise you to make your diet abstemious. Be sure that as a rational Christian sentinel you guard the door of your stomach, allowing nothing to pass your lips that will be an enemy to your health and life. God holds you responsible to obey the light He has given you on health reform. The rush of blood to the head must be overcome. There are large blood vessels in the limbs for the purpose of distributing the life-giving current to all parts of the body. The fire you kindle in your stomach is making your brain like a heated furnace. Eat much more sparingly, and eat simple food, which does not require heavy seasoning. Your animal passions should be starved, not pampered and fed. The congestion of blood in the brain is strengthening the animal instincts and weakening spiritual powers. . . .

What you need is less temporal food and much more spiritual food, more of the bread of life. The simpler your diet, the better it will be for you.

Clogs the Machinery

(1870) 2T 412, 413

157. My brother, you have much to learn. You indulge your appetite by eating more food than your system can convert into good blood. It is sin to be intemperate in the quantity of food eaten, even if the quality is unobjectionable. Many feel that if they do not eat meat and the grosser articles of food, they may eat of simple food until they cannot well eat more. This is a mistake. Many professed health reformers are nothing less than gluttons. They lay upon the digestive organs so great a burden that the vitality of the system is exhausted in the effort to dispose of it. It also has a depressing influence upon the intellect; for the brain nerve power is called upon to assist the stomach in its work. Overeating, even of the simplest food, benumbs the sensitive nerves of the brain, and weakens its vitality. Overeating has a worse effect upon the system than overworking; the energies of the soul are more effectually prostrated by intemperate eating than by intemperate working.

The digestive organs should never be burdened with a quantity or quality of food which it will tax the system to appropriate. All that is taken into the stomach, above what the system can use to convert into good blood, clogs the machinery; for it cannot be made into either flesh or blood, and its presence burdens the liver, and produces a morbid condition of the system. The stomach is overworked in its efforts to dispose of it, and then there is a sense of languor, which is interpreted to mean hunger, and without allowing the digestive organs time to rest from their severe labor, to recruit their energies, another immoderate amount is taken into the stomach, to set the weary machinery again in motion. The system receives less nourishment from too great a quantity of food, even of the right quality, than from a moderate quantity taken at regular periods.

DIGESTION AIDED BY MODERATE EXERCISE

My brother, your brain is benumbed. A man who disposes of the quantity of food that you do, should be a laboring man. Exercise is important to digestion, and to a healthy condition of body and mind. You need physical exercise. You move and act as if you were wooden, as though you had no elasticity. Healthy, active exercise is what you need. This will invigorate the mind. Neither study nor violent exercise should be engaged in immediately after a full meal; this would be a violation of the laws of the system. Immediately after eating there is a strong draft upon the nervous energy. The brain force is called into active exercise to assist the stomach; therefore, when the mind or body is taxed heavily after eating, the process of digestion is hindered. The vitality of the system, which is needed to carry on the work in one direction, is called away and set to work in another.

(1890) C.T.B.H. 101

158. Exercise aids the dyspeptic by giving the digestive organs a healthy tone. To engage in deep study or violent exercise immediately after eating, hinders the digestive process; for the vitality of the system, which is needed to carry on the work of digestion, is called away to other parts. But

a short walk after a meal, with the head erect and the shoulders back, exercising moderately, is a great benefit. The mind is diverted from self to the beauties of nature. The less the attention is called to the stomach, the better. If you are in constant fear that your food will hurt you, it most assuredly will. Forget your troubles; think of something cheerful.

[Overeating causes excess flow of blood to the brain—276]
[Exercise especially needful to those of sluggish temperament —225]
[Disturbed sleep resulting from late suppers—270]
[The cause of that faint feeling—213, 218, 245, 269, 270, 561, 705, 707]
[Indulgence weakens digestive organs and lessens power to assimilate—202]
[The stomach needs quiet rest—267]

Aided by Pure Air

(1868) 1T 702

159. The influence of pure, fresh air is to cause the blood to circulate healthfully through the system. It refreshes the body, and tends to render it strong and healthy, while at the same time its influence is decidedly felt upon the mind, imparting a degree of composure and serenity. It excites the appetite, and renders the digestion of food more perfect, and induces sound and sweet sleep.

(1905) M.H. 272, 273

160. The lungs should be allowed the greatest freedom possible. Their capacity is developed by free action; it diminishes if they are cramped and compressed. Hence the ill effects of the practice so common, especially in sedentary pursuits, of stooping at one's work. In this position it is impossible to breathe deeply. Superficial breathing soon becomes a habit, and the lungs lose their power to expand. A similar effect is produced by tight lacing. . . .

Thus an insufficient supply of oxygen is received. The blood moves sluggishly. The waste, poisonous matter, which should be thrown off in the exhalations from the lungs, is retained, and the blood becomes impure. Not only the lungs, but the stomach, liver, and brain are affected. The skin becomes sallow, digestion is retarded; the heart is depressed; the brain is clouded; the thoughts are confused; **gloom set-**

tles upon the spirits; the whole system becomes depressed and inactive, and peculiarly susceptible to disease.

Hindered by Liquid Diet

(1872) 3T 74

161. Had your physical health been unimpaired, you would have made an eminently useful woman. You have long been diseased, and this has affected your imagination so that your thoughts have been concentrated upon yourself, and the imagination has affected the body. Your habits have not been good in many respects. Your food has not been of the right quantity or quality. You have eaten too largely, and of a poor quality of food, which could not be converted into good blood. You have educated the stomach to this kind of diet. This, your judgment has taught you, was the best, because you realized the least disturbance from it. But this was not a correct experience. Your stomach was not receiving that vigor that it should from your food. Taken in a liquid state, your food would not give healthful vigor or tone to the system. But when you change this habit, and eat more solids and less liquids, your stomach will feel disturbed. Notwithstanding this, you should not yield the point; you should educate your stomach to bear a more solid diet.

Letter 9, 1887

162. I told them that the preparation of their food was wrong, and that living principally on soups and coffee and bread was not health reform; that so much liquid taken into the stomach was not healthful, and that all who subsisted on such a diet placed a great tax upon the kidneys, and so much watery substance debilitated the stomach.

I was thoroughly convinced that many in the establishment were suffering with indigestion because of eating this kind of food. The digestive organs were enfeebled and the blood impoverished. Their breakfast consisted of coffee and bread with the addition of prune sauce. This was not healthful. The stomach, after rest and sleep, was better able to take care of a substantial meal than when wearied

with work. Then the noon meal was generally soup, sometimes meat. The stomach is small, but the appetite, unsatisfied, partakes largely of this liquid food; so it is burdened.

[Fruit will allay the irritation that calls for so much drink at
meals—475]

Food to Be Warm, but Not Hot

(1870) 2T 603

163. I would advise all to take something warm into
the stomach, every morning at least. You can do this without much labor.

Letter 14, 1901

164. Hot drinks are not required, except as a medicine.
The stomach is greatly injured by a large quantity of hot
food and hot drink. Thus the throat and digestive organs,
and through them the other organs of the body, are enfeebled.

Vital Force Depleted by Cold Food

(1905) M.H. 305

165. Food should not be eaten very hot or very cold. If
food is cold, the vital force of the stomach is drawn upon
in order to warm it before digestion can take place. Cold
drinks are injurious for the same reason; while the free use
of hot drinks is debilitating.

[Vitality drawn upon in warming much cold food in stomach
—124]

[C.T.B.H. 51] (1890) C.H. 119, 120

166. Many make a mistake in drinking cold water with
their meals. Food should not be washed down. Taken with
meals, water diminishes the flow of saliva; and the colder
the water, the greater the injury to the stomach. Ice water
or ice lemonade, taken with meals, will arrest digestion until
the system has imparted sufficient warmth to the stomach
to enable it to take up its work again. Masticate slowly,
and allow the saliva to mingle with the food.

The more liquid there is taken into the stomach with the
meals, the more difficult it is for the food to digest; for the
liquid must first be absorbed.

[Drinking water with meals—731]

A Caution to Busy People

Letter 274, 1908

167. I am instructed to say to the workers in our sanitariums and to the teachers and students in our schools that there is need of guarding ourselves upon the point of appetite. There is danger of becoming lax in this respect, and of letting our individual cares and responsibilities so absorb our time that we shall not take time to eat as we should. My message to you is, Take time to eat, and do not crowd into the stomach a great variety of foods at one meal. To eat hurriedly of several kinds of food at a meal is a serious mistake.

Eat Slowly, Masticate Thoroughly

[C.T.B.H. 51, 52] (1890) C.H. 120

168. In order to secure healthy digestion, food should be eaten slowly. Those who wish to avoid dyspepsia, and those who realize their obligation to keep all their powers in a condition which will enable them to render the best service to God, will do well to remember this. If your time to eat is limited, do not bolt your food, but eat less, and masticate slowly. The benefit derived from food does not depend so much on the quantity eaten as on its thorough digestion; nor the gratification of taste so much on the amount of food swallowed as on the length of time it remains in the mouth. Those who are excited, anxious, or in a hurry, would do well not to eat until they have found rest or relief; for the vital powers, already severely taxed, cannot supply the necessary digestive fluids.

(1905) M.H. 305

169. Food should be eaten slowly, and should be thoroughly masticated. This is necessary, in order that the saliva may be properly mixed with the food, and the digestive fluids be called into action.

A Lesson to Be Repeated

Letter 27, 1905

170. If we would work for the restoration of health, it is necessary to restrain the appetite, to eat slowly, and only a

limited variety at one meal. This instruction needs to be
repeated frequently. It is not in harmony with the principles of health reform to have so many different dishes at
one meal.

MS 3, 1897

171. Great care should be taken when the change is made
from a flesh meat to a vegetarian diet to supply the table
with wisely prepared, well-cooked articles of food. So much
porridge eating is a mistake. The dry food that requires
mastication is far preferable. The health food preparations
are a blessing in this respect. Good brown bread and rolls,
prepared in a simple manner yet with painstaking effort,
will be healthful. Bread should never have the slightest
taint of sourness. It should be cooked until it is most thoroughly done. Thus all softness and stickiness will be avoided.

For those who can use them, good vegetables, prepared in
a healthful manner, are better than soft mushes or porridge.
Fruits used with thoroughly cooked bread two or three days
old will be more healthful than fresh bread. This, with slow
and thorough mastication, will furnish all that the system
requires.

R. & H., May 8, 1883

172. To make rolls, use soft water and milk, or a little
cream; make a stiff dough, and knead it as for crackers.
Bake on the grate of the oven. These are sweet and delicious. They require thorough mastication, which is a
benefit both to the teeth and to the stomach. They make
good blood, and impart strength.

Avoid Undue Anxiety

Letter 142, 1900

173. It is impossible to prescribe by weight the quantity
of food which should be eaten. It is not advisable to follow
this process, for by so doing the mind becomes self-centered.
Eating and drinking become altogether too much a matter
of thought. . . . There are many who have carried a heavy
weight of responsibility as to the quantity and quality of food
best adapted to nourish the system. Some, especially dys-

peptics, have worried so much in regard to their bill of fare that they have not taken sufficient food to nourish the system. They have done great injury to the house they live in, and we fear have spoiled themselves for this life.

(1905) M.H. 321

174. Some are continually anxious lest their food, however simple and healthful, may hurt them. To these let me say: Do not think that your food will injure you; do not think about it at all. Eat according to your best judgment; and when you have asked the Lord to bless the food for the strengthening of your body, believe that He hears your prayer, and be at rest.

[Extremes in prescribing exact number and quantity of foods —317]

(1905) M.H. 306

175. Another serious evil is eating at improper times, as after violent or excessive exercise, when one is much exhausted or heated. Immediately after eating there is a strong draft upon the nervous energies; and when mind or body is heavily taxed just before or just after eating, digestion is hindered. When one is excited, anxious, or hurried, it is better not to eat until rest or relief is found.

The stomach is closely related to the brain; and when the stomach is diseased, the nerve power is called from the brain to the aid of the weakened digestive organs. When these demands are too frequent, the brain becomes congested. When the brain is constantly taxed, and there is lack of physical exercise, even plain food should be eaten sparingly. At mealtime cast off care and anxious thought; do not feel hurried, but eat slowly and with cheerfulness, with your heart filled with gratitude to God for all His blessings.

Combination of Foods

Letter 213, 1902

176. Knowledge in regard to proper food combinations is of great worth, and is to be received as wisdom from God.

R. & H., July 29, 1884

177. Do not have too great a variety at a meal; three or four dishes are a plenty. At the next meal you can have a

change. The cook should tax her inventive powers to vary the dishes she prepares for the table, and the stomach should not be compelled to take the same kinds of food meal after meal.

(1868) 2T 63

178. There should not be many kinds at any one meal, but all meals should not be composed of the same kinds of food without variation. Food should be prepared with simplicity, yet with a nicety which will invite the appetite.

Letter 73a, 1896

179. It would be much better to eat only two or three different kinds of food at a meal than to load the stomach with many varieties.

MS 86, 1897

180. Many are made sick by the indulgence of their appetite. . . . So many varieties are introduced into the stomach that fermentation is the result. This condition brings on acute disease, and death frequently follows.

Letter 54, 1896

181. The variety of food at one meal causes unpleasantness, and destroys the good which each article, if taken alone, would do the system. This practice causes constant suffering, and often death.

Letter 73a, 1896

182. If your work is sedentary, take exercise every day, and at each meal eat only two or three kinds of simple food, taking no more of these than will satisfy the demands of hunger.

[Further suggestions to sedentary workers—225]

(1902) 7T 257

183. Disturbance is created by improper combinations of food; fermentation sets in; the blood is contaminated and the brain confused.

The habit of overeating, or of eating too many kinds of food at one meal, frequently causes dyspepsia. Serious injury is thus done to the delicate digestive organs. In vain the stomach protests, and appeals to the brain to reason from cause to effect. The excessive amount of food eaten, or the improper combination, does its injurious work. In vain do disagreeable premonitions give warning. Suffering is the consequence. Disease takes the place of health.

War in the Stomach

(1892) G.W. 174 (old edition)

184. Another cause, both of ill health and of inefficiency in labor, is indigestion. It is impossible for the brain to do its best work when the digestive powers are abused. Many eat hurriedly of various kinds of food, which set up a war in the stomach, and thus confuse the brain.

MS 3, 1897

185. It is not well to take a great variety of foods at one meal. When fruit and bread, together with a variety of other foods that do not agree, are crowded into the stomach at one meal, what can we expect but that a disturbance will be created?

MS 93, 1901

186. Many eat too rapidly. Others eat at one meal food which does not agree. If men and women would only remember how greatly they afflict the soul when they afflict the stomach, and how deeply Christ is dishonored when the stomach is abused, they would be brave and self-denying, giving the stomach opportunity to recover its healthy action. While sitting at the table we may do medical missionary work by eating and drinking to the glory of God.

Peaceful Stomachs and Peaceful Dispositions

MS 41, 1908

187. We must care for the digestive organs, and not force upon them a great variety of food. He who gorges himself with many kinds of food at a meal is doing himself injury. It is more important that we eat that which will agree with us than that we taste of every dish that may be placed before us. There is no door in our stomach by which we can look in and see what is going on; so we must use our mind, and reason from cause to effect. If you feel all wrought up, and everything seems to go wrong, perhaps it is because you are

suffering the consequences of eating a great variety of food.

The digestive organs have an important part to act in our life happiness. God has given us intelligence, that we may learn what we should use as food. Shall we not, as sensible men and women, study whether the things we eat will be in agreement, or whether they will cause trouble? People who have a sour stomach are very often of a sour disposition. Everything seems to be contrary to them, and they are inclined to be peevish and irritable. If we would have peace among ourselves, we should give more thought than we do to having a peaceful stomach.

[Harmful effects of too great variety of food and wrong combinations 141, 225, 226, 227, 264, 387, 546, 551, 722]

[Combination of many foods in our restaurants—415]

[Care in food combination for the sick—441, 467]

[E. G. White careful in her food combinations—Appendix I:19, 23, 25]

Fruits and Vegetables

(1905) M.H. 299, 300

188. There should not be a great variety at any one meal, for this encourages overeating, and causes indigestion.

It is not well to eat fruit and vegetables at the same meal. If the digestion is feeble, the use of both will often cause distress, and inability to put forth mental effort. It is better to have the fruit at one meal, and the vegetables at another.

The meals should be varied. The same dishes, prepared in the same way, should not appear on the table meal after meal and day after day. The meals are eaten with greater relish, and the system is better nourished, when the food is varied.

Rich Desserts and Vegetables

Letter 142, 1900

189. Puddings, custards, sweet cake, and vegetables, all served at the same meal, will cause a disturbance in the stomach.

Letter 312, 1908

190. You need to keep in your house the very best kind of help for the work of preparing your food. In the night

seasons, it seemed that Elder ———— was taken sick, and an experienced physician said to you, "I took notice of your diet. You eat too great a variety at one meal. Fruit and vegetables taken at one meal produce acidity of the stomach; then impurity of the blood results, and the mind is not clear because the digestion is imperfect." You should understand that every organ of the body is to be treated with respect. In the matter of diet, you must reason from cause to effect.

Sugar and Milk

(1905) M.H. 302

191. Far too much sugar is ordinarily used in food. Cakes, sweet puddings, pastries, jellies, jams, are active causes of indigestion. Especially harmful are the custards and puddings in which milk, eggs, and sugar are the chief ingredients. The free use of milk and sugar taken together should be avoided.

[C.T.B.H. 57] (1890) C.H. 154

192. Some use milk and a large amount of sugar on mush, thinking that they are carrying out health reform. But the sugar and the milk combined are liable to cause fermentation in the stomach, and are thus harmful.

[See milk and sugar—533, 534, 535, 536]

Rich and Complicated Mixtures

Letter 72, 1896

193. The less that condiments and desserts are placed upon our tables, the better it will be for all who partake of the food. All mixed and complicated foods are injurious to the health of human beings. Dumb animals would never eat such a mixture as is often placed in the human stomach. . . .

The richness of food and complicated mixtures of food are health destroying.

[Rich foods and variety of dishes not best for camp meeting diet—74]
[Combination of spiced meat, rich cakes and pies—673]
[See Section XIX, "Desserts"]

SECTION VI

Improper Eating a Cause of Disease

Quotations in Section VI

Improper Eating a Cause of Disease

A Heritage of Degeneracy

[C.T.B.H. 7-11] (1890) C.H. 19-23

194. MAN came from the hand of his Creator perfect in organization and beautiful in form. The fact that he has for six thousand years withstood the ever-increasing weight of disease and crime is conclusive proof of the power of endurance with which he was first endowed. And although the antediluvians generally gave themselves up to sin without restraint, it was more than two thousand years before the violation of natural law was sensibly felt. Had Adam originally possessed no greater physical power than men now have, the race would ere this have become extinct.

Through the successive generations since the fall, the tendency has been continually downward. Disease has been transmitted from parents to children, generation after generation. Even infants in the cradle suffer from afflictions caused by the sins of their parents.

Moses, the first historian, gives quite a definite account of social and individual life in the early days of the world's history, but we find no record that an infant was born blind, deaf, crippled, or imbecile. Not an instance is recorded of a natural death in infancy, childhood, or early manhood. Obituary notices in the book of Genesis run thus: "And all the days that Adam lived were nine hundred and thirty years; and he died." "And all the days of Seth were nine hundred and twelve years; and he died." Concerning others the record states, "He died in a good old age, an old man, and full of years." It was so rare for a son to die before his father, that such an occurrence was considered worthy of record: "Haran died before his father Terah." The patriarchs from Adam to Noah, with few exceptions, lived nearly a thousand years. Since then the average length of life has been decreasing.

At the time of Christ's first advent, the race had already

so degenerated that not only the old, but the middle-aged and the young, were brought from every city to the Saviour, to be healed of their diseases. Many labored under a weight of misery inexpressible.

The violation of physical law, with its consequent suffering and premature death, has so long prevailed that these results are regarded as the appointed lot of humanity; but God did not create the race in such a feeble condition. This state of things is not the work of Providence, but of man. It has been brought about by wrong habits,—by violating the laws that God has made to govern man's existence. A continual transgression of nature's laws is a continual transgression of the law of God. Had men always been obedient to the law of the ten commandments, carrying out in their lives the principles of those precepts, the curse of disease now flooding the world would not exist.

"Know ye not that your body is the temple of the Holy Ghost which is in you, which ye have of God, and ye are not your own? for ye are bought with a price; therefore glorify God in your body and in your spirit, which are God's." When men take any course which needlessly expends their vitality or beclouds their intellect, they sin against God; they do not glorify Him in their body and spirit, which are His.

Yet despite the insult which man has offered Him, God's love is still extended to the race; and He permits light to shine, enabling man to see that in order to live a perfect life he must obey the natural laws which govern his being. How important, then, that man should walk in this light, exercising all his powers, both of body and mind, to the glory of God!

We are in a world that is opposed to righteousness, or purity of character, and especially to growth in grace. Wherever we look, we see defilement and corruption, deformity and sin. How opposed is all this to the work that must be accomplished in us just previous to receiving the gift of immortality! God's elect must stand untainted amid the corruptions teeming around them in these last days. Their bodies must be made holy, their spirits pure. If this work is to be accomplished, it must be undertaken at once, earnestly and understandingly. The Spirit of God should have perfect control, influencing every action. . . .

Men have polluted the soul temple, and God calls upon them to awake, and to strive with all their might to win back their God-given manhood. Nothing but the grace of God can convict and convert the heart; from Him alone can the slaves of custom obtain power to break the shackles that bind them. It is impossible for a man to present his body a living sacrifice, holy, acceptable to God, while continuing to indulge habits that are depriving him of physical, mental, and moral vigor. Again the apostle says, "Be not conformed to this world; but be ye transformed by the renewing of your mind, that ye may prove what is that good, and acceptable, and perfect will of God."

Willing Ignorance of the Laws of Life

(1872) 3T 140, 141

195. The strange absence of principle which characterizes this generation, and which is shown in their disregard of the laws of life and health, is astonishing. Ignorance prevails upon this subject, while light is shining all round them. With the majority, their principal anxiety is, What shall I eat? what shall I drink? and wherewith shall I be clothed? Notwithstanding all that is said and written in regard to how we should treat our bodies, appetite is the great law which governs men and women generally.

The moral powers are weakened, because men and women will not live in obedience to the laws of health, and make this great subject a personal duty. Parents bequeath to their offspring their own perverted habits, and loathsome diseases corrupt the blood and enervate the brain. The majority of men and women remain in ignorance of the laws of their being, and indulge appetite and passion at the expense of intellect and morals, and seem willing to remain in ignorance of the result of their violation of nature's laws. They indulge the depraved appetite in the use of slow poisons, which corrupt the blood, and undermine the nervous forces, and in consequence bring upon themselves sickness and death. Their friends call the result of this course the dispensation of Providence. In this they insult Heaven. They rebelled against the laws of nature, and suffered the punishment of thus abusing her laws. Suffering and mortality now prevail everywhere, especially among children. How great is the contrast between this generation and those who lived during the first two thousand years!

Social Results of Uncontrolled Appetite

[C.T.B.H. 44, 45] (1890) C.H. 112

196. Against every transgression of the laws of life, nature will utter her protest. She bears abuse as long as she can; but finally the retribution comes, and it falls upon the mental as well as the physical powers. Nor does it end with the transgressor; the effects of his indulgence are seen in his offspring, and thus the evil is passed down from generation to generation.

The youth of today are a sure index to the future of society; and as we view them, what can we hope for that future? The majority are fond of amusement and averse to work. They lack moral courage to deny self and to respond to the claims of duty. They have but little self-control, and become excited and angry on the slightest occasion. Very many in every age and station of life are without principle or conscience; and with their idle, spendthrift habits they are rushing into vice and are corrupting society, until our world is becoming a second Sodom. If the appetites and passions were under the control of reason and religion, society would present a widely different aspect. God never designed that the present woeful condition of things should exist; it has been brought about through the gross violation of nature's laws.

Violated Laws—Natural and Spiritual

(1898) D.A. 824

197. To many of the afflicted ones who received healing, Christ said, "Sin no more, lest a worse thing come unto thee." Thus He taught that disease is the result of violating God's laws, both natural and spiritual. The great misery

in the world would not exist, did men but live in harmony with the Creator's plan.

Christ had been the guide and teacher of ancient Israel, and He taught them that health is the reward of obedience to the laws of God. The great Physician who healed the sick in Palestine had spoken to His people from the pillar of cloud, telling them what they must do, and what God would do for them. "If thou wilt diligently hearken to the voice of the Lord Thy God," He said, "and wilt do that which is right in His sight, and wilt give ear to His commandments, and keep all His statutes, I will put none of these diseases upon thee, which I have brought upon the Egyptians; for I am the Lord that healeth thee." Christ gave to Israel definite instruction in regard to their habits of life, and He assured them, "The Lord will take away from thee all sickness." When they fulfilled the conditions, the promise was verified to them. "There was not one feeble person among their tribes."

These lessons are for us. There are conditions to be observed by all who would preserve health. All should learn what these conditions are. The Lord is not pleased with ignorance in regard to His laws, either natural or spiritual. We are to be workers together with God for the restoration of health to the body as well as to the soul.

Self-inflicted Suffering

(1866) H. to L., ch. 3, p. 49

198. The human family have brought upon themselves diseases of various forms by their own wrong habits. They have not studied how to live healthfully, and their transgression of the laws of their being has produced a deplorable state of things. The people have seldom accredited their sufferings to the true cause—their own wrong course of action. They have indulged in intemperance in eating, and made a god of their appetite. In all their habits they have manifested a recklessness in regard to health and life; and when, as the result, sickness has come upon them they have made themselves believe that God was the author of it, when their own wrong course of action has brought the sure result.

(1905) M.H. 234, 235

199. Disease never comes without a cause. The way is prepared, and disease invited, by disregard of the laws of health. Many suffer in consequence of the transgression of their parents. While they are not responsible for what their parents have done, it is nevertheless their duty to ascertain what are and what are not violations of the laws of health. They should avoid the wrong habits of their parents, and by correct living, place themselves in better conditions.

The greater number, however, suffer because of their own wrong course of action. They disregard the principles of health by their habits of eating, drinking, dressing, and working. Their transgression of nature's laws produces the sure result; and when sickness comes upon them, many do not credit their suffering to the true cause, but murmur against God because of their afflictions. But God is not responsible for the suffering that follows disregard of natural law. . . .

Intemperate eating is often the cause of sickness, and what nature most needs is to be relieved of the undue burden that has been placed upon her.

[Parents sow seeds of disease and death—635]
[The penalty inevitable—11, 29, 30, 221, 227, 228, 250, 251, 294]

Sickness follows Indulgence of Appetite

(1905) M.H. 227

200. Many persons bring disease upon themselves by their self-indulgence. They have not lived in accordance with natural law or the principles of strict purity. Others have disregarded the laws of health in their habits of eating and drinking, dressing, or working.

Y.I., May 31, 1894

201. The mind does not wear out nor break down so often on account of diligent employment and hard study, as on account of eating improper food at improper times, and of careless inattention to the laws of health. . . . Diligent study is not the principal cause of the breaking down of the mental powers. The main cause is improper diet, irregular

neals, and a lack of physical exercise. Irregular hours for
ating and sleeping sap the brain forces.

(1900) 6T 372, 373

202. Many are suffering, and many are going into the
rave, because of the indulgence of appetite. They eat what
uits their perverted taste, thus weakening the digestive or-
ans and injuring their power to assimilate the food that is to
ustain life. This brings on acute disease, and too often
eath follows. The delicate organism of the body is worn out
y the suicidal practices of those who ought to know better.

The churches should be stanch and true to the light which
;od has given. Each member should work intelligently to
ut away from his life practice every perverted appetite.

[Diseases from poverty-stricken diet difficult to cure—315]
[Effect of improper eating on temper and home atmosphere—
34]
[Effects of mistaken reform—316]

Preparing the Way for Drunkenness

(1905) M.H. 334

203. Often intemperance begins in the home. By the use
f rich, unhealthful food the digestive organs are weakened
nd a desire is created for food that is still more stimulating.
'hus the appetite is educated to crave continually something
tronger. The demand for stimulants becomes more frequent
nd more difficult to resist. The system becomes more or less
lled with poison, and the more debilitated it becomes, the
reater is the desire for these things. One step in the wrong
irection prepares the way for another. Many who would
ot be guilty of placing on their table wine or liquor of any
ind will load their table with food which creates such a
iirst for strong drink that to resist the temptation is almost
npossible. Wrong habits of eating and drinking destroy
ie health and prepare the way for drunkenness.

Diseased Liver Through Wrong Diet

(1868) 2T 67-70

204. Last Sabbath, as I was speaking your pale faces rose
istinctly before me, as I had been shown them. I saw your

condition of health, and the ailments you have suffered unde
so long. I was shown that you have not lived healthfully
Your appetites have been unhealthy, and you have gratifie
the taste at the expense of the stomach. You have taken int
your stomachs articles which it is impossible to convert int
good blood. This has laid a heavy tax on the liver, for th
reason that the digestive organs are deranged. You botl
have diseased livers. The health reform would be a grea
benefit to you both, if you would strictly carry it out. Thi
you have failed to do. Your appetites are morbid, and be
cause you do not relish a plain, simple diet, composed of un
bolted wheat flour, vegetables and fruits prepared withou
spices or grease, you are continually transgressing the law
which God has established in your system. While you d
this, you must suffer the penalty; for to every transgressio
is affixed a penalty. Yet you wonder at your continued poo
health. Be assured that God will not work a miracle to sav
you from the result of your own course of action. . . .

RICH FOOD AND FEVERS

There is no treatment which can relieve you of you
present difficulties while you eat and drink as you do. Yo
can do that for yourselves which the most experienced phy
sician can never do. Regulate your diet. In order to gratif
the taste, you frequently place a severe tax upon your diges
tive organs by receiving into the stomach food which is no
the most healthful, and at times in immoderate quantitie
This wearies the stomach, and unfits it for the reception c
even the most healthful foods. You keep your stomachs con
stantly debilitated, because of your wrong habits of eating
Your food is made too rich. It is not prepared in a simpl
natural manner, but is totally unfitted for the stomach whe
you have prepared it to suit your taste. Nature is burdene
and endeavors to resist your efforts to cripple her. Chil
and fevers are the result of those attempts to rid herself c
the burden you lay upon her. You have to suffer the penalt
of nature's violated laws. God has established laws in you
system which you cannot violate without suffering the pur

shment. You have consulted taste without reference to
health. You have made some changes, but have merely
taken the first steps in reform diet. God requires of us
temperance in all things. "Whether therefore ye eat, or
drink, or whatsoever ye do, do all to the glory of God."

BLAMING PROVIDENCE

Of all the families I am acquainted with, none need the
benefit of the health reform more than yours. You groan
under pains and prostrations which you cannot account for,
and you try to submit with as good a grace as you can, thinking affliction is your lot, and Providence has thus ordained
it. If you could have your eyes opened, and could see the
steps taken in your lifetime to walk right into your present
condition of poor health, you would be astonished at your
blindness in not seeing the real state of the case before. You
have created unnatural appetites, and do not derive half that
enjoyment from your food which you would if you had not
used your appetites wrongfully. You have perverted nature,
and have been suffering the consequences, and painful has
it been.

THE PRICE OF A "GOOD MEAL"

Nature bears abuse as long as she can without resisting;
then she arouses and makes a mighty effort to rid herself of
the encumbrances and evil treatment she has suffered. Then
come headache, chills, fevers, nervousness, paralysis, and
other evils too numerous to mention. A wrong course of
eating or drinking destroys health and with it the sweetness
of life. Oh, how many times have you purchased what you
called a good meal at the expense of a fevered system, loss
of appetite, and loss of sleep! Inability to enjoy food, a
sleepless night, hours of suffering,—all for a meal in which
taste was gratified!

Thousands have indulged their perverted appetites, have
eaten a good meal, as they called it, and as the result, have
brought on a fever, or some other acute disease, and certain
death. That was enjoyment purchased at immense cost. Yet
many have done this, and these self-murderers have been

eulogized by their friends and the minister, and carried directly to heaven at their death. What a thought! Glutton in heaven! No, no; such will never enter the pearly gate of the golden city of God. Such will never be exalted to the right hand of Jesus, the precious Saviour, the suffering Man of Calvary, whose life was one of constant self-denial and sacrifice. There is a place appointed for all such among the unworthy, who can have no part in the better life, the immortal inheritance.

Effect of Improper Eating Upon the Disposition

Letter 274, 1908

205. Many spoil their dispositions by eating improperly. We should be just as careful to learn the lessons of health reform as we are to have our studies perfectly prepared; for the habits that we adopt in this direction are helping to form our characters for the future life. It is possible for one to spoil his spiritual experience by an ill-use of the stomach.

Appeals for Reform

(1905) M.H. 308

206. Where wrong habits of diet have been indulged, there should be no delay in reform. When dyspepsia has resulted from the abuse of the stomach, efforts should be made carefully to preserve the remaining strength of the vital forces, by removing every overtaxing burden. The stomach may never entirely recover health after long abuse; but a proper course of diet will save further debility, and many will recover more or less fully. It is not easy to prescribe rules that will meet every case; but with attention to right principles in eating, great reforms may be made, and the cook need not be continually toiling to tempt the appetite.

Abstemiousness in diet is rewarded with mental and moral vigor; it also aids in the control of the passions.

(1905) M.H. 295

207. Those foods should be chosen that best supply the elements needed for building up the body. In this choice appetite is not a safe guide. Through wrong habits of eat-

ing, the appetite has become perverted. Often it demands food that impairs health and causes weakness instead of strength. We cannot safely be guided by the customs of society. The disease and suffering that everywhere prevail are largely due to popular errors in regard to diet.

(1909) 9T 160

208. Only when we are intelligent in regard to the principles of healthful living, can we be fully aroused to see the evils resulting from improper diet. Those who, after seeing their mistakes, have courage to change their habits, will find that the reformatory process requires a struggle and much perseverance; but when correct tastes are once formed, they will realize that the use of the food which they formerly regarded as harmless, was slowly but surely laying the foundation for dyspepsia and other diseases.

(1909) 9T 156

209. God requires of His people continual advancement. We need to learn that indulged appetite is the greatest hindrance to mental improvement and soul sanctification. With all our profession of health reform many of us eat improperly. Indulgence of appetite is the greatest cause of physical and mental debility, and lies largely at the foundation of feebleness and premature death. Let the individual who is seeking to possess purity of spirit bear in mind that in Christ there is power to control the appetite.

[Overeating a cause of disease: See Section VII, "Overeating," and Section VIII, "Control of Appetite"]

[Relation of flesh diet to disease—668-677, 689, 690, 691, 692, 713, 722]

[Disease caused by use of tea and coffee—734, 736, 737, 741]

SECTION VII

Overeating

Quotations in Section VII

Overeating

A Common, but Serious Sin

Letter 17, 1895

210. OVERTAXING the stomach is a common sin, and when too much food is used, the entire system is burdened. Life and vitality, instead of being increased, are decreased. This is as Satan plans to have it. Man uses up his vital forces in unnecessary labor in taking care of an excess of food.

By taking too much food, we not only improvidently waste the blessings of God, provided for the necessities of nature, but do great injury to the whole system. We defile the temple of God; it is weakened and crippled; and nature cannot do its work wisely and well, as God has made provision that it should. Because of the selfish indulgence of his appetite, man has oppressed nature's power by compelling it to do work it should never be required to do.

Were all men acquainted with the living, human machinery, they would not be guilty of doing this, unless, indeed, they loved self-indulgence so well that they would continue their suicidal course and die a premature death, or live for years a burden to themselves and to their friends.

Clogging the Human Machinery

[C.T.B.H. 51] (1890) C.H. 119

211. It is possible to eat immoderately, even of wholesome food. It does not follow that because one has discarded the use of hurtful articles of diet, he can eat just as much as he pleases. Overeating, no matter what the quality of the food, clogs the living machine, and thus hinders it in its work.

Signs, Sept. 1, 1887

212. Intemperance in eating, even of healthful food, will have an injurious effect upon the system, and will blunt the mental and moral faculties.

Letter 73a, 1896
213. Nearly all the members of the human family eat more than the system requires. This excess decays and becomes a putrid mass. . . . If more food, even of a simple quality, is placed in the stomach than the living machinery requires, this surplus becomes a burden. The system makes desperate efforts to dispose of it, and this extra work causes a tired, weary feeling. Some who are continually eating call this all-gone feeling hunger, but it is caused by the overworked condition of the digestive organs.

[Effects of overeating even of simple, healthful food—33, 157]

(1900) 6T 343
214. Needless worries and burdens are created by the desire to make a display in entertaining visitors. In order to prepare a great variety for the table, the housewife overworks; because of the many dishes prepared, the guests overeat; and disease and suffering, from overwork on the one hand and overeating on the other, is the result. These elaborate feasts are a burden and an injury.

Health Reformer, June, 1878
215. Gluttonous feasts, and food taken into the stomach at untimely seasons, leave an influence upon every fiber of the system; and the mind also is seriously affected by what we eat and drink.

(1876) 4T 96
216. Close application to severe labor is injurious to the growing frames of the young; but where hundreds have broken down their constitutions by overwork alone, inactivity, overeating, and delicate idleness have sown the seeds of disease in the system of thousands that are hurrying to swift and sure decay.

Gluttony a Capital Offense

(1880) 4T 454, 455
217. Some do not exercise control over their appetites, but indulge taste at the expense of health. As the result, the brain is clouded, their thoughts are sluggish, and they fail

to accomplish what they might if they were self-denying and abstemious. These rob God of the physical and mental strength which might be devoted to His service if temperance were observed in all things.

Paul was a health reformer. Said he, "I keep under my body, and bring it into subjection; lest that by any means, when I have preached to others, I myself should be a castaway." He felt that a responsibility rested upon him to preserve all his powers in their strength, that he might use them to the glory of God. If Paul was in danger from intemperance, we are in greater danger, because we do not feel and realize as he did the necessity of glorifying God in our bodies and spirits, which are His. Overeating is the sin of this age.

The word of God places the sin of gluttony in the same catalogue with drunkenness. So offensive was this sin in the sight of God that He gave directions to Moses that a child who would not be restrained on the point of appetite, but would gorge himself with anything his taste might crave, should be brought by his parents before the rulers of Israel, and should be stoned to death. The condition of the glutton was considered hopeless. He would be of no use to others, and was a curse to himself. No dependence could be placed upon him in anything. His influence would be ever contaminating others, and the world would be better without such a character; for his terrible defects would be perpetuated. None who have a sense of their accountability to God will allow the animal propensities to control reason. Those who do this are not Christians, whoever they may be, and however exalted their profession. The injunction of Christ is, "Be ye therefore perfect, even as your Father which is in heaven is perfect." He here shows us that we may be as perfect in our sphere as God is in His sphere.

The Course Plan Incites to Gluttony

(1905) M.H. 306, 307

218. Many who discard flesh meats and other gross and injurious articles think that because their food is simple and

wholesome they may indulge appetite without restraint, and they eat to excess, sometimes to gluttony. This is an error. The digestive organs should not be burdened with a quantity or quality of food which it will tax the system to appropriate.

Custom has decreed that the food should be placed upon the tables in courses. Not knowing what is coming next, one may eat a sufficiency of food which perhaps is not the best suited to him. When the last course is brought on, he often ventures to overstep the bounds, and take the tempting dessert, which, however, proves anything but good for him. If all the food intended for a meal is placed on the table at the beginning, one has opportunity to make the best choice.

Sometimes the result of overeating is felt at once. In other cases there is no sensation of pain; but the digestive organs lose their vital force, and the foundation of physical strength is undermined.

The surplus food burdens the system, and produces morbid, feverish conditions. It calls an undue amount of blood to the stomach, causing the limbs and extremities to chill quickly. It lays a heavy tax on the digestive organs, and when these organs have accomplished their task, there is a feeling of faintness or languor. Some who are continually overeating call this all-gone feeling hunger; but it is caused by the overworked condition of the digestive organs. At times there is numbness of the brain, with disinclination to mental or physical effort.

These unpleasant symptoms are felt because nature has accomplished her work at an unnecessary outlay of vital force, and is thoroughly exhausted. The stomach is saying, "Give me rest." But with many the faintness is interpreted as a demand for more food; so instead of giving the stomach rest, another burden it placed upon it. As a consequence the digestive organs are often worn out when they should be capable of doing good work.

[Organs may lose vital force though no pain is felt—155]
[God's workers to practice temperance in eating—117]
[E. G. White could not ask God's blessing on her work if she overate—Appendix I:7]

The Cause of Physical and Mental Debility

(1890) C.T.B.H. 154

219. As a people, with all our profession of health reform, we eat too much. Indulgence of appetite is the greatest cause of physical and mental debility, and lies at the foundation of a large share of the feebleness which is apparent everywhere.

(1870) 2T 362-365

220. Many who have adopted the health reform have left off everything hurtful; but does it follow that because they have left off these things, they can eat just as much as they please? They sit down to the table, and instead of considering how much they should eat, they give themselves up to appetite and eat to great excess. And the stomach has all it can do, or all it should do, the rest of that day, to worry away with the burden imposed upon it. All the food that is put into the stomach, from which the system cannot derive benefit, is a burden to nature in her work. It hinders the living machine. The system is clogged, and cannot successfully carry on its work. The vital organs are unnecessarily taxed, and the brain nerve power is called to the stomach to help the digestive organs carry on their work of disposing of an amount of food which does the system no good. . . .

And what influence does overeating have upon the stomach? It becomes debilitated, the digestive organs are weakened, and disease, with all its train of evils, is brought on as the result. If persons were diseased before, they thus increase the difficulties upon them, and lessen their vitality every day they live. They call their vital powers into unnecessary action to take care of the food that they place in their stomachs. What a terrible condition is this to be in!

We know something of dyspepsia by experience. We have had it in our family; and we feel that it is a disease much to be dreaded. When a person becomes a thorough dyspeptic, he is a great sufferer, mentally and physically; and his friends must also suffer, unless they are as unfeeling as brutes.

And yet will you say, "It is none of your business what I eat, or what course I pursue?" Does anybody around dyspeptics suffer? Just take a course that will irritate them in any way. How natural to be fretful! They feel bad, and it appears to them that their children are very bad. They cannot speak calmly to them, nor, without especial grace, act calmly in their families. All around them are affected by the disease upon them; all have to suffer the consequences of their infirmity. They cast a dark shadow. Then, do not your habits of eating and drinking affect others? They certainly do. And you should be very careful to preserve yourself in the best condition of health, that you may render to God perfect service, and do your duty in society and to your family.

But even health reformers can err in the quantity of food. They can eat immoderately of a healthful quality of food.

MS 93, 1901

221. The Lord has instructed me that as a general rule, we place too much food in the stomach. Many make themselves uncomfortable by overeating, and sickness is often the result. The Lord did not bring this punishment on them. They brought it on themselves; and God desires them to realize that pain is the result of transgression.

Many eat too rapidly. Others eat at one meal food which does not agree. If men and women would only remember how greatly they afflict the soul when they afflict the stomach, and how deeply Christ is dishonored when the stomach is abused, they would be brave and self-denying, giving the stomach opportunity to recover its healthy action. While sitting at the table we may do medical missionary work by eating and drinking to the glory of God.

Drowsiness During Church Service

(1870) 2T 374

222. When we eat immoderately, we sin against our own bodies. Upon the Sabbath, in the house of God, gluttons will sit and sleep under the burning truths of God's word. They can neither keep their eyes open, nor comprehend the solemn discourses given. Do you think that such are glorifying God in their bodies and spirits, which are His? No;

they dishonor Him. And the dyspeptic—what has made him dyspeptic is taking this course. Instead of observing regularity, he has let appetite control him, and has eaten between meals. Perhaps, if his habits are sedentary, he has not had the vitalizing air of heaven to help in the work of digestion; he may not have had sufficient exercise for his health.

(1905) M.H. 307

223. We should not provide for the Sabbath a more liberal supply or a greater variety of food than for other days. Instead of this, the food should be more simple, and less should be eaten, in order that the mind may be clear and vigorous to comprehend spiritual things. A clogged stomach means a clogged brain. The most precious words may be heard and not appreciated, because the mind is confused by an improper diet. By overeating on the Sabbath, many do more than they think, to unfit themselves for receiving the benefit of its sacred opportunities.

[Drowsiness in Sabbath services—93]
[Abstemious diet imparts mental and moral vigor—85, 117, 206]
[Effects of overeating on spirituality—56, 57, 59, 251]
[Effects of overeating on the mind—74]
[Overeating at camp meeting—57, 124]
[Suicidal practices—202]
[Desserts a temptation to overeating—538, 547, 550]
[A source of church trials—65]
[Gluttony the prevailing sin of the age—35]
[Overeating leads to dissipation—244]
[Keeping a clean conscience—263]
[Intemperance and overeating encouraged by mothers—351, 354]

A Cause of Forgetfulness

Letter 17, 1895

224. The Lord has given me light for you on the subject of temperance in all things. You are intemperate in your eating. Frequently you place in your stomach double the quantity of food your system requires. This food decays; your breath becomes offensive; your catarrhal difficulties are aggravated; your stomach is overworked; and life and energy are called from the brain to work the mill which

grinds the material you have placed in your stomach. In this, you have shown little mercy to yourself.

You are a gormand when at the table. This is one great cause of your forgetfulness and loss of memory. You say things which I know you have said, and then turn square about, and say that you said something entirely different. I knew this, but passed it over as the sure result of overeating. Of what use would it be to speak about it? It would not cure the evil.

Counsel to Sedentary Workers and Ministers

(1905) M.H. 308-310

225. Overeating is especially harmful to those who are sluggish in temperament; these should eat sparingly, and take plenty of physical exercise. There are men and women of excellent natural ability who do not accomplish half what they might if they would exercise self-control in the denial of appetite.

Many writers and speakers fail here. After eating heartily they give themselves to sedentary occupations, reading, study, or writing, allowing no time for physical exercise. As a consequence, the free flow of thought and words is checked. They cannot write or speak with the force and intensity necessary in order to reach the heart; their efforts are tame and fruitless.

Those upon whom rest important responsibilities, those, above all, who are guardians of spiritual interests, should be men of keen feeling and quick perception. More than others, they need to be temperate in eating. Rich and luxurious food should have no place upon their tables.

Every day men in positions of trust have decisions to make upon which depend results of great importance. Often they have to think rapidly, and this can be done successfully by those only who practice strict temperance. The mind strengthens under the correct treatment of the physical and mental powers. If the strain is not too great, new vigor comes with every taxation. But often the work of those who have important plans to consider and important decisions to make is affected for evil by the results of improper diet. A disordered stomach produces a disordered, uncer-

ain state of mind. Often it causes irritability, harshness,
or injustice. Many a plan that would have been a blessing
to the world has been set aside, many unjust, oppressive,
even cruel measures have been carried, as the result of diseased conditions due to wrong habits of eating.

Here is a suggestion for all whose work is sedentary or
chiefly mental; let those who have sufficient moral courage
and self-control try it: At each meal take only two or three
kinds of simple food, and eat no more than is required to
satisfy hunger. Take active exercise every day, and see if
you do not receive benefit.

Strong men who are engaged in active physical labor are
not compelled to be as careful as to the quantity or quality
of their food as are persons of sedentary habits; but even
these would have better health if they would practice self-
control in eating and drinking.

Some wish that an exact rule could be prescribed for
their diet. They overeat, and then regret it, and so they
keep thinking about what they eat and drink. This is not
as it should be. One person cannot lay down an exact rule
for another. Every one should exercise reason and self-
control and should act from principle.

[Late suppers particularly harmful—270]

Indigestion and Board Meetings

(1902) 7T 257, 258

226. At bountiful tables, men often eat much more than
can be easily digested. The overburdened stomach cannot
do its work properly. The result is a disagreeable feeling
of dullness in the brain, and the mind does not act quickly.
Disturbance is created by improper combinations of food;
fermentation sets in; the blood is contaminated and the brain
confused.

The habit of overeating, or of eating too many kinds of
food at one meal, frequently causes dyspepsia. Serious injury is thus done to the delicate digestive organs. In vain
the stomach protests, and appeals to the brain to reason from
cause to effect. The excessive amount of food eaten, or the

improper combination, does its injurious work. In vain do disagreeable premonitions give warning. Suffering is the consequence. Disease takes the place of health.

Some may ask, What has this to do with board meetings? Very much. The effects of wrong eating are brought into council and board meetings. The brain is affected by the condition of the stomach. A disordered stomach is productive of a disordered, uncertain state of mind. A diseased stomach produces a diseased condition of the brain, and often makes one obstinate in maintaining erroneous opinions. The supposed wisdom of such a one is foolishness with God.

I present this as a cause of the situation in many council and board meetings, where questions demanding careful study have been given but little consideration, and decisions of the greatest importance have been hurriedly made. Often when there should have been unanimity of sentiment in the affirmative, decided negatives have entirely changed the atmosphere pervading a meeting. These results have been presented to me again and again.

I present these matters now because I am instructed to say to my brethren in the ministry, By intemperance in eating, you disqualify yourselves for seeing clearly the difference between sacred and common fire. And by this intemperance you also reveal your disregard for the warnings that the Lord has given you. His word to you is: "Who is among you that feareth the Lord, that obeyeth the voice of His servant, that walketh in darkness, and hath no light? Let him trust in the name of the Lord, and stay upon his God." . . . Shall we not draw near to the Lord, that He may save us from all intemperance in eating and drinking, from all unholy, lustful passion, all wickedness? Shall we not humble ourselves before God, putting away everything that corrupts the flesh and the spirit, that in His fear we may perfect holiness of character?

No Recommendation of Health Reform

(1880) 4T 416, 417

227. Our preachers are not particular enough in regard to their habits of eating. They partake of too large quan-

tities of food, and of too great a variety at one meal. Some are reformers only in name. They have no rules by which to regulate their diet, but indulge in eating fruit or nuts between their meals, and thus impose too heavy burdens upon the digestive organs. Some eat three meals a day, when two would be more conducive to physical and spiritual health. If the laws which God has made to govern the physical system are violated, the penalty must surely follow.

Because of imprudence in eating, the senses of some seem to be half paralyzed, and they are sluggish and sleepy. These pale-faced ministers who are suffering in consequence of selfish indulgence of the appetite, are no recommendation of health reform. When suffering from overwork, it would be much better to drop out a meal occasionally, and thus give nature a chance to rally. Our laborers could do more by their example to advance health reform than by preaching it. When elaborate preparations are made for them by well-meaning friends, they are strongly tempted to disregard principle; but by refusing the dainty dishes, the rich condiments, the tea and coffee, they may prove themselves to be practical health reformers. Some are now suffering in consequence of transgressing the laws of life, thus causing a stigma to rest on the cause of health reform.

Excessive indulgence in eating, drinking, sleeping, or seeing, is sin. The harmonious, healthy action of all the powers of body and mind results in happiness; and the more elevated and refined the powers the more pure and unalloyed the happiness.

Digging Their Graves With Their Teeth

(1880) 4T 408, 409

228. The reason why many of our ministers complain of sickness is, they fail to take sufficient exercise, and indulge in overeating. They do not realize that such a course endangers the strongest constitution. Those who, like yourself, are sluggish in temperament, should eat very sparingly, and not shun physical taxation. Many of our ministers are digging their graves with their teeth. The system,

in taking care of the burden placed upon the digestive organs, suffers, and a severe draft is made upon the brain. For every offense committed against the laws of health, the transgressor must pay the penalty in his own body.

SECTION VIII

Control of Appetite

Quotations in Section VIII

Control of Appetite

Failure in Self-control the First Sin

(1864) Sp. Gifts IV, 120

229. ADAM and Eve in Eden were noble in stature, and perfect in symmetry and beauty. They were sinless, and in perfect health. What a contrast to the human race now! Beauty is gone. Perfect health is not known. Everywhere we look we see disease, deformity, and imbecility. I inquired the cause of this wonderful degeneracy, and was pointed back to Eden. The beautiful Eve was beguiled by the serpent to eat of the fruit of the only tree of which God had forbidden them to eat, or even touch it, lest they die.

Eve had everything to make her happy. She was surrounded by fruit of every variety. Yet the fruit of the forbidden tree appeared more desirable to her than the fruit of all the other trees in the garden of which she could freely eat. She was intemperate in her desires. She ate, and through her influence, her husband ate also, and a curse rested upon them both. The earth also was cursed because of their sin. And since the fall, intemperance in almost every form has existed. The appetite has controlled reason. The human family have followed in a course of disobedience, and, like Eve, have been beguiled by Satan to disregard the prohibitions God has made, flattering themselves that the consequences would not be as fearful as had been apprehended. The human family have violated the laws of health, and have run to excess in almost everything. Disease has been steadily increasing. The cause has been followed by the effect.

Noah's Day and Ours

[C.T.B.H. 11, 12] (1890) C.H. 23, 24

230. Jesus, seated on the Mount of Olives, gave instruction to His disciples concerning the signs which should pre-

cede His coming: "As the days of Noah were, so shall also the coming of the Son of man be. For as in the days that were before the flood they were eating and drinking, marrying and giving in marriage, until the day that Noah entered into the ark, and knew not until the flood came and took them all away; so shall also the coming of the Son of man be." The same sins that brought judgments upon the world in the days of Noah, exist in our day. Men and women now carry their eating and drinking so far that it ends in gluttony and drunkenness. This prevailing sin, the indulgence of perverted appetite, inflamed the passions of men in the days of Noah, and led to widespread corruption. Violence and sin reached to heaven. This moral pollution was finally swept from the earth by means of the flood. The same sins of gluttony and drunkenness benumbed the moral sensibilities of the inhabitants of Sodom, so that crime seemed to be the delight of the men and women of that wicked city. Christ thus warns the world: "Likewise also as it was in the days of Lot: they did eat, they drank, they bought, they sold, they planted, they builded; but the same day that Lot went out of Sodom it rained fire and brimstone from heaven and destroyed them all. Even thus shall it be in the day when the Son of man is revealed."

Christ has here left us a most important lesson. He would lay before us the danger of making our eating and drinking paramount. He presents the result of unrestrained indulgence of appetite. The moral powers are enfeebled, so that sin does not appear sinful. Crime is lightly regarded, and passion controls the mind, until good principles and impulses are rooted out, and God is blasphemed. All this is the result of eating and drinking to excess. This is the very condition of things which Christ declares will exist at His second coming.

The Saviour presents to us something higher to toil for than merely what we shall eat and drink, and wherewithal we shall be clothed. Eating, drinking, and dressing are carried to such excess that they become crimes. They are among the marked sins of the last days, and constitute a sign of Christ's soon coming. Time, money, and strength, which belong to the Lord, but which He has entrusted to us, are wasted in superfluities of dress and luxuries for the perverted appetite, which lessen vitality, and bring suffering and decay. It is impossible to present our bodies a living sacrifice to God when we continually fill them with corruption and disease by our own sinful indulgence.

[C.T.B.H. 42, 43] (1890) C.H. 108-110

231. One of the strongest temptations that man has to meet is upon the point of appetite. In the beginning the Lord made man upright. He was created with a perfectly balanced mind, the size and strength of all his organs being fully and harmoniously developed. But through the seductions of the wily foe, the prohibition of God was disregarded, and the laws of nature wrought out their full penalty. . . .

Since the first surrender to appetite, mankind have been growing more and more self-indulgent, until health has been sacrificed on the altar of appetite. The inhabitants of the antediluvian world were intemperate in eating and drinking. They would have flesh meats, although God had at that time given man no permission to eat animal food. They ate and drank till the indulgence of their depraved appetite knew no bounds, and they became so corrupt that God could bear with them no longer. Their cup of iniquity was full, and He cleansed the earth of its moral pollution by a flood.

SODOM AND GOMORRAH

As men multiplied upon the earth after the flood, they again forgot God, and corrupted their ways before Him. Intemperance in every form increased, until almost the whole world was given up to its sway. Entire cities have been swept from the face of the earth because of the debasing crimes and revolting iniquity that made them a blot upon the fair field of God's created works. The gratification of unnatural appetite led to the sins that caused the destruction of Sodom and Gomorrah. God ascribes the fall of Babylon to her gluttony and drunkenness. Indulgence of appetite and passion was the foundation of all their sins.

Esau Conquered by Appetite

(1868) 2T 38

232. Esau lusted for a favorite dish, and sacrificed his birthright to gratify appetite. After his lustful appetite had been gratified, he saw his folly, but found no space for repentance though he sought it carefully and with tears. There are very many who are like Esau. He represents a class who have a special, valuable blessing within their reach,—the immortal inheritance, life that is as enduring as the life of God, the Creator of the universe, happiness immeasurable, and an eternal weight of glory,—but who have so long indulged their appetites, passions, and inclinations, that their power to discern and appreciate the value of eternal things is weakened.

Esau had a special, strong desire for a particular article of food, and he had so long gratified self that he did not feel the necessity of turning from the tempting, coveted dish. He thought upon it, making no special effort to restrain his appetite, until the power of appetite bore down every other consideration, and controlled him, and he imagined that he would suffer great inconvenience, and even death, if he could not have that particular dish. The more he thought upon it, the more his desire strengthened, until his birthright, which was sacred, lost its value and its sacredness.

Israel's Lust for Flesh

[C.T.B.H. 43, 44] (1890) C.H. 111, 112

233. When the God of Israel brought His people out of Egypt, He withheld flesh meats from them in a great measure, but gave them bread from heaven, and water from the flinty rock. With this they were not satisfied. They loathed the food given them, and wished themselves back in Egypt, where they could sit by the fleshpots. They preferred to endure slavery, and even death, rather than to be deprived of flesh. God granted their desire, giving them flesh, and leaving them to eat till their gluttony produced a plague, from which many of them died.

ALL THESE ARE ENSAMPLES

Example after example might be cited to show the effects of yielding to appetite. It seemed a small matter to our first parents to transgress the command of God in that one act,— the eating from a tree that was so beautiful to the sight and so pleasant to the taste,—but it broke their allegiance to God, and opened the gates to a flood of guilt and woe that has deluged the world.

THE WORLD TODAY

Crime and disease have increased with every succeeding generation. Intemperance in eating and drinking, and the indulgence of the baser passions, have benumbed the nobler faculties of man. Reason, instead of being the ruler, has come to be the slave of appetite to an alarming extent. An increasing desire for rich food has been indulged, until it has become the fashion to crowd all the delicacies possible into the stomach. Especially at parties of pleasure is the appetite indulged with but little restraint. Rich dinners and late suppers are served, consisting of highly seasoned meats, with rich sauces, cakes, pies, ices, tea, coffee, etc. No wonder that, with such a diet, people have sallow complexions, and suffer untold agonies from dyspepsia.

(1864) Sp. Gifts IV, 131, 132

234. The present corrupt state of the world was presented before me. The sight was terrible. I have wondered that the inhabitants of the earth were not destroyed, like the people of Sodom and Gomorrah. I have seen reason enough for the present state of degeneracy and mortality in the world. Blind passion controls reason, and every high consideration with many is sacrificed to lust.

The first great evil was intemperance in eating and drinking. Men and women have made themselves slaves to appetite. They are intemperate in labor. A great amount of hard labor is performed to obtain food for their tables which greatly injures the already overtaxed system. Women spend a great share of their time over a heated cookstove, preparing food, highly seasoned with spices to gratify the taste.

As a consequence, the children are neglected and do not receive moral and religious instruction. The overworked mother neglects to cultivate a sweetness of temper, which is the sunshine of the dwelling. Eternal considerations become secondary. All the time has to be employed in preparing these things for the appetite which ruin health, sour the temper, and becloud the reasoning faculties.

(1890) C.T.B.H. 16

235. We meet intemperance everywhere. We see it on the cars, the steamboats, and wherever we go; and we should ask ourselves what we are doing to rescue souls from the tempter's grasp. Satan is constantly on the alert to bring the race fully under his control. His strongest hold on man is through the appetite, and this he seeks to stimulate in every possible way. All unnatural excitants are harmful, and they cultivate the desire for liquor. How can we enlighten the people, and prevent the terrible evils that result from the use of these things? Have we done all that we can do in this direction?

Worshiping at the Shrine of Perverted Appetite

(1882) 5T 196, 197

236. God has granted to this people great light, yet we are not placed beyond the reach of temptation. Who among us are seeking help from the gods of Ekron? Look on this picture—not drawn from imagination. In how many, even among Seventh-day Adventists, may its leading characteristics be seen? An invalid—apparently very conscientious, yet bigoted and self-sufficient—freely avows his contempt for the laws of health and life, which divine mercy has led us as a people to accept. His food must be prepared in a manner to satisfy his morbid cravings. Rather than sit at a table where wholesome food is provided, he will patronize restaurants, because he can there indulge appetite without restraint. A fluent advocate of temperance, he disregards its foundation principles. He wants relief, but refuses to obtain it at the price of self-denial. That man is worshiping at the shrine of perverted appetite. He is an idolater.

The powers which, sanctified and ennobled, might be employed to honor God, are weakened and rendered of little service. An irritable temper, a confused brain, and unstrung nerves, are among the results of his disregard of nature's laws. He is inefficient, unreliable.

Christ's Victory in Our Behalf

(1876) 4T 44

237. In the wilderness of temptation Christ met the great leading temptations that would assail man. There He encountered, single-handed, the wily, subtle foe, and overcame him. The first great temptation was upon appetite; the second, presumption; the third, love of the world. Satan has overcome his millions by tempting them to the indulgence of appetite. Through the gratification of the taste, the nervous system becomes excited and the brain power enfeebled, making it impossible to think calmly or rationally. The mind is unbalanced. Its higher, nobler faculties are perverted to serve animal lust, and the sacred, eternal interests are not regarded. When this object is gained, Satan can come with his two other leading temptations and find ready access. His manifold temptations grow out of these three great leading points.

(1898) D.A. 122, 123

238. Of all the lessons to be learned from our Lord's first great temptation, none is more important than that bearing upon the control of the appetites and passions. In all ages, temptations appealing to the physical nature have been most effectual in corrupting and degrading mankind. Through intemperance, Satan works to destroy the mental and moral powers that God gave to man as a priceless endowment. Thus it becomes impossible for men to appreciate things of eternal worth. Through sensual indulgence, Satan seeks to blot from the soul every trace of likeness to God.

The uncontrolled indulgence and consequent disease and degradation that existed at Christ's first advent, will again exist, with intensity of evil, before His second coming. Christ declares that the condition of the world will be as in the days before the flood, and as in Sodom and Gomorrah. Every imagination of the thoughts of the heart will be evil continually. Upon the very verge of that fearful time we are now living, and to us should come home the lesson of the Saviour's fast. Only by the inexpressible anguish which Christ endured, can we estimate the evil of unrestrained indulgence. His example declares that our only hope of eternal life is through bringing the appetites and passions into subjection to the will of God.

LOOK TO THE SAVIOUR

In our own strength it is impossible for us to deny the clamors of our fallen nature. Through this channel Satan will bring temptation upon us. Christ knew that the enemy would come to every human being, to take advantage of hereditary weakness, and by his false insinuations to ensnare all whose trust is not in God. And by passing over the ground which man must travel, our Lord has prepared the way for us to overcome. It is not His will that we should be placed at a disadvantage in the conflict with Satan. He would not have us intimidated and discouraged by the assaults of the serpent. "Be of good cheer," He says; "I have overcome the world."

Let him who is struggling against the power of appetite, look to the Saviour in the wilderness of temptation. See Him in His agony upon the cross, as He exclaimed, "I thirst." He has endured all that it is possible for us to bear. His victory is ours.

Jesus rested upon the wisdom and strength of His heavenly Father. He declared, "The Lord God will help Me; therefore shall I not be confounded. . . . And I know that I shall not be ashamed. . . . Behold, the Lord God will help Me." Pointing to His own example, He says to us, "Who is among you that feareth the Lord, . . . that walketh in darkness, and hath no light? Let him trust in the name of the Lord, and stay upon his God."

"The prince of this world cometh," saith Jesus, "and hath nothing in Me." There was in Him nothing that responded to Satan's sophistry. He did not consent to sin. Not even by a thought did He yield to temptation. So it may be with us. Christ's humanity was united with divinity; He was fitted for the conflict by the indwelling of the Holy Spirit. And He came to make us partakers of the divine nature. So long as we are united to Him by faith, sin has no more dominion over us. God reaches for the hand of faith in us to direct it to lay fast hold upon the divinity of Christ, that we may attain to perfection of character.

(1875) 3T 561

239. Satan comes to man, as he came to Christ, with his overpowering temptations to indulge appetite. He well knows his power to overcome man upon this point. He overcame Adam and Eve in Eden upon appetite, and they lost their blissful home. What accumulated misery and crime have filled our world in consequence of the fall of Adam. Entire cities have been blotted from the face of the earth because of the debasing crimes and revolting iniquity that made them a blot upon the universe. Indulgence of appetite was the foundation of all their sins.

(1890) C.T.B.H. 16

240. Christ began the work of redemption just where the ruin began. His first test was on the same point where Adam failed. It was through temptations addressed to the appetite that Satan had overcome a large proportion of the human race, and his success had made him feel that the control of this fallen planet was in his hands. But in Christ he found one who was able to resist him, and he left the field of battle a conquered foe. Jesus says, "He hath nothing in Me." His victory is an assurance that we too may come off victors in our conflicts with the enemy. But it is not our heavenly Father's purpose to save us without an effort on our part to cooperate with Christ. We must act our part, and divine power, uniting with our effort, will bring victory.

[For our sakes Christ exercised self-control stronger than hunger or death—295]

[Christ strengthened to endure by His fast; His victory an encouragement to all—296]

[When most fiercely tempted, Christ ate nothing—70]
[The strength of temptation to indulge appetite measured by anguish of Christ during His fast—298]

Daniel's Example in Overcoming

(1890) C.T.B.H. 22, 23

241. Temptations to the indulgence of appetite possess a power which can be overcome only by the help that God can impart. But with every temptation we have the promise of God that there shall be a way of escape. Why, then, are so many overcome? It is because they do not put their trust in God. They do not avail themselves of the means provided for their safety. The excuses offered for the gratification of perverted appetite, are therefore of no weight with God.

Daniel valued his human capabilities, but he did not trust in them. His trust was in that strength which God has promised to all who will come to Him in humble dependence, relying wholly upon His power.

He purposed in his heart that he would not defile himself with the portion of the king's meat, nor with the wine which he drank; for he knew that such a diet would not strengthen his physical powers or increase his mental capability. He would not use wine, nor any other unnatural stimulant; he would do nothing to becloud his mind; and God gave him "knowledge and skill in all learning and wisdom," and also "understanding in all visions and dreams.". . .

Daniel's parents had trained him in his childhood to habits of strict temperance. They had taught him that he must conform to nature's laws in all his habits; that his eating and drinking had a direct influence upon his physical, mental, and moral nature, and that he was accountable to God for his capabilities; for he held them all as a gift from God, and must not, by any course of action, dwarf or cripple them. As the result of this teaching, the law of God was exalted in his mind, and reverenced in his heart. During the early years of his captivity, Daniel was passing through an ordeal which was to familiarize him with courtly grandeur, with hypocrisy, and with paganism. A strange school in-

eed to fit him for a life of sobriety, industry, and faithful-
ess! And yet he lived uncorrupted by the atmosphere of
vil with which he was surrounded.

The experience of Daniel and his youthful companions
lustrates the benefits that may result from an abstemious
iet, and shows what God will do for those who will co-
perate with Him in the purifying and uplifting of the soul.
hey were an honor to God, and a bright and shining light
a the court of Babylon.

In this history we hear the voice of God addressing us
adividually, bidding us gather up all the precious rays of
ght upon this subject of Christian temperance, and place
urselves in right relation to the laws of health.

[R. & H., Jan. 25, 1881] C.H. 66

242. What if Daniel and his companions had made a
ompromise with those heathen officers, and had yielded to
ie pressure of the occasion by eating and drinking as was
ustomary with the Babylonians? That single instance of
eparture from principle would have weakened their sense
f right and their abhorrence of wrong. Indulgence of
ppetite would have involved the sacrifice of physical vigor,
learness of intellect, and spiritual power. One wrong step
ould probably have led to others, until, their connection
ith heaven being severed, they would have been swept
way by temptation.

[Daniel's clearness of mind due to simple diet and life of
rayer—117]
[More about Daniel—33, 34, 117]

Our Christian Duty

(1868) 2T 65

243. When we realize the requirements of God, we shall
ee that He requires us to be temperate in all things. The
id of our creation is to glorify God in our bodies and spirits
hich are His. How can we do this when we indulge the
ppetite to the injury of the physical and moral powers?
od requires that we present our bodies a living sacrifice.
hen the duty is enjoined on us to preserve that body in the
ery best condition of health, that we may comply with His

requirements. "Whether, therefore, ye eat or drink, or whatsoever ye do, do all to the glory of God."

(1900) 6T 374, 375

244. The apostle Paul writes: "Know ye not that they which run in a race run all, but one receiveth the prize? So run, that ye may obtain. And every man that striveth for the mastery is temperate in all things. Now they do it to obtain a corruptible crown; but we an incorruptible. I therefore so run, not as uncertainly; so fight I, not as one that beateth the air; but I keep under my body, and bring it into subjection; lest that by any means, when I have preached to others, I myself should be a castaway." 1 Cor. 9:24-27.

There are many in the world who indulge pernicious habits. Appetite is the law that governs them; and because of their wrong habits, the moral sense is clouded and the power to discern sacred things is to a great extent destroyed. But it is necessary for Christians to be strictly temperate. They should place their standard high. Temperance in eating, drinking, and dressing is essential. Principle should rule instead of appetite or fancy. Those who eat too much or whose food is of an objectionable quality, are easily led into dissipation, and into other "foolish and hurtful lusts, which drown men in destruction and perdition." 1 Tim. 6:9. The "laborers together with God" should use every jot of their influence to encourage the spread of true temperance principles.

It means much to be true to God. He has claims upon all who are engaged in His service. He desires that mind and body be preserved in the best condition of health, every power and endowment under the divine control, and as vigorous as careful, strictly temperate habits can make them. We are under obligation to God to make an unreserved consecration of ourselves to Him, body and soul, with all the faculties appreciated as His entrusted gifts, to be employed in His service.

All our energies and capabilities are to be constantly strengthened and improved during this probationary period. Only those who appreciate these principles, and have been trained to care for their bodies intelligently and in the fear of God, should be chosen to take responsibilities in this work. Those who have been long in the truth, yet who cannot distinguish between the pure principles of righteousness and the principles of evil, whose understanding in regard to justice, mercy, and the love of God is clouded, should be relieved of responsibilities. Every church needs a clear, sharp testimony, giving the trumpet a certain sound.

If we can arouse the moral sensibilities of our people on the subject of temperance, a great victory will be gained. Temperance in all things of this life is to be taught and practiced. Temperance in eating, drinking, sleeping, and dressing is one of the grand principles of the religious life. Truth brought into the sanctuary of the soul will guide in the treatment of the body. Nothing that concerns the health of the human agent is to be regarded with indifference. Our eternal welfare depends upon the use we make during this life of our time, strength, and influence.

Slaves to Appetite

(1864) Sp. Gifts IV, 129-131

245. There is a class who profess to believe the truth, who do not use tobacco, snuff, tea, or coffee, yet they are guilty of gratifying the appetite in a different manner. They crave highly seasoned meats, with rich gravies, and their appetite has become so perverted that they cannot be satisfied with even meat, unless prepared in a manner most injurious. The stomach is fevered, the digestive organs are taxed, and yet the stomach labors hard to dispose of the load forced upon it. After the stomach has performed its task it becomes exhausted, which causes faintness. Here many are deceived, and think that it is the want of food which produces such feelings, and without giving the stomach time to rest, they take more food, which for the time removes the faintness. And the more the appetite is indulged, the more will be its clamors for gratification. This faintness is generally the result of meat eating, and eating frequently, and too much. . . .

Because it is the fashion, in harmony with morbid appetite, rich cake, pies, and puddings, and every hurtful thing, are crowded into the stomach. The table must be loaded down with a variety, or the depraved appetite cannot be satisfied. In the morning, these slaves to appetite often have impure breath, and a furred tongue. They do not enjoy health, and wonder why they suffer with pains, headaches, and various ills. Many eat three times a day, and again just before going to bed. In a short time the digestive organs are worn out, for they have had no time to rest. These become miserable dyspeptics, and wonder what has made them so. The cause has brought the sure result. A second meal should never be eaten until the stomach has had time to rest from the labor of digesting the preceding meal. If a third meal be eaten at all, it should be light, and several hours before going to bed.

Many are so devoted to intemperance that they will not change their course of indulging in gluttony under any considerations. They would sooner sacrifice health, and die prematurely, than to restrain their intemperate appetite. And there are many who are ignorant of the relation their eating and drinking has to health. Could such be enlightened, they might have moral courage to deny the appetite, and eat more sparingly, and of that food alone which was healthful and by their own course of action save themselves a great amount of suffering.

EDUCATE THE APPETITE

Persons who have indulged their appetite to eat freely of meat, highly seasoned gravies, and various kinds of rich cakes and preserves, cannot immediately relish a plain, wholesome, and nutritious diet. Their taste is so perverted they have no appetite for a wholesome diet of fruits, plain bread, and vegetables. They need not expect to relish at first food so different from that which they have been indulging themselves to eat. If they cannot at first enjoy plain food, they should fast until they can. That fast will prove to them of greater benefit than medicine, for the abused stomach will find that rest which it has long needed, and real hunger can be satisfied with a plain diet. It will take time for the taste to recover from the abuses which it has received, and to gain its natural tone. But perseverance in a self-denying course of eating and drinking will soon make plain, wholesome food palatable, and it will soon be eaten with greater satisfaction than the epicure enjoys over his rich dainties.

The stomach is not fevered with meat, and overtaxed, but is in a healthy condition, and can readily perform its task. There should be no delay in reform. Efforts should be made to preserve carefully the remaining strength of the vital forces, by lifting off every overtaxing burden. The stomach may never fully recover health, but a proper course of diet will save further debility, and many will recover more or less, unless they have gone very far in gluttonous self-murder.

Those who permit themselves to become slaves to a gluttonous appetite, often go still further, and debase themselves by indulging their corrupt passions, which have become excited by intemperance in eating and in drinking. They give loose rein to their debasing passions, until health and intellect greatly suffer. The reasoning faculties are, in a great measure, destroyed by evil habits.

Effect of Indulgence, Physical, Mental, Moral

(1890) C.T.B.H. 83

246. Many students are deplorably ignorant of the fact that diet exerts a powerful influence upon the health. Some have never made a determined effort to control the appetite, or to observe proper rules in regard to diet. They eat too much, even at their meals, and some eat between meals whenever the temptation is presented. If those who profess to be Christians desire to solve the questions so perplexing to them, why their minds are so dull, why their religious aspirations are so feeble, they need not, in many instances, go farther than the table; here is cause enough, if there were no other.

Many separate themselves from God by their indulgence of appetite. He who notices the fall of a sparrow, who numbers the very hairs of the head, marks the sin of those who indulge perverted appetite at the expense of weakening the physical powers, benumbing the intellect, and deadening the moral perceptions.

A Future Day of Remorse

(1882) 5T 135

247. Many are incapacitated for labor both mentally and physically by overeating and the gratification of the lustful passions. The animal propensities are strengthened, while the moral and spiritual nature is enfeebled. When we shall stand around the great white throne, what a record will the lives of many then present. Then will they see what they might have done had they not debased their God-given powers. Then will they realize what height of intellectual greatness they might have attained, had they given to God all the physical and mental strength He had entrusted to them. In their agony of remorse they will long to have their lives to live over again.

[Mental and physical effects of overeating—219, 220]

Unnatural Appetite to Be Restrained

(1890) C.T.B.H. 150, 151

248. Providence has been leading the people of God out from the extravagant habits of the world, away from the indulgence of appetite and passion, to take their stand upon the platform of self-denial, and temperance in all things. The people whom God is leading will be peculiar. They will not be like the world. If they follow the leadings of God, they will accomplish His purposes, and will yield their will to His will. Christ will dwell in the heart. The temple of God will be holy. Your body, says the apostle, is the temple of the Holy Ghost. God does not require His children to deny themselves to the injury of physical strength. He requires them to obey natural law, in order to preserve physical health. Nature's path is the road He marks out, and it is broad enough for any Christian. With a lavish hand God has provided us with rich and varied bounties for our sustenance and enjoyment. But in order for us to enjoy the natural appetite, which will preserve health and prolong

life, He restricts the appetite. He says, Beware! restrain, deny, unnatural appetite. If we create a perverted appetite, we violate the laws of our being, and assume the responsibility of abusing our bodies and of bringing disease upon ourselves.

(1909) 9T 153, 154

249. Those who have received instruction regarding the evils of the use of flesh foods, tea, and coffee, and rich and unhealthful food preparations, and who are determined to make a covenant with God by sacrifice, will not continue to indulge their appetite for food that they know to be unhealthful. God demands that the appetites be cleansed, and that self-denial be practiced in regard to those things which are not good. This is a work that will have to be done before His people can stand before Him a perfected people.

Health Reformer, September, 1871

250. God has not changed, neither does He propose to change our physical organism, in order that we may violate a single law without feeling the effects of its violation. But many willingly close their eyes to the light. . . . By indulging their inclinations and appetites, they violate the laws of life and health; and if they obey conscience, they must be controlled by principle in their eating and dressing, rather than be led by inclination, fashion, and appetite.

Usefulness of God's Workers Depends Upon Controlled Appetite

Letter 158, 1909

251. Present before the people the need of resisting the temptation to indulge appetite. This is where many are failing. Explain how closely body and mind are related, and show the need of keeping both in the very best condition. . . .

All who indulge the appetite, waste the physical energies, and weaken the moral power, will sooner or later feel the retribution that follows the transgression of physical law.

Christ gave His life to purchase redemption for the sinner. The world's Redeemer knew that indulgence of appetite was bringing physical debility and deadening the perceptive faculties so that sacred and eternal things could not be discerned. He knew that self-indulgence was perverting the moral powers, and that man's great need was conversion,—in heart and mind and soul, from the life of self-indulgence to one of self-denial and self-sacrifice. May the Lord help you as His servant to appeal to the ministers and to arouse the sleeping churches. Let your labors as a physician and a minister be in harmony. It is for this that our sanitariums are established, to preach the truth of true temperance. . . .

As a people, we need to reform, and especially do ministers and teachers of the word need to reform. I am instructed to say to our ministers and to the presidents of our conferences: Your usefulness as laborers for God in the work of recovering perishing souls, depends much on your success in overcoming appetite. Overcome the desire to gratify appetite, and if you do this your passions will be easily controlled. Then your mental and moral powers will be stronger. "And they overcame . . . by the blood of the Lamb, and by the word of their testimony."

An Appeal to a Fellow Worker

Letter 49, 1892

252. The Lord has chosen you to do His work, and if you work carefully, prudently, and bring your habits of eating in strict control to knowledge and reason, you would have many more pleasant, comfortable hours than if you acted unwisely. Put on the brakes, hold your appetite under strict charge, and then leave yourself in the hands of God. Prolong your life by careful supervision of yourself.

Abstemiousness Increases Vigor

(1875) 3T 490-492

253. Men who are engaged in giving the last message of warning to the world, a message which is to decide the destiny of souls, should make a practical application in their own lives of the truths they preach to others. They should be examples to the people in their eating, in their drinking, and in their chaste conversation and deportment. Gluttony, indulgence of the baser passions, and grievous sins, are hidden under the garb of sanctity by many professed repre-

sentatives of Christ throughout our world. There are men of excellent natural ability whose labor does not accomplish half what it might if they were temperate in all things. Indulgence of appetite and passion beclouds the mind, lessens physical strength, and weakens moral power. Their thoughts are not clear. Their words are not spoken in power, are not vitalized by the Spirit of God so as to reach the hearts of the hearers.

As our first parents lost Eden through the indulgence of appetite, our only hope of regaining Eden is through the firm denial of appetite and passion. Abstemiousness in diet, and control of all the passions, will preserve the intellect and give mental and moral vigor, enabling men to bring all their propensities under the control of the higher powers, and to discern between right and wrong, the sacred and the common. All who have a true sense of the sacrifice made by Christ in leaving His home in heaven to come to this world that He might by His own life show man how to resist temptation, will cheerfully deny self and choose to be partakers with Christ of His sufferings.

The fear of the Lord is the beginning of wisdom. Those who overcome as Christ overcame will need to constantly guard themselves against the temptations of Satan. The appetite and passions should be restricted and under the control of enlightened conscience, that the intellect may be unimpaired, the perceptive powers clear, so that the workings of Satan and his snares may not be interpreted to be the providence of God. Many desire the final reward and victory which are to be given to overcomers, but are not willing to endure toil, privation, and denial of self, as did their Redeemer. It is only through obedience and continual effort that we shall overcome as Christ overcame.

The controlling power of appetite will prove the ruin of thousands, when, if they had conquered on this point, they would have had moral power to gain the victory over every other temptation of Satan. But those who are slaves to appetite will fail in perfecting Christian character. The continual transgression of man for six thousand years has brought sickness, pain, and death as its fruits. And as we near the close of time, Satan's temptation to indulge appetite will be more powerful and more difficult to overcome.

[The path of self-denial in eating is the path to health—473]

Relation of Habits to Sanctification

R. & H., Jan. 25, 1881

254. It is impossible for any to enjoy the blessing of sanctification while they are selfish and gluttonous. These groan under a burden of infirmities because of wrong habits of eating and drinking, which do violence to the laws of life and health. Many are enfeebling their digestive organs by indulging perverted appetite. The power of the human constitution to resist the abuses put upon it is wonderful; but persistent wrong habits in excessive eating and drinking will enfeeble every function of the body. Let these feeble ones consider what they might have been, had they lived temperately, and promoted health instead of abusing it. In the gratification of perverted appetite and passion, even professed Christians cripple nature in her work and lessen physical, mental, and moral power. Some who are doing this, claim to be sanctified to God; but such a claim is without foundation. . . .

"A son honoreth his father, and a servant his master; if then I be a Father, where is Mine honor? and if I be a Master, where is My fear? saith the Lord of hosts unto you, O priests, that despise My name. And ye say, Wherein have we despised Thy name? Ye offer polluted bread upon Mine altar; and ye say, Wherein have we polluted Thee? In that ye say, The table of the Lord is contemptible. And if ye offer the blind for sacrifice, is it not evil? and if ye offer the lame and sick, is it not evil? offer it now unto thy governor; will he be pleased with thee, or accept thy person? saith the Lord of hosts. Ye brought that which was torn, and the lame, and the sick; thus ye brought an offering; should I accept this of your hand? saith the Lord."

Let us give careful heed to these warnings and reproofs. Though addressed to ancient Israel, they are no less applicable to the people of God today. And we should consider the

words of the apostle in which he appeals to his brethren, by
the mercies of God, to present their bodies, "a living sacrifice, holy, acceptable unto God." This is true sanctification.
It is not merely a theory, an emotion, or a form of words,
but a living, active principle, entering into the everyday life.
It requires that our habits of eating, drinking, and dressing,
be such as to secure the preservation of physical, mental,
and moral health, that we may present to the Lord our
bodies—not an offering corrupted by wrong habits but—
"a living sacrifice, holy, acceptable unto God."

Let none who profess godliness regard with indifference
the health of the body, and flatter themselves that intemperance is no sin, and will not affect their spirituality. A close
sympathy exists between the phyical and the moral nature.

Decision of Character Required

Letter 166, 1903

255. To deny appetite requires decision of character.
For want of this decision multitudes are ruined. Weak,
pliable, easily led, many men and women fail utterly of
becoming what God desires them to be. Those who are destitute of decision of character cannot make a success of the
daily work of overcoming. The world is full of besotted,
intemperate, weak-minded men and women, and how hard
it is for them to become genuine Christians.

What does the great Medical Missionary say?—"If any
man will come after Me, let him deny himself, and take up his
cross, and follow Me." It is Satan's work to tempt men to
tempt their fellow men. He strives to induce men to be
laborers together with him in his work of destruction. He
strives to lead them to give themselves so wholly to the indulgence of appetite and to the exciting amusements and follies
which human nature naturally craves, but which the word of
God decidedly forbids, that they can be ranked as his helpers
—working with him to destroy the image of God in man.

Through the strong temptations of principalities and
powers, many are ensnared. Slaves to the caprice of appetite, they are besotted and degraded. . . .

"What? know ye not that your body is the temple of the Holy Ghost which is in you, which ye have of God, and ye are not your own? For ye are bought with a price: therefore glorify God in your body, and in your spirit, which are God's."

Those who have a constant realization that they stand in this relation to God will not place in the stomach food which pleases the appetite, but which injures the digestive organs. They will not spoil the property of God by indulging in improper habits of eating, drinking, or dressing. They will take great care of the human machinery, realizing that they must do this in order to work in copartnership with God. He wills that they should be healthy, happy, and useful. But in order for them to be this, they must place their wills on the side of His will.

Health Reformer, May, 1878

256. Bewitching temptations to follow the lust of the flesh, the lust of the eyes, and the pride of life, are to be met on every side. The exercise of firm principle, and strict control of the appetites and passions, in the name of Jesus the Conqueror, will alone carry us safely through life.

The Futile Attempt to Reform Gradually

MS 86, 1897

257. Some say, when an effort is made to enlighten them on this point [use of liquor and tobacco], I will leave off by degrees. But Satan laughs at all such decisions. He says, They are secure in my power. I have no fear of them on that ground. But he knows that he has no power over the man who, when sinners entice him, has moral courage to say No squarely and positively. Such a one has dismissed the companionship of the devil, and as long as he holds to Jesus Christ, he is safe. He stands where heavenly angels can connect with him, giving him moral power to overcome.

Peter's Appeal

(1890) C.T.B.H. 53, 54

258. The apostle Peter understood the relation between the mind and the body, and raised his voice in warning to his

brethren: "Dearly beloved, I beseech you, as strangers and pilgrims, abstain from fleshly lusts, which war against the soul." Many regard this text as a warning against licentiousness only; but it has a broader meaning. It forbids every injurious gratification of appetite or passion. Every perverted appetite becomes a warring lust. Appetite was given us for a good purpose, not to become the minister of death by being perverted, and thus degenerating into "lusts which war against the soul." . . .

The strength of the temptation to indulge appetite can be measured only by the inexpressible anguish of our Redeemer in that long fast in the wilderness. He knew that the indulgence of perverted appetite would so deaden man's perceptions that sacred things could not be discerned. Adam fell by the indulgence of appetite; Christ overcame by the denial of appetite. And our only hope of regaining Eden is through firm self-control. If the power of indulged appetite was so strong upon the race, that, in order to break its hold, the divine Son of God, in man's behalf, had to endure a fast of nearly six weeks, what a work is before the Christian! Yet, however great the struggle, he may overcome. By the help of that divine power which withstood the fiercest temptations that Satan could invent, he, too, may be entirely successful in his warfare with evil, and at last may wear the victor's crown in the kingdom of God.

By the Power of the Will and the Grace of God

(1890) C.T.B.H. 37

259. Through appetite, Satan controls the mind and the whole being. Thousands who might have lived, have passed into the grave, physical, mental, and moral wrecks, because they sacrificed all their powers to the indulgence of appetite. The necessity for the men of this generation to call to their aid the power of the will, strengthened by the grace of God, in order to withstand the temptations of Satan, and resist the least indulgence of perverted appetite, is far greater than it was several generations ago. But the present generation have less power of self-control than had those who lived then.

(1881) 4T 574

260. Few have moral stamina to resist temptation, especially of the appetite, and to practice self-denial. To some it is a temptation too strong to be resisted to see others eat the third meal; and they imagine they are hungry, when the feeling is not a call of the stomach for food, but a desire of the mind that has not been fortified with firm principle, and disciplined to self-denial. The walls of self-control and self-restriction should not in a single instance be weakened and broken down. Paul, the apostle to the Gentiles, says, "I keep under my body, and bring it into subjection; lest that by any means, when I have preached to others, I myself should be a castaway."

Those who do not overcome in little things, will have no moral power to withstand greater temptations.

(1905) M.H. 323

261. Carefully consider your diet. Study from cause to effect. Cultivate self-control. Keep appetite under the control of reason. Never abuse the stomach by overeating, but do not deprive yourself of the wholesome, palatable food that health demands.

(1900) 6T 336

262. In your association with unbelievers, do not allow yourselves to be swerved from right principles. If you sit at their table, eat temperately, and only of food that will not confuse the mind. Keep clear of intemperance. You cannot afford to weaken your mental or physical powers, lest you become unable to discern spiritual things. Keep your mind in such a condition that God can impress it with the precious truths of His word.

A Question of Moral Courage

(1870) 2T 374

263. Some of you feel as though you would like to have somebody tell you how much to eat. This is not the way it should be. We are to act from a moral and religious standpoint. We are to be temperate in all things, because an incorruptible crown, a heavenly treasure, is before us. And

now I wish to say to my brethren and sisters, I would have moral courage to take my position and to govern myself. I would not want to put that on some one else. You eat too much and then you are sorry, and so you keep thinking upon what you eat and drink. Just eat that which is for the best and go right away, feeling clear in the sight of Heaven, and not having remorse of conscience. We do not believe in removing temptations entirely away from either children or grown persons. We all have a warfare before us, and must stand in a position to resist the temptations of Satan; and we want to know that we possess the power in ourselves to do this.

Letter 324, 1905

264. I am given a message to give to you: Eat at regular periods. By wrong habits of eating, you are preparing yourself for future suffering. It is not always safe to comply with invitations to meals, even though given by your brethren and friends, who wish to lavish upon you many kinds of food. You know that you can eat two or three kinds of food at a meal without injury to your digestive organs. When you are invited out to a meal, shun the many varieties of food that those who have invited you set before you. This you must do if you would be a faithful sentinel. When food is placed before us, which, if eaten, would cause the digestive organs hours of hard work, we must not, if we eat this food, blame those who set it before us for the result. God expects us to decide for ourselves to eat that food only which will not cause suffering to the digestive organs.

[The body to be servant to the mind—35]
[Early education of the appetite—346, 353]
[Appetite to be denied with interest and zeal—65]
[Prayer for healing by the intemperate—29]
[Effects of indulgence on influence and usefulness—72]

Victory Through Christ

(1890) C.T.B.H. 19

265. Christ fought the battle upon the point of appetite, and came off victorious; and we also can conquer through strength derived from Him. Who will enter in through the

gates into the city?—Not those who declare that they cannot break the force of appetite. Christ has resisted the power of him who would hold us in bondage; though weakened by His long fast of forty days, He withstood temptation, and proved by this act that our cases are not hopeless. I know that we cannot obtain the victory alone; and how thankful we should be that we have a living Saviour, who is ready and willing to aid us!

(1905) M.H. 176

266. A pure and noble life, a life of victory over appetite and lust, is possible to every one who will unite his weak, wavering human will to the omnipotent, unwavering will of God.

SECTION IX

Regularity in Eating

Quotations in Section IX

Regularity in Eating

PART I—NUMBER OF MEALS

Rest Needed by the Stomach

Letter 73a, 1896

267. THE stomach must have careful attention. It must not be kept in continual operation. Give this misused and much-abused organ some peace and quiet and rest. After the stomach has done its work for one meal, do not crowd more work upon it before it has had a chance to rest and before a sufficient supply of gastric juice is provided by nature to care for more food. Five hours at least should elapse between each meal, and always bear in mind that if you would give it a trial, you would find that two meals are better than three.

Eat a Substantial Breakfast

Letter 3, 1884

268. It is the custom and order of society to take a slight breakfast. But this is not the best way to treat the stomach. At breakfast time the stomach is in a better condition to take care of more food than at the second or third meal of the day. The habit of eating a sparing breakfast and a large dinner is wrong. Make your breakfast correspond more nearly to the heartiest meal of the day.

Late Suppers

(1905) M.H. 304

269. For persons of sedentary habits, late suppers are particularly harmful. With them the disturbance created is often the beginning of disease that ends in death.

In many cases the faintness that leads to a desire for food is felt because the digestive organs have been too severely taxed during the day. After disposing of one meal, the digestive organs need rest. At least five or six hours should intervene between the meals; and most persons who give the plan a trial, will find that two meals a day are better than three.

(1865) H. to L., ch. 1, pp. 55-57

270. Many indulge in the pernicious habit of eating just before sleeping hours. They may have taken three regular meals; yet because they feel a sense of faintness, as though hungry, will eat a lunch or fourth meal. By indulging this wrong practice, it has become a habit, and they feel as though they could not sleep without taking a lunch before retiring. In many cases, the cause of this faintness is because the digestive organs have been already too severely taxed through the day in disposing of unwholesome food forced upon the stomach too frequently, and in too great quantities. The digestive organs thus taxed become weary, and need a period of entire rest from labor to recover their exhausted energies. A second meal should never be eaten until the stomach has had time to rest from the labor of digesting the preceding meal. If a third meal be eaten at all, it should be light, and several hours before going to bed.

But with many, the poor, tired stomach may complain of weariness in vain. More food is forced upon it, which sets the digestive organs in motion, again to perform the same round of labor through the sleeping hours. The sleep of such is generally disturbed with unpleasant dreams, and in the morning they awake unrefreshed. There is a sense of languor and loss of appetite. A lack of energy is felt through the entire system. In a short time the digestive organs are worn out, for they have had no time to rest. These become miserable dyspeptics, and wonder what has made them so. The cause has brought the sure result. If this practice be indulged in a great length of time, the health will become seriously impaired. The blood becomes impure, the complexion sallow, and eruptions will frequently appear. You will often hear complaints from such, of frequent pains and soreness in the region of the stomach, and while performing labor, the stomach becomes so tired that they are obliged to desist from work, and rest. They seem to be at loss to account for this state of things; for, setting this aside, they are apparently healthy.

THE CAUSE AND CURE OF THAT ALL-GONE FEELING

Those who are changing from three meals a day, to two, will at first be troubled more or less with faintness, especially about the time they have been in the habit of eating their third meal. But if they persevere for a short time, this faintness will disappear.

The stomach, when we lie down to rest, should have its work all done, that it may enjoy rest, as well as other portions of the body. The work of digestion should not be carried on through any period of the sleeping hours. After the stomach, which has been overtaxed, has performed its task, it becomes exhausted, which causes faintness. Here many are deceived, and think that it is the want of food which produces such feelings, and without giving the stomach time to rest, they take more food, which for the time removes the faintness. And the more the appetite is indulged, the more will be its clamors for gratification. This faintness is generally the result of meat eating, and eating frequently, and too much. The stomach becomes weary by being kept constantly at work, disposing of food not the most healthful. Having no time for rest, the digestive organs become enfeebled, hence the sense of "goneness," and desire for frequent eating. The remedy such require, is to eat less frequently and less liberally, and be satisfied with plain, simple food, eating twice, or, at most, three times a day. The stomach must have its regular periods for labor and rest; hence eating irregularly and between meals, is a most pernicious violation of the laws of health. With regular habits, and proper food, the stomach will gradually recover.

R. & H., May 8, 1883

271. The stomach may be so educated as to desire food eight times a day, and feel faint if it is not supplied. But this is no argument in favor of so frequent eating.

[Awaking with impure breath and furred tongue—245]

The Two-Meal Plan

(1903) Ed. 205

272. In most cases, two meals a day are preferable to three. Supper, when taken at an early hour, interferes with the digestion of the previous meal. When taken later, it is not itself digested before bedtime. Thus the stomach fails of securing proper rest. The sleep is disturbed, the brain and nerves are wearied, the appetite for breakfast is impaired, the whole system is unrefreshed, and is unready for the day's duties.

[Two-meal plan for children—343, 344]

(1905) M.H. 321

273. The practice of eating but two meals a day is generally found a benefit to health; yet under some circumstances, persons may require a third meal. This should, however, if taken at all, be very light, and of food most easily digested. Crackers—the English biscuit—or zwieback, and fruit, or cereal coffee, are the foods best suited for the evening meal.

[C.T.B.H. 58] (1890) C.H. 156

274. Most people enjoy better health while eating two meals a day than three; others, under their existing circumstances, may require something to eat at suppertime; but this meal should be very light. Let no one think himself a criterion for all,—that every one must do exactly as he does.

Never cheat the stomach out of that which health demands, and never abuse it by placing upon it a load which it should not bear. Cultivate self-control. Restrain appetite; keep it under the control of reason. Do not feel it necessary to load down your table with unhealthful food when you have visitors. The health of your family and the influence upon your children should be considered, as well as the habits and tastes of your guests.

(1881) 4T 574

275. To some it is a temptation too strong to be resisted to see others eat the third meal, and they imagine they are

hungry, when the feeling is not a call of the stomach for food, but a desire of the mind that has not been fortified with firm principle, and disciplined to self-denial.

[For context see—260]

As a Remedy for Irritability

(1880) 4T 501, 502

276. The course of Brother H has not been what it should have been. His likes and dislikes are very strong and he has not kept his own feelings under the control of reason. Brother H, your health is greatly injured by over-eating, and eating at improper times. This causes a determination of blood to the brain. The mind becomes confused, and you have not the proper control of yourself. You appear like a man whose mind is unbalanced. You make strong moves, are easily irritated, and view things in an exaggerated and perverted light. Plenty of exercise in the open air, and an abstemious diet, are essential to your health. You should not eat more than two meals a day. If you feel that you must eat at night, take a drink of cold water, and in the morning you will feel much better for not having eaten.

None to Be Forced to Discard Their Third Meal

Letter 145, 1901

277. With regard to the diet question, this matter must be handled with such wisdom that no overbearing will appear. It should be shown that to eat two meals is far better for the health than to eat three. But there must be no authoritative forcing seen. No one connected with the sanitarium should be compelled to adopt the two-meal system. Persuasion is more appropriate than force. . . .

The days are now growing shorter, and it will be a good time to present this matter. As the days shorten, let dinner be a little later, and then the third meal will not be felt necessary.

Letter 200, 1902

278. In regard to the third meal, do not make eating but two meals compulsory. Some do best healthwise when eating three light meals, and when they are restricted to two, they feel the change severely.

[Possibility of harm through discarding third meal at our sanitariums—424]

Not to Be a Test

Letter 30, 1903

279. I eat only two meals a day. But I do not think that the number of meals should be made a test. If there are those who are better in health when eating three meals, it is their privilege to have three. I choose two meals. For thirty-five years I have practiced the two-meal system.

Objectionable Results of Enforcing the Two-Meal Plan in Training Schools

Letter 141, 1899

280. The impression is upon many minds that the diet question is being carried to extremes. When students combine physical and mental taxation, so largely as they do at this school (Avondale), the objection to the third meal is to a great extent removed. Then no one needs to feel abused. Those who conscientiously eat only two meals need not change in this at all. . . .

The fact that some, teachers and students, have the privilege of eating in their rooms, is not creating a healthful influence. There must be harmonious action in the conducting of meals. If those who only eat two meals have the idea that they must eat enough at the second meal to answer for the third meal also, they will injure their digestive organs. Let the students have the third meal, prepared without vegetables, but with simple, wholesome food, such as fruit and bread.

[For ministers two meals more conducive to physical and spiritual health—227]

[Two-meal plan followed by E. G. White—Appendix I:4, 5, 20, 22, 23]

[Mrs. White's table set twice a day—27]

PART II—EATING BETWEEN MEALS

The Importance of Regularity

MS 1, 1876

281. After the regular meal is eaten, the stomach should be allowed to rest for five hours. Not a particle of food should be introduced into the stomach till the next meal. In this interval the stomach will perform its work, and will then be in a condition to receive more food.

In no case should the meals be irregular. If dinner is eaten an hour or two before the usual time, the stomach is unprepared for the new burden; for it has not yet disposed of the food eaten at the previous meal, and has not vital force for new work. Thus the system is overtaxed.

Neither should the meals be delayed one or two hours, to suit circumstances, or in order that a certain amount of work may be accomplished. The stomach calls for food at the time it is accustomed to receive it. If that time is delayed, the vitality of the system decreases, and finally reaches so low an ebb that the appetite is entirely gone. If food is then taken, the stomach is unable to properly care for it. The food cannot be converted into good blood.

If all would eat at regular periods, not tasting anything between meals, they would be ready for their meals, and would find a pleasure in eating that would repay them for their effort.

(1905) M.H. 303, 304

282. Regularity in eating is of vital importance. There should be a specified time for each meal. At this time, let every one eat what the system requires, and then take nothing more until the next meal. There are many who eat when the system needs no food, at irregular intervals, and between meals, because they have not sufficient strength of will to resist inclination. When traveling, some are constantly nibbling if anything eatable is within their reach. This is very injurious. If travelers would eat regularly of food that is simple and nutritious, they would not feel so great weariness, nor suffer so much from sickness.

(1905) M.H. 384

283. Regularity in eating should be carefully observed. Nothing should be eaten between meals, no confectionery, nuts, fruits, or food of any kind. Irregularities in eating destroy the healthful tone of the digestive organs, to the detriment of health and cheerfulness. And when the children come to the table, they do not relish wholesome food; their appetites crave that which is hurtful for them.

(1870) 2T 485

284. There has not been in this family the right management in regard to diet; there has been irregularity. There should have been a specified time for each meal, and the food should have been prepared in a simple form, and free from grease; but pains should have been taken to have it nutritious, healthful, and inviting. In this family, as also in many others, a special parade has been made for visitors: many dishes prepared and frequently made too rich, so that those seated at the table would be tempted to eat to excess. Then in the absence of company there was a great reaction, a falling off in the preparations brought on the table. The diet was spare, and lacked nourishment. It was considered not so much matter "just for ourselves." The meals were frequently picked up, and the regular time for eating not regarded. Every member of the family was injured by such management. It is a sin for any of our sisters to make such great preparations for visitors, and wrong their own families by a spare diet which will fail to nourish the system.

(1869) 2T 373

285. I am astonished to learn that, after all the light that has been given in this place, many of you eat between meals! You should never let a morsel pass your lips between your regular meals. Eat what you ought, but eat it at one meal, and then wait until the next.

[C.T.B.H. 50] (1890) C.H. 118

286. Many turn from light and knowledge, and sacrifice principle to taste. They eat when the system needs no food, and at irregular intervals, because they have no moral

stamina to resist inclination. As the result, the abused stomach rebels, and suffering follows. Regularity in eating is very important for health of body and serenity of mind. Never should a morsel of food pass the lips between meals.

(1869) 2T 374

287. And the dyspeptic,—what has made him dyspeptic is taking this course. Instead of observing regularity, he has let appetite control him, and has eaten between meals.

Health Reformer, May, 1877

288. Children are generally untaught in regard to the importance of when, how, and what they should eat. They are permitted to indulge their tastes freely, to eat at all hours, to help themselves to fruit when it tempts their eyes, and this, with the pie, cake, bread and butter, and sweetmeats eaten almost constantly, makes them gormands and dyspeptics. The digestive organs, like a mill which is continually kept running, become enfeebled, vital force is called from the brain to aid the stomach in its overwork, and thus the mental powers are weakened. The unnatural stimulation and wear of the vital forces make them nervous, impatient of restraint, self-willed, and irritable.

[Importance to children of regularity in diet—343, 344, 345, 346, 348]

(1875) 3T 564

289. Many parents, to avoid the task of patiently educating their children to habits of self-denial, and teaching them how to make a right use of all the blessings of God, indulge them in eating and drinking whenever they please. Appetite and selfish indulgence, unless positively restrained, grow with the growth and strengthen with the strength.

[For context see 347]

R. & H., July 29, 1884

290. It is quite a common custom with people of the world to eat three times a day, beside eating at irregular intervals between meals; and the last meal is generally the most hearty, and is often taken just before retiring. This is reversing the natural order; a hearty meal should never be taken so late in the day. Should these persons change

their practice, and eat but two meals a day, and nothing between meals, not even an apple, a nut, or any kind of fruit, the result would be seen in a good appetite and greatly improved health.

R. & H., July 29, 1884

291. When traveling, some are almost constantly nibbling, if there is anything within their reach. This is a most pernicious practice. Animals that do not have reason, and that know nothing of mental taxation, may do this without injury, but they are no criterion for rational beings, who have mental powers that should be used for God and humanity.

Health Reformer, June, 1878

292. Gluttonous feasts, and food taken into the stomach at untimely seasons, leave an influence upon every fiber of the system.

(1892) G.W. 174 (old edition)

293. Many eat at all hours, regardless of the laws of health. Then gloom covers the mind. How can men be honored with divine enlightenment, when they are so reckless in their habits, so inattentive to the light which God has given in regard to these things? Brethren, is it not time for you to be converted on these points of selfish indulgence?

R. & H., May 8, 1883

294. Three meals a day and nothing between meals—not even an apple—should be the utmost limit of indulgence. Those who go further violate nature's laws and will suffer the penalty.

[Ministers who disregard this rule—227]
[Eating between meals at camp meetings—124]
[Children should not eat candies, fruits, nuts, or anything between meals—344]
[Allowing children to eat at any hour—348, 355, 361]
[Results to students—246]

SECTION X

Fasting

Quotations in Section X

Fasting

Christ's Victory Through Denial of Appetite

(1898) D.A. 117, 118

295. With Christ, as with the holy pair in Eden, appetite was the ground of the first great temptation. Just where the ruin began, the work of our redemption must begin. As by the indulgence of appetite Adam fell, so by the denial of appetite Christ must overcome. "And when He had fasted forty days and forty nights, He was afterward an hungered. And when the tempter came to Him, he said, If Thou be the Son of God, command that these stones be made bread. But He answered and said, It is written, Man shall not live by bread alone, but by every word that proceedeth out of the mouth of God."

From the time of Adam to that of Christ, self-indulgence had increased the power of the appetites and passions, until they had almost unlimited control. Thus men had become debased and diseased, and of themselves it was impossible for them to overcome. In man's behalf, Christ conquered by enduring the severest test. For our sake He exercised a self-control stronger than hunger or death. And in this first victory were involved other issues that enter into all our conflicts with the powers of darkness.

When Jesus entered into the wilderness, He was shut in by the Father's glory. Absorbed in communion with God, He was lifted above human weakness. But the glory departed, and He was left to battle with temptation. It was pressing upon Him every moment. His human nature shrank from the conflict that awaited Him. For forty days He fasted and prayed. Weak and emaciated from hunger, worn and haggard with mental agony, "His visage was so marred more than any man, and His form more than the sons of men." Now was Satan's opportunity. Now he supposed that he could overcome Christ.

185

Letter 158, 1909

296. Christ entered upon the test upon the point of appetite, and for nearly six weeks resisted temptation in behalf of man. That long fast in the wilderness was to be a lesson to fallen man for all time. Christ was not overcome by the strong temptations of the enemy, and this is encouragement for every soul who is struggling against temptation. Christ has made it possible for every member of the human family to resist temptation. All who would live godly lives may overcome as Christ overcame, by the blood of the Lamb, and the word of their testimony. That long fast of the Saviour strengthened Him to endure. He gave evidence to man that He would begin the work of overcoming just where ruin began,—on the point of appetite.

(1869) 2T 202, 203

297. When Christ was the most fiercely beset by temptation, He ate nothing. He committed Himself to God, and through earnest prayer, and perfect submission to the will of His Father, came off conqueror. Those who profess the truth for these last days, above every other class of professed Christians, should imitate the great Exemplar in prayer.

[For context see 70]

(1875) 3T 486

298. The Redeemer of the world knew that the indulgence of appetite would bring physical debility, and so deaden the perceptive organs that sacred and eternal things would not be discerned. Christ knew that the world was given up to gluttony, and that this indulgence would pervert the moral powers. If the indulgence of appetite was so strong upon the race that in order to break its power, the divine Son of God, in behalf of man, was required to fast nearly six weeks, what a work is before the Christian in order that he may overcome even as Christ overcame! The strength of the temptation to indulge perverted appetite can be measured only by the inexpressible anguish of Christ in that long fast in the wilderness.

As a Preparation for Study of the Scriptures

(1870) 2T 692

299. There are in the Scriptures some things which are hard to be understood, and which, according to the language of Peter, the unlearned and unstable wrest unto their own destruction. We may not, in this life, be able to explain the meaning of every passage of Scripture; but there are no vital points to practical truth that will be clouded in mystery.

When the time shall come, in the providence of God, for the world to be tested upon the truth for that time, minds will be exercised by His Spirit to search the Scriptures, even with fasting and with prayer, until link after link is searched out, and united in a perfect chain.

Every fact which immediately concerns the salvation of souls will be made so clear that none need err, or walk in darkness.

(1870) 2T 650, 651

300. Difficult points of present truth have been reached by the earnest efforts of a few who were devoted to the work. Fasting and fervent prayer to God have moved the Lord to unlock His treasuries of truth to their understanding.

[R. & H., July 26, 1892] L. & T. 47

301. Those who sincerely desire truth will not be reluctant to lay open their positions for investigation and criticism, and will not be annoyed if their opinions and ideas are crossed. This was the spirit cherished among us forty years ago. We would come together burdened in soul, praying that we might be one in faith and doctrine; for we knew that Christ is not divided. One point at a time was made the subject of investigation. Solemnity characterized these councils of investigation. The Scriptures were opened with a sense of awe. Often we fasted, that we might be better fitted to understand the truth.

When Special Divine Help Is Needed

Letter 73, 1896

302. For certain things, fasting and prayer are recommended and appropriate. In the hand of God they are a

means of cleansing the heart and promoting a receptiv
frame of mind. We obtain answers to our prayers becaus
we humble our souls before God.

(1892) G.W. 236 (old edition)

303. It is in the order of God that those who bear respon
sibilities should often meet together to counsel with one an
other and to pray earnestly for that wisdom which He alon
can impart. Unitedly make known your troubles to God
Talk less; much precious time is lost in talk that brings n
light. Let brethren unite in fasting and prayer for the wis
dom that God has promised to supply liberally.

(1867) 1T 624

304. Whenever it is necessary for the advancement o
the cause of truth and the glory of God, that an opponent b
met, how carefully, and with what humility, should they [th
advocates of truth] go into the conflict. With heart search
ing, confession of sin, and earnest prayer, and often fastin,
for a time, they should entreat that God would especiall
help them, and give His saving, precious truth a gloriou
victory, that error might appear in its true deformity, an
its advocates be completely discomfited.

[The Saviour's fast a lesson to us, who live in fearful time
—238]

The True Fast

[Letter 73, 1896] M.M. 283

305. The true fasting which should be recommended t
all, is abstinence from every stimulating kind of food, an
the proper use of wholesome, simple food, which God ha
provided in abundance. Men need to think less about wha
they shall eat and drink of temporal food, and much more i
regard to the food from heaven, that will give tone an
vitality to the whole religious experience.

R. & H., Feb. 11, 1904

306. Now and onward till the close of time the people o
God should be more earnest, more wide-awake, not trustin
in their own wisdom, but in the wisdom of their Leade
They should set aside days for fasting and prayer. Entir

bstinence from food may not be required, but they should eat sparingly of the most simple food.

Letter 206, 1908

307. All the fasting in the world will not take the place of simple trust in the word of God. "Ask," He says, "and e shall receive." . . . You are not called upon to fast forty days. The Lord bore that fast for you in the wilderness of temptation. There would be no virtue in such a fast; but here is virtue in the blood of Christ.

MS 28, 1900

308. The spirit of true fasting and prayer is the spirit which yields mind, heart, and will to God.

As a Remedy for Disease

(1905) M.H. 235

309. Intemperate eating is often the cause of sickness, and what nature most needs is to be relieved of the undue burden that has been placed upon her. In many cases of sickness, the very best remedy is for the patient to fast for a meal or two, that the overworked organs of digestion may have an opportunity to rest. A fruit diet for a few days has often brought great relief to brain workers. Many times a short period of entire abstinence from food, followed by simple, moderate eating, has led to recovery through nature's own recuperative effort. An abstemious diet for a month or two would convince many sufferers that the path of self-denial is the path to health.

(1902) 7T 134

310. There are some who would be benefited more by abstinence from food for a day or two every week than by any amount of treatment or medical advice. To fast one day a week would be of incalculable benefit to them.

(1864) Sp. Gifts IV, 133, 134

311. Indulging in eating too frequently, and in too large quantities, overtaxes the digestive organs, and produces a feverish state of the system. The blood becomes impure, and then diseases of various kinds occur. . . .

The sufferers in such cases can do for themselves that which others cannot do as well for them. They should commence to relieve nature of the load they have forced upon her. They should remove the cause. Fast a short time, and give the stomach a chance for rest. Reduce the feverish state of the system by a careful and understanding application of water. These efforts will help nature in her struggles to free the system of impurities.

[Sp. Gifts IV, 130, 131] (1864) C.H. 148

312. Persons who have indulged their appetite to eat freely of meat, highly seasoned gravies, and various kinds of rich cakes and preserves, cannot immediately relish a plain, wholesome, and nutritious diet. Their taste is so perverted that they have no appetite for a wholesome diet of fruits, plain bread, and vegetables. They need not expect to relish at first food so different from that which they have been indulging themselves to eat. If they cannot at first enjoy plain food, they should fast until they can. That fast will prove to them of greater benefit than medicine, for the abused stomach will find that rest which it has long needed, and real hunger can be satisfied with a plain diet. It will take time for the taste to recover from the abuses which it has received, and to gain its natural tone. But perseverance in a self-denying course of eating and drinking will soon make plain, wholesome food palatable, and it will soon be eaten with greater satisfaction than the epicure enjoys over his rich dainties.

Guard Against Enfeebling Abstinence

(1870) 2T 384, 385

313. In cases of severe fever, abstinence from food for a short time will lessen the fever, and make the use of water more effectual. But the acting physician needs to understand the real condition of the patient, and not allow him to be restricted in diet for a great length of time until his system becomes enfeebled. While the fever is raging, food may irritate and excite the blood; but as soon as the strength of the fever is broken, nourishment should be given in a careful, judicious manner. If food is withheld too long, the

stomach's craving for it will create fever, which will be relieved by a proper allowance of food of a right quality. It gives nature something to work upon. If there is a great desire expressed for food, even during the fever, to gratify that desire with a moderate amount of simple food would be less injurious than for the patient to be denied. When he can get his mind upon nothing else, nature will not be overburdened with a small portion of simple food.

Advice to an Aged Minister

Letter 2, 1872

314. I have been informed that you have taken but one meal a day for a period of time; but I know it to be wrong in your case, for I have been shown that you needed a nutrious diet, and that you were in danger of being too abstemious. Your strength would not admit of your severe discipline. . . .

I think that you have erred in fasting two days. God did not require it of you. I beg of you to be cautious and eat freely good, wholesome food twice a day. You will surely decrease in strength and your mind become unbalanced unless you change your course of abstemious diet.

Quotations in Section XI

Extremes in Diet

The Value of a Consistent Course

[C.T.B.H. 55] (1890) C.H. 153-155

315. MANY of the views held by Seventh-day Adventists differ widely from those held by the world in general. Those who advocate an unpopular truth should, above all others, seek to be consistent in their own life. They should not try to see how different they can be from others, but how near they can come to those whom they wish to influence, that they may help them to the positions they themselves so highly prize. Such a course will commend the truths they hold.

Those who are advocating a reform in diet should, by the provision they make for their own table, present the advantages of hygiene in the best light. They should so exemplify its principles as to commend it to the judgment of candid minds.

There is a large class who will reject any reform movement, however reasonable, if it lays a restriction upon the appetite. They consult taste, instead of reason and the laws of health. By this class, all who leave the beaten track of custom and advocate reform will be opposed, and accounted radical, let them pursue ever so consistent a course. But no one should permit opposition or ridicule to turn him from the work of reform, or cause him to lightly regard it. He who is imbued with the spirit which actuated Daniel, will not be narrow or conceited, but he will be firm and decided in standing for the right. In all his associations, whether with his brethren or with others, he will not swerve from principle, while at the same time he will not fail to manifest a noble, Christlike patience. When those who advocate hygienic reform carry the matter to extremes, people are not to blame if they become disgusted. Too often our religious faith is thus brought into disrepute, and in many cases those who witness such exhibitions of inconsistency can never afterward be brought to think that there is anything good in the reform. These extremists do more harm in a few months than they can undo in a lifetime. They are engaged in a work which Satan loves to see go on.

Two classes have been presented before me: first, those who are not living up to the light which God has given them; secondly, those who are too rigid in carrying out their one-sided ideas of reform, and enforcing them on others. When they take a position, they stand to it stubbornly, and carry nearly everything over the mark.

The first class adopted the reform because some one else did. They did not obtain a clear understanding of its principles for themselves. Many of those who profess the truth have received it because some one else did, and for their life they could not give the reason of their faith. This is why they are so unstable. Instead of weighing their motives in the light of eternity, instead of obtaining a practical knowledge of the principles underlying all their actions, instead of digging down to the bottom and building upon a right foundation for themselves, they are walking in the light of another's torch, and will surely fail.

The other class take wrong views of the reform. They adopt too meager a diet. They subsist upon a poor quality of food, prepared without reference to the nourishment of the system. It is important that food be prepared with care, so that the appetite, when not perverted, can relish it.

Because we, from principle, discard the use of those things which irritate the stomach and destroy health, the idea should never be given that it is of little consequence what we eat. I do not recommend an impoverished diet. Many who need the benefits of healthful living, and from conscientious motives adopt what they believe to be such, are deceived by supposing that a meager bill of fare, prepared without painstaking, and consisting mostly of mushes, and so-called gems, heavy and sodden, is what is meant by a reformed diet. Some use milk and a large amount of sugar on mush, thinking that they are carrying out health reform. But the sugar and milk combined are liable to cause fermentation in the stomach, and are thus harmful. The free use of sugar in any form tends to clog the system, and is not unfrequently a cause of disease. Some think that they must eat only just such an amount, and just such a quality, and confine themselves to two or three kinds of food. But in eating too small an amount, and that not of the best quality, they do not receive sufficient nourishment. . . .

Narrow ideas, and overstraining of small points, have been a great injury to the cause of hygiene. There may be such an effort at economy in the preparation of food, that, instead of a healthful diet, it becomes a poverty-stricken diet. What is the result?—Poverty of the blood. I have seen several cases of disease most difficult to cure, which were due to impoverished diet. The persons thus afflicted were not compelled by poverty to adopt a meager diet, but did so in order to follow out their own erroneous ideas of what constitutes health reform. Day after day, meal after meal, the same articles of food were prepared without variation, until dyspepsia and general debility resulted.

Mistaken Ideas of Reform

(1905) M.H. 318-320

316. Not all who profess to believe in dietetic reform are really reformers. With many persons the reform consists merely in discarding certain unwholesome foods. They do not understand clearly the principles of health, and their tables, still loaded with harmful dainties, are far from being an example of Christian temperance and moderation.

Another class, in their desire to set a right example, go to the opposite extreme. Some are unable to obtain the most desirable foods, and instead of using such things as would best supply the lack, they adopt an impoverished diet. Their food does not supply the elements needed to make good blood. Their health suffers, their usefulness is impaired, and their example tells against rather than in favor of reform in diet.

Others think that since health requires a simple diet, there need be little care in the selection or the preparation of food. Some restrict themselves to a very meager diet, not having sufficient variety to supply the needs of the system, and they suffer in consequence.

Those who have but a partial understanding of the principles of reform are often the most rigid, not only in carrying out their views themselves, but in urging them on their families and their neighbors. The effect of their mistaken reforms, as seen in their own ill-health, and their efforts to force their views upon others, give many a false idea of dietetic reform, and lead them to reject it altogether.

Those who understand the laws of health, and who are governed by principle, will shun the extremes, both of indulgence and of restrictions. Their diet is chosen, not for the mere gratification of appetite, but for the upbuilding of the body. They seek to preserve every power in the best condition for the highest service to God and man. The appetite is under the control of reason and conscience, and they are rewarded with health of body and mind. While they do not urge their views offensively upon others, their example is a testimony in favor of right principles. These persons have a wide influence for good.

There is a real common sense in dietetic reform. The subject should be studied broadly and deeply, and no one should criticize others because their practice is not, in all things, in harmony with his own. It is impossible to make an unvarying rule to regulate every one's habits, and no one should think himself a criterion for all. Not all can eat the same things. Foods that are palatable and wholesome to one person may be distasteful, and even harmful, to another. Some cannot use milk, while others thrive on it. Some persons cannot digest peas and beans; others find them wholesome. For some the coarser grain preparations are good food, while others cannot use them.

Avoid an Impoverished Diet

(1870) 2T 366, 367

317. But what about an impoverished diet? I have spoken of the importance of the quantity and quality of food

being in strict accordance with the laws of health. But we would not recommend an impoverished diet. I have been shown that many take a wrong view of the health reform, and adopt too poor a diet. They subsist upon a cheap, poor quality of food, prepared without care or reference to the nourishment of the system. It is important that the food should be prepared with care, that the appetite, when not perverted, can relish it. Because we from principle discard the use of meat, butter, mince pies, spices, lard, and that which irritates the stomach and destroys health, the idea should never be given that it is of but little consequence what we eat.

There are some who go to extremes. They must eat just such an amount and just such a quality, and confine themselves to two or three things. They allow only a few things to be placed before them or their families to eat. In eating a small amount of food, and that not of the best quality, they do not take into the stomach that which will suitably nourish the system. Poor food cannot be converted into good blood. An impoverished diet will impoverish the blood.

[C.T.B.H. 49, 50] (1890) C.H. 118

318. Because it is wrong to eat merely to gratify perverted taste, it does not follow that we should be indifferent in regard to our food. It is a matter of the highest importance. No one should adopt an impoverished diet. Many are debilitated from disease, and need nourishing, well-cooked food. Health reformers, above all others, should be careful to avoid extremes. The body must have sufficient nourishment.

MS 59, 1912

319.
Dear Brother ———,

In the past you have practiced health reform too rigorously for your own good. Once, when you were very sick, the Lord gave me a message to save your life. You have been too strenuous in restricting your diet to certain articles of food. While I was praying for you, words were given me for you to set you in the right path. The message was sent that you were to allow yourself a more generous diet. The use of flesh meat was not advised. Directions were given as to the food to be taken. You followed the directions given, rallied, and are still with us.

I often think of the instruction then given you. I have been given so many precious messages to bear to the sick and the afflicted. For this I am grateful, and I praise the Lord.

Vary the Menus

(1868) 2T 63

320. We advise you to change your habits of living; but while you do this we caution you to move understandingly. I am acquainted with families who have changed from a meat diet to one that is impoverished. Their food is so poorly prepared that the stomach loathes it, and such have told me that the health reform did not agree with them; that they were decreasing in physical strength. Here is one reason why some have not been successful in their efforts to simplify their food. They have a poverty-stricken diet. Food is prepared without painstaking, and there is a continual sameness. There should not be many kinds at any one meal, but all meals should not be composed of the same kinds of food without variation. Food should be prepared with simplicity, yet with a nicety which will invite the appetite. You should keep grease out of your food. It defiles any preparation of food you may make. Eat largely of fruits and vegetables.

Y.I., May 31, 1894

321. Many have misinterpreted health reform, and have received perverted ideas of what constitutes right living. Some honestly think that a proper dietary consists chiefly of porridge. To eat largely of porridge would not ensure health to the digestive organs, for it is too much like liquid.

Consideration for Individual Needs

(1869) 2T 254

322. You have erred, and thought it was pride which led your wife to desire to have things more comfortable around her. She has been stinted, and dealt closely with by you. She needs a more generous diet, a more plentiful supply of food upon her table; and in her house she needs things as

comfortable and convenient as you can make them, things to make her work as easy as possible. But you have viewed matters from a wrong standpoint. You have thought that almost anything which could be eaten was good enough if you could live upon it and retain strength. You have pleaded the necessity of spare diet to your feeble wife. But she cannot make good blood or flesh upon the diet to which you could confine yourself and flourish. Some persons cannot subsist upon the same food upon which others can do well, even though it be prepared in the same manner.

You are in danger of becoming an extremist. Your system could not convert a very coarse, poor diet into good blood. Your blood-making organs are in good condition. But your wife requires a more select diet. Let her eat the same food which your system could convert into good blood, and her system could not appropriate it. She lacks vitality, and needs a generous, strengthening diet. She should have a good supply of fruit, and not be confined to the same things from day to day. She has a slender hold of life. She is diseased, and the wants of her system are far different from those of a healthy person.

Not to Be the Cause of a Time of Trouble

(1859) 1T 205, 206

323. I saw that you had mistaken notions about afflicting your bodies, depriving yourselves of nourishing food. These things lead some of the church to think that God is surely with you, or you would not deny self, and sacrifice thus. But I saw that none of these things will make you more holy. The heathen do all this, but receive no reward for it. A broken and contrite spirit before God is in His sight of great price. I saw that your views concerning these things are erroneous, and that you are looking at the church and watching them, noticing little things, when your attention should be turned to your own soul's interest. God has not laid the burden of His flock upon you. You think that the church is upon the background, because they cannot see things as you do, and because they do not follow the same rigid course

which you think you are required to pursue. I saw that you are deceived in regard to your own duty and the duty of others. Some have gone to extremes in regard to diet. They have taken a rigid course, and lived so very plain that their health has suffered, disease has strengthened in the system, and the temple of God has been weakened. . . .

I saw that God does not require any one to take a course of such rigid economy as to weaken or injure the temple of God. There are duties and requirements in His word to humble the church and cause them to afflict their souls, and there is no need of making crosses and manufacturing duties to distress the body in order to cause humility. All this is outside of the word of God.

The time of trouble is just before us; and then stern necessity will require the people of God to deny self, and to eat merely enough to sustain life; but God will prepare us for that time. In that fearful hour our necessity will be God's opportunity to impart His strengthening power, and to sustain His people. . . .

Those who labor with their hands must nourish their strength to perform this labor, and those also who labor in word and doctrine must nourish their strength; for Satan and his evil angels are warring against them to tear down their strength. They should seek rest of body and mind from wearing labor when they can, and should eat of nourishing, strengthening food to build up their strength; for they will be obliged to exercise all the strength they have. I saw that it does not glorify God in the least for any of His people to make a time of trouble for themselves. There is a time of trouble just before God's people, and He will prepare them for that fearful conflict.

When Health Reform Becomes Health Deform

Letter 37, 1901

324. I have something to say in reference to extreme views of health reform. Health reform becomes health deform, a health destroyer, when it is carried to extremes. You will not be successful in sanitariums, where the sick

are treated, if you prescribe for the patients the same diet you have prescribed for yourself and your wife. I assure you that your ideas in regard to diet for the sick are not advisable. The change is too great. While I would discard flesh meat as injurious, something less objectionable may be used, and this is found in eggs. Do not remove milk from the table or forbid its being used in the cooking of food. The milk used should be procured from healthy cows, and should be sterilized.

Those who take an extreme view of health reform are in danger of preparing tasteless dishes. This has been done over and over again. The food has become so insipid as to be refused by the stomach. The food given the sick should be varied. They should not be given the same dishes over and over again. . . .

I have told you what I have because I have received light that you are injuring your body by a poverty-stricken diet. I must say to you that it will not be best for you to instruct the students as you have done in regard to the diet question, because your ideas in regard to discarding certain things will not be for the help of those who need help.

Brother and Sister ——, I have all confidence in you, and I greatly desire that you may have physical health, in order that you may have perfect soundness spiritually. It is the lack of suitable food that has caused you to suffer so keenly. You have not taken the food essential to nourish your frail physical strength. You must not deny yourself of good, wholesome food.

At one time Doctor —— tried to teach our family to cook according to health reform, as he viewed it, without salt or anything else to season the food. Well, I determined to try it, but I became so reduced in strength that I had to make a change; and a different policy was entered upon with great success. I tell you this because I know that you are in positive danger. Food should be prepared in such a way that it will be nourishing. It should not be robbed of that which the system needs.

The Lord calls upon Brother and Sister —— to reform, to take periods of rest. It is not right for you to take burdens as you have done in the past. Unless you take heed, you will sacrifice that life which is so precious in the sight of the Lord. "Ye are not your own; for ye are bought with a price: therefore glorify God in your body, and in your spirit, which are God's." . . .

Do not go to extremes in regard to the health reform. Some of our people are very careless in regard to health reform. But because some are far behind, you must not, in order to be an example to them, be an extremist. You must not deprive yourself of that class of food which makes good blood. Your devotion to true principles is leading you to submit yourself to a diet which is giving you an experience that will not recommend health reform. This is your danger. When you see that you are becoming weak physically, it is essential for you to make changes, and at once. Put into your diet something you have left out. It is your duty to do this. Get eggs of healthy fowls. Use these eggs cooked or raw. Drop them uncooked into the best unfermented wine you can find. This will supply that which is necessary to your system. Do not for a moment suppose that it will not be right to do this. . . .

We appreciate your experience as a physician, and yet I say that milk and eggs should be included in your diet. These things cannot at present be dispensed with, and the doctrine of dispensing with them should not be taught.

You are in danger of taking too radical a view of health reform, and of prescribing for yourself a diet that will not sustain you. . . .

I do hope that you will heed the words I have spoken to you. It has been presented to me that you will not be able to exert the most successful influence in health reform unless in some things you become more liberal to yourself and to others. The time will come when milk cannot be used as freely as it is now used; but the present time is not the time to discard it. And eggs contain properties which are remedial agencies in counteracting poisons. And while warnings have been given against the use of these articles of diet in families where the children were addicted to, yes, steeped in, habits of self-abuse; yet we should not consider it a denial of principle to use eggs of hens which are well cared for and suitably fed. . . .

God calls upon those for whom Christ died to take proper care of themselves, and set a right example to others. My brother, you are not to make a test for the people of God, upon the question of diet; for they will lose confidence in teachings that are strained to the farthest point of extension. The Lord desires His people to be sound on every point in health reform, but we must not go to extremes. . . .

The reason for Doctor ——'s poor health is his over-drawing on his bank stock of health, and then failing to replace the amount drawn out by wholesome, nutritious, palatable food. My brother, devote your whole life to Him who was crucified for you, but do not tie yourself down to a meager diet; for thus you misrepresent health reform.

While working against gluttony and intemperance, we are to remember the means and appliances of gospel truth, which commend themselves to sound judgment. In order to do our work in straight, simple lines, we must recognize the conditions to which the human family are subjected. God has made provisions for those who live in the different countries of the world. Those who desire to be co-workers with God must consider carefully how they teach health reform in God's great vineyard. They must move carefully in specifying just what food should and should not be eaten. The human messenger must unite with the divine Helper in presenting the message of mercy to the multitudes God would save.

We are to be brought into connection with the masses. Should health reform be taught them in its most extreme form, harm would be done. We ask them to leave off eating meat and drinking tea and coffee. This is well. But some say that milk also should be given up. This is a subject that needs to be carefully handled. There are poor families whose diet consists of bread and milk, and, if they can get it, a little fruit. All flesh food should be discarded, but vegetables should be made palatable with a little milk or cream or something equivalent. The poor say, when health reform is presented to them, "What shall we eat? We cannot afford to buy the nut foods." As I preach the gospel to the poor, I am instructed to tell them to eat that food which is most nourishing. I cannot say to them: You must not eat eggs, or milk, or cream; you must use no butter in the preparation of food. The gospel must be preached to the poor, and the time has not yet come to prescribe the strictest diet.

The time will come when we may have to discard some of the articles of diet we now use, such as milk and cream and eggs; but my message is that you must not bring yourself to a time of trouble beforehand, and thus afflict yourself with death. Wait till the Lord prepares the way before you.

The reforms that are strained to the highest tension might accommodate a certain class, who can obtain all they need to take the place of the things discarded; but this class forms a very small minority of the people to whom these tests seem unnecessary. There are those who try to abstain from what is declared to be harmful. They fail to supply the system with proper nourishment, and as a consequence become weak and unable to work. Thus health reform is brought to disrepute. The work we have tried to build up solidly is confused with strange things that God has not required. The energies of the church are crippled.

But God will interfere to prevent the results of these too-strenuous ideas. The gospel is to harmonize the sinful race. It is to bring the rich and the poor together at the feet of Jesus. . . .

But I wish to say that when the time comes that it is no longer safe to use milk, cream, butter, and eggs, God will reveal this. No extremes in health reform are to be advocated. The question of using milk and butter and eggs will work out its own problem. At present we have no burden on this line. Let your moderation be known unto all men.

Letter 37, 1904

325. Last night I was in my sleep talking with Doctor ——. I said to him: You must still exercise care in regard to extremes in diet. You must not go to extremes either in your own case or in regard to the food provided

for the helpers and the patients at the sanitarium. The patients pay a good price for their board, and they should have liberal fare. Some may come to the sanitarium in a condition demanding stern denial of appetite and the simplest fare, but as their health improves, they should be liberally supplied with nourishing food.

[Sanitariums to avoid extremes in diet—427, 428, 429]

The Food Should be Made Appetizing

(1867) 2T 538

326. Health reformers, above all others, should be careful to shun extremes. The body must have sufficient nourishment. We cannot subsist upon air merely; neither can we retain health unless we have nourishing food. Food should be prepared in good order, so that it is palatable.

(1909) 9T 161-163

327. A diet lacking in the proper elements of nutrition, brings reproach upon the cause of health reform. We are mortal, and must supply ourselves with food that will give proper nourishment to the body.

Some of our people, while conscientiously abstaining from eating improper foods, neglect to supply themselves with the elements necessary for the sustenance of the body. Those who take an extreme view of health reform are in danger of preparing tasteless dishes, making them so insipid that they are not satisfying. Food should be prepared in such a way that it will be appetizing as well as nourishing. It should not be robbed of that which the system needs. I use some salt, and always have, because salt, instead of being deleterious, is actually essential for the blood. Vegetables should be made palatable with a little milk or cream, or something equivalent.

While warnings have been given regarding the dangers of disease through butter, and the evil of the free use of eggs by small children, yet we should not consider it a violation of principle to use eggs from hens that are well cared for and suitably fed. Eggs contain properties that are remedial agencies in counteracting certain poisons.

Some, in abstaining from milk, eggs, and butter, have failed to supply the system with proper nourishment, and as a consequence, have become weak and unable to work. Thus health reform is brought into disrepute. The work that we have tried to build up solidly is confused with strange things that God has not required, and the energies of the church are crippled. But God will interfere to prevent the results of these too strenuous ideas. The gospel is to harmonize the sinful race. It is to bring the rich and poor together at the feet of Jesus.

The time will come when we may have to discard some of the articles of diet we now use, such as milk and cream and eggs; but it is not necessary to bring upon ourselves perplexity by premature and extreme restrictions. Wait until the circumstances demand it, and the Lord prepares the way for it.

Those who would be successful in proclaiming the principles of health reform must make the word of God their guide and counselor. Only as the teachers of health reform principles do this, can they stand on vantage ground. Let us never bear a testimony against health reform by failing to use wholesome, palatable food in place of the harmful articles of diet that we have discarded. Do not in any way encourage an appetite for stimulants. Eat only plain, simple, wholesome food, and thank God constantly for the principles of health reform. In all things be true and upright, and you will gain precious victories.

Harmful Influence of Extremists

(1870) 2T 374, 375

328. And while we would caution you not to overeat, even of the best quality of food, we would also caution those that are extremists not to raise a false standard, and then endeavor to bring everybody to it.

(1870) 2T 384-387

329. I was shown that both B and C have dishonored the cause of God. They have brought upon it a stain which will never be fully wiped out. I was shown the family of our dear Brother D. If this brother had received proper help at the right time, every member of his family would have been alive today. It is a wonder that the laws of the land

have not been enforced in this instance of maltreatment. That family were perishing for food—the plainest, simplest food. They were starving in a land of plenty. A novice was practicing upon them. The young man did not die of disease, but of hunger. Food would have strengthened the system, and kept the machinery in motion. . . .

It is time that something was done to prevent novices from taking the field and advocating health reform. Their works and words can be spared; for they do more injury than the wisest and most intelligent men, with the best influence they can exert, can counteract. It is impossible for the best-qualified advocates of health reform to fully relieve the minds of the public from the prejudice received through the wrong course of these extremists, and to place the great subject of health reform upon a right basis in the community where these men have figured. The door is also closed in a great measure, so that unbelievers cannot be reached by the present truth upon the Sabbath and the soon coming of our Saviour. The most precious truths are cast aside by the people as unworthy of a hearing. These men are referred to as representatives of health reformers and Sabbathkeepers in general. A great responsibility rests upon those who have thus proved a stumbling block to unbelievers.

Urging Personal Opinions and Personal Tests

Letter 39, 1901

330. The time has come when health reform will be received in its importance by many in high places and in low places. But we are to allow nothing to eclipse the message we have to bear, the third angel's message, connected with the messages of the first and second angel. We must not allow minor things to bind us in a small circle, where we cannot obtain access to the people at large.

The church and the world need all the influence, all the talents God has given us. All we have should be appropriated to His use. In presenting the gospel, keep out all your own opinions. We have a world-wide message, and the Lord wants His servants to guard sacredly the trust He has given them. To every man God has given his work. Then let no false message be borne. Let there be no straining into inconsistent problems the grand light of health reform. The inconsistencies of one rest upon the whole body of believers; therefore when one goes to extremes, great harm is done to the cause of God.

The carrying of things to extremes is a matter to be dreaded. It always results in my being compelled to speak to prevent matters from being misunderstood, so that the world will not have cause to think that Seventh-day Adventists are a body of extremists. When we seek to pull people out of the fire on the one hand, the very words which then have to be spoken to correct evils are used to justify indulgence on the other hand. May the Lord keep us from human tests and extremes.

Let no one advance extreme views in regard to what we shall eat and what we shall drink. The Lord has given light. Let our people accept the light and walk in the light. There needs to be a great increase in the knowledge of God and Jesus Christ. This knowledge is eternal life. An increase of piety, of good, humble, spiritual religion would place our people in a position where they could learn of the Great Teacher.

The time may come when it will not be safe to use milk. But if the cows are healthy and the milk thoroughly cooked, there is no necessity of creating a time of trouble beforehand. Let no one feel that he must bear a message as to what our people shall place on their tables in every particular. Those who take an extreme position will in the end see that the results are not what they thought they would be. The Lord will lead us by His own right hand, if we will be led. Love and purity—these are the fruits borne upon a good tree. Every one that loveth is born of God and knoweth God.

I was instructed to say to those in the —— Conference who had been so strenuous upon the subject of health reform, urging their ideas and views upon others, that God had not given them their message. I told them that if they would soften and subdue their inherited and cultivated tendencies, in which there is a large amount of stubbornness, they would see that they need to be converted. "If we love one another, God dwelleth in us, and His love is perfected in us. . . . God is love; and he that dwelleth in love dwelleth in God, and God in him." . . .

Human wisdom is to be combined with divine wisdom and the mercy of God. Let us hide self in Christ. Let us work diligently to reach the high standard God has set up for us,—moral transformation by the gospel. God calls upon us to advance in right lines, to make straight paths for our feet, lest the lame be turned out of the way. Then will Christ be satisfied.

Error on Side of People Preferable to Opposite Extreme

Letter 57, 1886

331. Brother and Sister —— carried the matter of indulgence in eating to extreme, and the institute became demoralized. Now the enemy would push you into the opposite extreme if he could, to have a poverty-stricken diet. Be careful to keep level heads and sensible ideas. Seek wisdom from heaven and move understandingly. If you take extremely radical positions, you will be obliged to back down, and then however conscientious you may have been, you have lost confidence in your own sound judgment, and our brethren and unbelievers will lose confidence in you. Be sure to go no faster than you have positive light from God. Take no man's ideas, but move intelligently in the fear of the Lord.

If you err, let it not be in getting as far from the people as possible, for then you cut the thread of your influence and can do them no good. Better err on the side of the people than altogether away from them, for there is hope in that case that you can carry the people with you, but there is no need of error on either side.

You need not go into the water, or into the fire, but take the middle path, avoiding all extremes. Do not let it appear that you are one-sided, ill-balanced managers. Do not have a meager, poor diet. Do not let any one influence you to have the diet poverty-stricken. Have your food prepared in a healthful, tasteful manner; have your food prepared with a nicety that will correctly represent health reform.

The great backsliding upon health reform is because unwise minds have handled it and carried it to such extremes that it has disgusted in place of converting people to it. I have been where these radical ideas have been carried out. Vegetables prepared with only water, and everything else in like manner. This kind of cookery is health *deform,* and there are some minds so constituted that they will accept anything that bears the features of rigorous diet or reform of any kind.

My brethren, I would have you temperate in all things, but be careful that you do not strain the point or run our institution into such a narrow channel that it comes out to a point. You must not fall into every man's notions, but be level-headed, calm, trusting in God.

Both Extremes to Be Avoided

(1900) 6T 373, 374

332. I know that many of our brethren are in heart and practice opposed to health reform. I advocate no extremes. But as I have been looking over my manuscripts, I have seen the decided testimonies borne and the warnings of dangers that come to our people through imitating the customs and practices of the world in self-indulgence, gratification of appetite, and pride of apparel. My heart is sick and sad over the existing state of things. Some say that some of our brethren have pressed these questions too strongly. But because some may have acted indiscreetly in pressing their sentiments concerning health reform on all occasions, will any dare to keep back the truth on this subject? The people of the world are generally far in the opposite extreme of indulgence and intemperance in eating and drinking; and as the result, lustful practices abound.

There are many now under the shadow of death who have prepared to do a work for the Master, but who have not felt that a sacred obligation rested upon them to observe the laws of health. The laws of the physical system are indeed the laws of God; but this fact seems to have been forgotten. Some have limited themselves to a diet that cannot sustain them in health. They have not provided nourishing food to take the place of injurious articles; and they have not considered that tact and ingenuity must be exercised in preparing food in the most healthful manner. The system must be properly nourished in order to perform its work. It is contrary to health reform, after cutting off the great variety of unwholesome dishes, to go to the opposite extreme, reducing the quantity and quality of the food to a low standard. Instead of health reform this is health deform.

[Importance of instruction in preparing wholesome, appetizing food—see Cooking Schools in Section XXV]

SECTION XII

Diet During Pregnancy

Quotations in Section XII

Diet During Pregnancy

Prenatal Influences

(1905) M.H. 372, 373

333. THE effect of prenatal influences is by many parents looked upon as a matter of little moment; but Heaven does not so regard it. The message sent by an angel of God, and twice given in the most solemn manner, shows it to be deserving of our most careful thought.

In the words spoken to the Hebrew mother, God speaks to all mothers in every age. "Let her beware," the angel said; "all that I commanded her, let her observe." The well-being of the child will be affected by the habits of the mother. Her appetites and passions are to be controlled by principle. There is something for her to shun, something for her to work against, if she fulfills God's purpose for her in giving her a child. If before the birth of her child she is self-indulgent, if she is selfish, impatient, and exacting, these traits will be reflected in the disposition of the child. Thus many children have received as a birthright almost unconquerable tendencies to evil.

But if the mother unswervingly adheres to right principles, if she is temperate and self-denying, if she is kind, gentle, and unselfish, she may give her child these same precious traits of character. Very explicit was the command prohibiting the use of wine by the mother. Every drop of strong drink taken by her to gratify appetite endangers the physical, mental, and moral health of her child, and is a direct sin against her Creator.

Many advisers urge that every wish of the mother should be gratified; that if she desires any article of food, however harmful, she should freely indulge her appetite. Such advice is false and mischievous. The mother's physical needs should in no case be neglected. Two lives are depending upon her, and her wishes should be tenderly regarded, her needs generously supplied. But at this time above all

217

others she should avoid, in diet and in every other line, whatever would lessen physical or mental strength. By the command of God Himself she is placed under the most solemn obligation to exercise self-control.

(1890) C.T.B.H. 37, 38

334. When the Lord would raise up Samson as a deliverer of His people, He enjoined upon the mother correct habits of life before the birth of her child. And the same prohibition was to be imposed, from the first, upon the child; for he was to be consecrated to God as a Nazarite from his birth.

The angel of God appeared to the wife of Manoah, and informed her that she should have a son; and in view of this he gave her the important directions: "Now therefore beware, I pray thee, and drink not wine nor strong drink, and eat not any unclean thing."

God had important work for the promised child of Manoah to do, and it was to secure for him the qualifications necessary for this work, that the habits of both the mother and the child were to be so carefully regulated. "Neither let her drink wine nor strong drink," was the angel's instruction for the wife of Manoah, "nor eat any unclean thing; all that I commanded her let her observe." The child will be affected for good or evil by the habits of the mother. She must herself be controlled by principle, and must practice temperance and self-denial, if she would seek the welfare of her child

"Let Her Beware"

Signs, Feb. 26, 1902

335. The words spoken to the wife of Manoah contain a truth that the mothers of today would do well to study. In speaking to this one mother, the Lord spoke to all the anxious, sorrowing mothers of that time, and to all the mothers of succeeding generations. Yes, every mother may understand her duty. She may know that the character of her children will depend vastly more upon her habits before their birth and her personal efforts after their birth than upon external advantages or disadvantages.

"Let her beware," the angel said. Let her stand prepared to resist temptation. Her appetites and passions are to be controlled by principle. Of every mother it may be said, "Let her beware." There is something for her to shun, something for her to work against, if she fulfills God's purpose for her in giving her a child. . . .

The mother who is a fit teacher for her children must, before their birth, form habits of self-denial and self-control; for she transmits to them her own qualities, her own strong or weak traits of character. The enemy of souls understands this matter much better than do many parents. He will bring temptation upon the mother, knowing that if she does not resist him, he can through her affect her child. The mother's only hope is in God. She may flee to Him for grace and strength. She will not seek help in vain. He will enable her to transmit to her offspring qualities that will help them to gain success in this life and to win eternal life.

Appetite Not to Run Riot

(1870) 2T 381-383

336. It is an error generally committed to make no difference in the life of a woman previous to the birth of her children. At this important period the labor of the mother should be lightened. Great changes are going on in her system. It requires a greater amount of blood, and therefore an increase of food of the most nourishing quality to convert into blood. Unless she has an abundant supply of nutritious food, she cannot retain her physical strength, and her offspring is robbed of vitality. Her clothing also demands attention. Care should be taken to protect the body from a sense of chilliness. She should not call vitality unnecessarily to the surface to supply the want of sufficient clothing. If the mother is deprived of an abundance of wholesome, nutritious food, she will lack in the quantity and quality of blood. Her circulation will be poor and her child will lack in the very same things. There will be an inability in the offspring to appropriate food which it can convert into good blood to nourish the system. The prosperity of mother and child depends much upon good, warm

clothing, and a supply of nourishing food. The extra draf
upon the vitality of the mother must be considered and pro
vided for.

But, on the other hand, the idea that women, because o
their special condition, may let the appetite run riot, is a
mistake based on custom, but not on sound sense. The appe
tite of women in this condition may be variable, fitful, an
difficult to gratify; and custom allows her to have anythin
she may fancy, without consulting reason as to whether sucl
food can supply nutrition for her body and for the growth o
her child. The food should be nutritious, but should not b
of an exciting quality. Custom says that if she wants flesl
meats, pickles, spiced food, or mince pies, let her have them
appetite alone is to be consulted. This is a great mistake
and does much harm. The harm cannot be estimated. I
ever there is need of simplicity of diet and special care as t
the quality of food eaten, it is in this important period.

Women who possess principle, and who are well in
structed, will not depart from simplicity of diet at this tim
of all others. They will consider that another life is de
pendent upon them, and will be careful in all their habits, an
especially in diet. They should not eat that which is innu
tritious and exciting, simply because it tastes good. Ther
are too many counselors ready to persuade them to do thing
which reason would tell them they ought not to do.

Diseased children are born because of the gratification o
appetite by the parents. The system did not demand th
variety of food upon which the mind dwelt. Because onc
in the mind it must be in the stomach, is a great error whic
Christian women should reject. Imagination should not b
allowed to control the wants of the system. Those wh
allow the taste to rule, will suffer the penalty of transgress
ing the laws of their being. And the matter does not en
here; their innocent offspring also will be sufferers.

The blood-making organs cannot convert spices, minc
pies, pickles, and diseased flesh meats into good blood. An
if so much food is taken into the stomach that the digestiv
organs are compelled to overwork in order to dispose of i

and to free the system from irritating substances, the mother does injustice to herself, and lays the foundation of disease in her offspring. If she chooses to eat as she pleases, and what she may fancy, irrespective of consequences, she will bear the penalty, but not alone. Her innocent child must suffer because of her indiscretion.

Effects of Overwork and Impoverished Diet

(1865) H. to L., ch. 2, pp. 33, 34

337. The mother, in many cases previous to the birth of her children, is permitted to toil early and late, heating her blood. . . . Her strength should have been tenderly cherished. . . . Her burdens and cares are seldom lessened, and that period, which should be to her of all others a time of rest, is one of fatigue, sadness, and gloom. By too great exertion on her part, she deprives her offspring of that nutrition which nature has provided for it, and by heating her own blood, she imparts to it a bad quality of blood. The offspring is robbed of its vitality, robbed of physical and mental strength.

(1870) 2T 378, 379

338. I was shown the course of B in his own family. He has been severe and overbearing. He adopted the health reform as advocated by Brother C, and, like him, took extreme views of the subject; and not having a well-balanced mind, he has made terrible blunders, the results of which time will not efface. Aided by items gathered from books, he commenced to carry out the theory he had heard advocated by Brother C, and like him, made a point of bringing all up to the standard he had erected. He brought his own family to his rigid rules, but failed to control his own animal propensities. He failed to bring himself to the mark, and keep his body under. If he had had a correct knowledge of the system of health reform, he would have known that his wife was not in a condition to give birth to healthy children. His own unsubdued passions had borne sway without reasoning from cause to effect.

Before the birth of his children, he did not treat his wife as a woman in her condition should be treated. . . . He did not provide the quality and quantity of food that was necessary to nourish two lives instead of one. Another life was dependent upon her, and her system did not receive the nutritious wholesome food necessary to sustain her strength. There was a lack in the quantity and in the quality. Her system required changes, a variety and quality of food that was more nourishing. Her children were born with feeble digestive powers and impoverished blood. From the food the mother was compelled to receive, she could not furnish a good quality of blood, and therefore gave birth to children filled with humors.

Diet in Childhood

Quotations in Section XIII

Diet in Childhood

Counsel Based on Divine Instruction

Signs, Sept. 13, 1910

339. The inquiry of fathers and mothers should be, "What shall we do unto the child that shall be born unto us?" We have brought before the reader what God has said concerning the course of the mother before the birth of her children. But this is not all. The angel Gabriel was sent from the heavenly courts to give directions for the care of children after their birth, that parents might fully understand their duty.

About the time of Christ's first advent the angel Gabriel came to Zacharias with a message similar to that given to Manoah. The aged priest was told that his wife should bear a son, whose name should be called John. "And," said the angel, "thou shalt have joy and gladness; and many shall rejoice at his birth. For he shall be great in the sight of the Lord, and shall drink neither wine nor strong drink; and he shall be filled with the Holy Ghost." This child of promise was to be brought up with strictly temperate habits. An important work of reform was to be committed to him, to prepare the way for Christ.

Intemperance in every form existed among the people. Indulgence in wine and luxurious food was lessening physical strength, and debasing the morals to such an extent that the most revolting crimes did not appear sinful. The voice of John was to sound forth from the wilderness in stern rebuke for the sinful indulgences of the people, and his own abstemious habits were also to be a reproof of the excesses of his time.

THE TRUE BEGINNING OF REFORM

The efforts of our temperance workers are not sufficiently far-reaching to banish the curse of intemperance from our land. Habits once formed are hard to overcome. The reform should begin with the mother before the birth of her children; and if God's instructions were faithfully obeyed, intemperance would not exist.

It should be the constant effort of every mother to conform her habits to God's will, that she may work in harmony with Him to preserve her children from the health and life destroying vices of the present day. Let mothers place themselves without delay in right relations to their Creator, that they may by His assisting grace build around their children a bulwark against dissipation and intemperance. If mothers would but follow such a course, they might see their children, like the youthful Daniel, reach a high standard in moral and intellectual attainments, becoming a blessing to society and an honor to their Creator.

The Infant

(1905) M.H. 383

340. The best food for the infant is the food that nature provides. Of this it should not be needlessly deprived. It is a heartless thing for a mother, for the sake of convenience or social enjoyment, to seek to free herself from the tender office of nursing her little one.

The mother who permits her child to be nourished by another should consider well what the result may be. To a greater or less degree the nurse imparts her own temper and temperament to the nursing child.

Health Reformer, September, 1871

341. In order to keep pace with fashion, nature has been abused, instead of being consulted. Mothers sometimes depend upon a hireling, or a nursing bottle must be substituted, for the maternal breast. And one of the most delicate and gratifying duties a mother can perform for her dependent offspring, which blends her life with its own, and which awakens the most holy feelings in the hearts of women, is sacrificed to fashion's murderous folly.

There are mothers who will sacrifice their maternal duties in nursing their children simply because it is too much trouble to be confined to their offspring, which is the fruit of their own body. The ballroom and the exciting scenes of pleasure have had the influence to benumb the fine sensibilities of the soul. These have been more attractive to the fashionable mother than maternal duties to her children. Maybe she puts her children out to a hireling, to do those duties for them which should belong to herself exclusively. Her false habits make the necessary duties, which it should be her joy to perform, disagreeable to her, because the care of her children will interfere with the claims of fashionable life. A stranger performs the duties of the mother, and gives from her breast the food to sustain life.

Nor is this all. She also imparts her temper and her temperament to the nursing child. The child's life is linked to hers. If the hireling is a coarse type of woman, passionate and unreasonable; if she is not careful in her morals, the nursling will be, in all probability, of the same or a similar type. The same coarse quality of blood, coursing in the veins of the hireling nurse, is in that of the child. Mothers who will thus turn their children from their arms, and refuse the maternal duties, because they are a burden which they cannot well sustain, while devoting their lives to fashion, are unworthy the name of mother. They degrade the noble instincts and holy attributes of women, and choose to be butterflies of fashionable pleasure, having less sense of their responsibility to their posterity than the dumb brutes. Many mothers substitute the bottle for the breast. This is necessary because they have not nourishment for their children. But in nine cases out of ten their wrong habits of dressing, and of eating from their youth, have brought upon them inability to perform the duties nature designed they should. . . .

It ever has appeared to me to be cold, heartless business for mothers who can nurse their children to turn them from the maternal breast to the bottle. In that case, the greatest care is necessary to have the milk from a healthy cow, and to have the bottle, as well as the milk, perfectly sweet. This is frequently neglected, and as the result, the infant is made to suffer needlessly. Disturbances of the stomach and bowels are liable to occur, and the much-to-be-pitied infant becomes diseased, if it were healthy when born.

(1865) H. to L., ch. 2, pp. 39, 40

342. The period in which the infant receives its nourishment from the mother, is critical. Many mothers, while nursing their infants, have been permitted to overlabor, and to heat their blood in cooking, and the nursling has been seriously affected, not only with fevered nourishment from the mother's breast, but its blood has been poisoned by the unhealthy diet of the mother, which has fevered her whole system, thereby affecting the food of the infant. The infant will also be affected by the condition of the mother's mind. If she is unhappy, easily agitated, irritable, giving vent to outbursts of passion, the nourishment the infant receives from its mother will be inflamed, often producing colic, spasms, and, in some instances, causing convulsions and fits.

The character also of the child is more or less affected by the nature of the nourishment received from the mother. How important then that the mother, while nursing her infant, should preserve a happy state of mind, having the perfect control of her own spirit. By thus doing, the food of the child is not injured, and the calm, self-possessed course the mother pursues in the treatment of her child has very much to do in molding the mind of the infant. If it is nervous, and easily agitated, the mother's careful, unhurried manner will have a soothing and correcting influence, and the health of the infant can be very much improved.

Infants have been greatly abused by improper treatment. If it was fretful, it has generally been fed to keep it quiet, when, in most cases, the very reason of its fretfulness was because of its having received too much food, made injurious by the wrong habits of the mother. More food only made the matter worse, for its stomach was already overloaded.

Regularity in Eating

(1865) H. to L., ch. 2, p. 47

343. The first education children should receive from the mother in infancy should be in regard to their physical health. They should be allowed only plain food, of that quality that would preserve to them the best condition of

health, and that should be partaken of only at regular periods, not oftener than three times a day, and two meals would be better than three. If children are disciplined aright, they will soon learn that they can receive nothing by crying or fretting. A judicious mother will act in training her children, not merely in regard to her own present comfort, but for their future good. And to this end she will teach her children the important lesson of controlling the appetite, and of self-denial, that they should eat, drink, and dress in reference to health.

(1880) 4T 502

344. Your children should not be allowed to eat candies, fruit, nuts, or anything in the line of food, between their meals. Two meals a day are better for them than three. If the parents set the example, and move from principle, the children will soon fall into line. Irregularities in eating destroy the healthy tone of the digestive organs, and when your children come to the table, they do not relish wholesome food; their appetites crave that which is the most hurtful for them. Many times your children have suffered from fever and ague brought on by improper eating, when their parents were accountable for their sickness. It is the duty of parents to see that their children form habits conducive to health, thereby saving much distress.

Health Reformer, September, 1866

345. Children are also fed too frequently, which produces feverishness and suffering in various ways. The stomach should not be kept constantly at work, but should have its periods of rest. Without it children will be peevish and irritable and frequently sick.

[Children to be taught when and how to eat—288]
[Early training of Daniel—241]
[See Section IX, Regularity in Eating]

Early Education of the Appetite

(1905) M.H. 383-385

346. The importance of training children to right dietetic habits can hardly be overestimated. The little ones need to

learn that they eat to live, not live to eat. The training should begin with the infant in its mother's arms. The child should be given food only at regular intervals, and less frequently as it grows older. It should not be given sweets, or the food of older persons, which it is unable to digest. Care and regularity in the feeding of infants will not only promote health, and thus tend to make them quiet and sweet-tempered, but will lay the foundation of habits and will be a blessing to them in after years.

As children emerge from babyhood, great care should still be taken in educating their tastes and appetite. Often they are permitted to eat what they choose and when they choose, without reference to health. The pains and money so often lavished upon unwholesome dainties lead the young to think that the highest object in life, and that which yields the greatest amount of happiness, is to be able to indulge the appetite. The result of this training is gluttony, then comes sickness, which is usually followed by dosing with poisonous drugs.

Parents should train the appetites of their children, and should not permit the use of unwholesome foods. But in the effort to regulate the diet, we should be careful not to err in requiring children to eat that which is distasteful, or to eat more than is needed. Children have rights, they have preferences, and when these preferences are reasonable, they should be respected. . . .

Mothers who gratify the desires of their children at the expense of health and happy tempers, are sowing seeds of evil that will spring up and bear fruit. Self-indulgence grows with the growth of the little ones, and both mental and physical vigor are sacrificed. Mothers who do this work reap with bitterness the seed they have sown. They see their children grow up unfitted in mind and character to act a noble and useful part in society or in the home. The spiritual as well as the mental and physical powers suffer under the influence of unhealthful food. The conscience becomes stupefied, and the susceptibility to good impressions is impaired.

While the children should be taught to control the appetite, and to eat with reference to health, let it be made plain that they are denying themselves only that which would do them harm. They give up hurtful things for something better. Let the table be made inviting and attractive, as it is supplied with the good things which God has so bountifully bestowed. Let mealtime be a cheerful, happy time. As we enjoy the gifts of God, let us respond by grateful praise to the Giver.

(1875) 3T 564

347. Many parents, to avoid the task of patiently educating their children to habits of self-denial, and teaching them how to make a right use of all the blessings of God, indulge them in eating and drinking whenever they please. Appetite and selfish indulgence, unless positively restrained, grow with the growth and strengthen with the strength. When these children commence life for themselves, and take their place in society, they are powerless to resist temptation. Moral impurity and gross iniquity abound everywhere. The temptation to indulge taste and to gratify inclination has not lessened with the increase of years, and youth in general are governed by impulse, and are slaves to appetite. In the glutton, the tobacco devotee, the winebibber, and the inebriate, we see the evil results of defective education.

Indulgence and Depravity

(1864) Sp. Gifts IV, 132, 133

348. Children who eat improperly are often feeble, pale, and dwarfed and are nervous, excitable, and irritable. Everything noble is sacrificed to the appetite, and the animal passions predominate. The lives of many children from five to ten and fifteen years of age seem marked with depravity. They possess knowledge of almost every vice. The parents are, in a great degree, at fault in this matter, and to them will be accredited the sins of their children which their improper course has indirectly led them to commit. They tempt their children to indulge their appetite by placing upon their tables flesh meats and other food prepared with spices,

which have a tendency to excite the animal passions. By their example they teach their children intemperance in eating. They have been indulged to eat almost any hour of the day, which keeps the digestive organs constantly taxed. Mothers have had but little time to instruct their children. Their precious time was devoted to cooking various kinds of unwholesome food to place upon their tables.

Many parents have permitted their children to be ruined while they were trying to regulate their lives to fashion. If visitors are to come, they wish to have them sit down to as good a table as they would find among any of their circle of acquaintances. Much time and expense are devoted to this object. For the sake of appearance, rich food is prepared to suit the appetite, and even professed Christians make so much parade that they call around them a class whose principal object in visiting them is for the dainties they get to eat. Christians should reform in this respect. While they should courteously entertain their visitors, they should not be such slaves to fashion and appetite.

Study Simplicity

(1890) C.T.B.H. 141

349. Food should be so simple that its preparation will not absorb all the time of the mother. It is true, care should be taken to furnish the table with healthful food prepared in a wholesome and inviting manner. Do not think that anything you can carelessly throw together to serve as food is good enough for the children. But less time should be devoted to the preparation of unhealthful dishes for the table, to please a perverted taste, and more time to the education and training of the children. Let the strength which is now given to the unnecessary planning of what you shall eat and drink, and wherewithal you shall be clothed, be directed to keeping their persons clean and their clothes neat.

Letter 72, 1896

350. Highly seasoned meats, followed by rich pastry, is wearing out the vital organs of the digestion of children. Were they accustomed to plain, wholesome food, their appe-

tites would not crave unnatural luxuries and mixed preparations. . . . Meat given to children is not the best thing to
ensure success. . . . To educate your children to subsist on
a meat diet would be harmful to them. It is much easier to
create an unnatural appetite than to correct and reform the
taste after it has become second nature.

Fostering Intemperance

(1875) 3T 563

351. Many mothers who deplore the intemperance which
exists everywhere, do not look deep enough to see the cause.
They are daily preparing a variety of dishes and highly seasoned food, which tempt the appetite and encourage overeating. The tables of our American people are generally prepared in a manner to make drunkards. Appetite is the ruling
principle with a large class. Whoever will indulge appetite
in eating too often, and food not of a healthful quality, is
weakening his power to resist the clamors of appetite and
passion in other respects in proportion as he has strengthened the propensity to incorrect habits of eating. Mothers
need to be impressed with their obligation to God and to
the world to furnish society with children having well-
developed characters. Men and women who come upon the
stage of action with firm principles will be fitted to stand un-
sullied amid the moral pollutions of this corrupt age. . . .

The tables of many professed Christian women are daily
set with a variety of dishes which irritate the stomach and
produce a feverish condition of the system. Flesh meats
constitute the principal article of food upon the tables of
some families, until their blood is filled with cancerous and
scrofulous humors. Their bodies are composed of what they
eat. But when suffering and disease come upon them, it is
considered an affliction of Providence.

We repeat, intemperance commences at our tables. The
appetite is indulged until its indulgence becomes second nature. By the use of tea and coffee, an appetite is formed
for tobacco, and this encourages the appetite for liquors.

(1905) M.H. 334

352. Let parents begin a crusade against intemperance at their own fireside, in the principles they teach their children to follow from infancy, and they may hope for success.

[C.T.B.H. 46] (1890) C.H. 113

353. Parents should make it their first object to become intelligent in regard to the proper manner of dealing with their children, that they may secure to them sound minds in sound bodies. The principles of temperance should be carried out in all the details of home life. Self-denial should be taught to children, and enforced upon them, so far as consistent, from babyhood.

[Irritating foods that cause a thirst water will not quench— 558]

(1875) 3T 488, 489

354. Many parents educate the tastes of their children, and form their appetites. They indulge them in eating flesh meats, and in drinking tea and coffee. The highly seasoned flesh meats and the tea and coffee, which some mothers encourage their children to use, prepare the way for them to crave stronger stimulants, as tobacco. The use of tobacco encourages the appetite for liquor; and the use of tobacco and liquor invariably lessens nerve power.

If the moral sensibilities of Christians were aroused upon the subject of temperance in all things, they could, by their example, commencing at their tables, help those who are weak in self-control, who are almost powerless to resist the cravings of appetite. If we could realize that the habits we form in this life will affect our eternal interests, that our eternal destiny depends upon strictly temperate habits, we would work to the point of strict temperance in eating and drinking.

By our example and personal effort we may be the means of saving many souls from the degradation of intemperance, crime, and death. Our sisters can do much in the great work for the salvation of others by spreading their tables with only healthful, nourishing food. They may employ their precious time in educating the tastes and appetites of their children, in forming habits of temperance in all things, and in encouraging self-denial and benevolence for the good of others.

Notwithstanding the example that Christ gave us in the wilderness of temptation by denying appetite and overcoming its power, there are many Christian mothers, who, by their example and by the education which they are giving their children, are preparing them to become gluttons and winebibbers. Children are frequently indulged in eating what they choose and when they choose, without reference to health. There are many children who are educated gormands from their babyhood. Through indulgence of appetite they are made dyspeptics at an early age. Self-indulgence and intemperance in eating grow with their growth and strengthen with their strength. Mental and physical vigor are sacrificed through the indulgence of parents. A taste is formed for certain articles of food from which they can receive no benefit, but only injury, and as the system is taxed, the constitution becomes debilitated.

[The foundation of intemperance—203]

Teach an Abhorrence for Stimulants

(1890) C.T.B.H. 17

355. Teach your children to abhor stimulants. How many are ignorantly fostering in them an appetite for these things! In Europe I have seen nurses putting the glass of wine or beer to the lips of the innocent little ones, thus cultivating in them a taste for stimulants. As they grow older, they learn to depend more and more on these things, till little by little they are overcome, drift beyond the reach of help, and at last fill a drunkard's grave.

But it is not thus alone that the appetite is perverted and made a snare. The food is often such as to excite a desire for stimulating drinks. Luxurious dishes are placed before the children,—spiced foods, rich gravies, cakes, and pastries. This highly seasoned food irritates the stomach, and causes a craving for still stronger stimulants. Not only is the appetite tempted with unsuitable food, of which the children are allowed to eat freely at their meals, but they are permitted to eat between meals, and by the time they are twelve or fourteen years of age they are often confirmed dyspeptics.

You have perhaps seen a picture of the stomach of one who is addicted to strong drink. A similar condition is produced under the irritating influence of fiery spices. With the stomach in such a state, there is a craving for something more to meet the demands of the appetite, something stronger, and still stronger. Next you find your sons out on the street learning to smoke.

Foods Especially Injurious to Children

[C.T.B.H. 46, 47] (1890) C.H. 114

356. It is impossible for those who give the reins to appetite to attain to Christian perfection. The moral sensibilities of your children cannot be easily aroused, unless you are careful in the selection of their food. Many a mother sets a table that is a snare to her family. Flesh meats, butter, cheese, rich pastry, spiced foods, and condiments are freely partaken of by both old and young. These things do their work in deranging the stomach, exciting the nerves, and enfeebling the intellect. The blood-making organs cannot convert such things into good blood. The grease cooked in the food renders it difficult of digestion. The effect of cheese is deleterious. Fine-flour bread does not impart to the system the nourishment that is to be found in unbolted-wheat bread. Its common use will not keep the system in the best condition. Spices at first irritate the tender coating of the stomach, but finally destroy the natural sensitiveness of this delicate membrane. The blood becomes fevered, the animal propensities are aroused, while the moral and intellectual powers are weakened, and become servants to the baser passions. The mother should study to set a simple yet nutritious diet before her family.

Counteracting Evil Tendencies

(1875) 3T 567, 568

357. Will mothers of this generation feel the sacredness of their mission, and not try to vie with their wealthy neigh-

bors in appearances, but seek to excel them in faithfully performing the work of instructing their children for the better life? If children and youth were trained and educated to habits of self-denial and self-control, if they were taught that they eat to live instead of living to eat, there would be less disease and less moral corruption. There would be little necessity for temperance crusades, which amount to so little, if in the youth who form and fashion society, right principles in regard to temperance could be implanted. They would then have moral worth and moral integrity to resist, in the strength of Jesus, the pollutions of these last days. . . . Parents may have transmitted to their children tendencies to appetite and passion, which will make more difficult the work of educating and training these children to be strictly temperate, and to have pure and virtuous habits. If the appetite for unhealthful food and for stimulants and narcotics, has been transmitted to them as a legacy from their parents, what a fearfully solemn responsibility rests upon the parents to counteract the evil tendencies which they have given to their children! How earnestly and diligently should the parents work to do their duty, in faith and hope, to their unfortunate offspring!

Parents should make it their first business to understand the laws of life and health, that nothing shall be done by them in the preparation of food, or through any other habits, which will develop wrong tendencies in their children. How carefully should mothers study to prepare their tables with the most simple, healthful food, that the digestive organs may not be weakened, the nervous forces unbalanced, and the instruction which they should give their children counteracted, by the food placed before them. This food either weakens or strengthens the organs of the stomach, and has much to do in controlling the physical and moral health of the children, who are God's blood-bought property. What a sacred trust is committed to parents, to guard the physical and moral constitutions of their children, so that the nervous system may be well balanced, and the soul not be endangered! Those who indulge the appetite of their children, and do not control their passions, will see the terrible mistake they have made, in the tobacco-loving, liquor-drinking slave, whose senses are benumbed, and whose lips utter falsehoods and profanity.

The Cruel Kindness of Indulgence

(1873) 3T 141

358. I was shown that one great cause of the existing deplorable state of things is that parents do not feel under obligation to bring up their children to conform to physical law. Mothers love their children with an idolatrous love, and indulge their appetite when they know it will injure their health, and thereby bring upon them disease and unhappiness. This cruel kindness is manifested to a great extent in the present generation. The desires of children are gratified at the expense of health and happy tempers, because it is easier for the mother, for the time being, to gratify them than to withhold that for which they clamor.

Thus mothers are sowing the seed that will spring up and bear fruit. The children are not educated to deny their appetites and restrict their desires. And they become selfish, exacting, disobedient, unthankful, and unholy. Mothers who are doing this work will reap with bitterness the fruit of the seed they have sown. They have sinned against Heaven and against their children, and God will hold them accountable.

(1890) C.T.B.H. 76, 77

359. When parents and children meet at the final reckoning, what a scene will be presented! Thousands of children who have been slaves to appetite and debasing vice, whose lives are moral wrecks, will stand face to face with the parents who made them what they are. Who but the parents must bear this fearful responsibility? Did the Lord make these youth corrupt? Oh, no! Who, then, has done this fearful work? Were not the sins of the parents transmitted to the children in perverted appetites and passions? and was not the work completed by those who neglected to train them according to the pattern which God has given? Just as surely as they exist, all these parents will pass in review before God.

Observations While Traveling

Health Reformer, December, 1870

360. While upon the cars, I heard parents remark that the appetites of their children were delicate, and unless they had meat and cake, they could not eat. When the noon meal was taken, I observed the quality of food given to these children. It was fine wheaten bread, sliced ham coated with black pepper, spiced pickles, cake, and preserves. The pale, sallow complexion of these children plainly indicated the abuses the stomach was suffering. Two of these children observed another family of children eating cheese with their food, and they lost their appetite for what was before them until their indulgent mother begged a piece of the cheese to give to her children, fearing the dear children would fail to make out their meal. The mother remarked, My children love this or that, so much, and I let them have what they want; for the appetite craves the kinds of food the system requires.

This might be correct if the appetite had never been perverted. There is a natural and a depraved appetite. Parents who have taught their children to eat unhealthful, stimulating food, all their lives, until the taste is perverted, and they crave clay, slate pencils, burned coffee, tea grounds, cinnamon, cloves, and spices, cannot claim that the appetite demands what the system requires. The appetite has been falsely educated, until it is depraved. The fine organs of the stomach have been stimulated and burned, until they have lost their delicate sensitiveness. Simple, healthful food seems to them insipid. The abused stomach will not perform the work given it, unless urged to it by the most stimulating substances. If these children had been trained from their infancy to take only healthful food, prepared in the most simple manner, preserving its natural properties as much as possible, and avoiding flesh meats, grease, and all spices, the taste and appetite would be unimpaired. In its natural state, it might indicate, in a great degree, the food best adapted to the wants of the system.

While parents and children were eating of their dainties, my husband and myself partook of our simple repast, at our usual hour, at 1 P. M., of graham bread without butter, and a generous supply of fruit. We ate our meal with a keen relish, and with thankful hearts that we were not obliged to carry a popular grocery with us to provide for a capricious appetite. We ate heartily, and felt no sense of hunger until the next morning. The boy with his oranges, nuts, popcorn, and candies, found us poor customers.

The quality of food eaten by parents and children could not be converted into good blood or sweet tempers. The children were pale. Some had disgusting sores upon their faces and hands. Others were nearly blind with sore eyes, which greatly marred the beauty of the countenance. And still others showed no eruption upon the skin, but were afflicted with cough, catarrh, or difficulty of throat and lungs. I noticed a boy of three years, who was suffering with diarrhea. He had quite a fever, but seemed to think all he needed was food. He was calling, every few minutes, for cake, chicken, pickles. The mother answered his every call like an obedient slave; and when the food called for did not come as soon as was desired, as the cries and calls become unpleasantly urgent, the mother answered, "Yes, yes, darling, you shall have it." After the food was placed in his hand, it was thrown passionately upon the car floor, because it did not come soon enough. One little girl was partaking of her boiled ham, and spiced pickles, and bread and butter, when she espied a plate I was eating from. Here was something she did not have, and she refused to eat. The girl of six years said she would have a plate. I thought it was the nice red apple I was eating she desired; and although we had a limited amount, I felt such pity for the parents, that I gave her a fine apple. She snatched it from my hand, and disdainfully threw it quickly to the car floor. I thought, This child, if permitted to thus have her own way, will indeed bring her mother to shame.

This exhibition of passion was the result of the mother's course of indulgence. The quality of food she provided for her child was a continual tax to the digestive organs. The blood was impure, and the child sickly and irritable. The quality of food given daily to this child was of that nature to excite the lower order of passions, and depress the moral and intellectual. The parents were forming the habits of their child. They were making her selfish and unloving. They did not restrain her desires, or control her passions. What can they expect of such a child, should she come to maturity? Many do not seem to understand the relation the mind sustains to the body. If the system is deranged by improper food, the brain and nerves are affected, and the passions are easily excited.

A child of about ten years was afflicted with chills and fever, and was disinclined to eat. The mother urged her: "Eat a little of this sponge cake. Here is some nice chicken. Won't you have a taste of these preserves?" The child finally ate a large meal for a well person. The food urged upon her was not proper for the stomach in health, and should in no case be taken while sick. The mother, in about two hours, was bathing the head of the child, saying she could not understand why she should have such a burning fever. She had added fuel to the fire, and wondered that the fire burned. Had that child been left to let nature take her course, and the stomach take the rest so necessary for it, her sufferings might have been far less. These mothers were not prepared to bring up children. The greatest cause of human suffering is ignorance on the subject of how to treat our own bodies.

The inquiry with many is, What shall I eat, and how shall I live, to best enjoy the present time? Duty and principle are laid aside for present gratification. If we would have health, we must live for it. If we perfect Christian character, we must live for it. Parents are, in a great degree, responsible for the physical health and morals of their children. They should instruct their children and urge them to conform to the laws of health for their own sake, to save themselves unhappiness and suffering. How strange that mothers should indulge their children to the ruin of their physical, mental, and moral health! What can be the character of such fondness! These mothers make their children unfit for happiness in this life, and render the prospect of the future life very uncertain.

Cause of Irritability and Nervousness

[C.T.B.H. 61, 62] (1890) F.E. 150, 151

361. Regularity should be the rule in all the habits of children. Mothers make a great mistake in permitting them to eat between meals. The stomach becomes deranged by this practice, and the foundation is laid for future suffering. Their fretfulness may have been caused by unwholesome food, still undigested; but the mother feels that she cannot spend time to reason upon the matter, and correct her injurious management. Neither can she stop to soothe their impatient worrying. She gives the little sufferers a piece of cake or some other dainty to quiet them, but this only increases the evil. Some mothers, in their anxiety to do a great amount of work, get wrought up into such nervous haste that they are more irritable than the children, and by scolding and even blows they try to terrify the little ones into quietude.

Mothers often complain of the delicate health of their children, and consult the physician, when, if they would but exercise a little common sense, they would see that the trouble is caused by errors in diet.

We are living in an age of gluttony, and the habits to which the young are educated, even by many Seventh-day Adventists, are in direct opposition to the laws of nature. I was seated once at the table with several children under twelve years of age. Meat was plentifully served, and then a delicate, nervous girl called for pickles. A bottle of chow-chow, fiery with mustard and pungent with spices, was handed her, from which she helped herself freely. The child was proverbial for her nervousness and irritability of temper, and these fiery condiments were well calculated to produce such a condition. The oldest child thought he could not eat a meal without meat, and showed great dissatisfaction, and even disrespect, if it was not provided for him. The mother had indulged him in his likes and dislikes till she had become little better than a slave to his caprices. The lad had not been provided with work, and he spent the greater portion of his time in reading that which was useless or worse than useless. He complained almost constantly of headache, and had no relish for simple food.

Parents should provide employment for their children. Nothing will be a more sure source of evil than indolence. Physical labor that brings healthful weariness to the muscles, will give an appetite for simple, wholesome food, and the youth who is properly employed will not rise from the table grumbling because he does not see before him a platter of meat and various dainties to tempt his appetite.

Jesus, the Son of God, in laboring with His hands at the carpenter's trade, gave an example to all youth. Let those who scorn to take up the common duties of life remember that Jesus was subject to His parents, and contributed His share toward the sustenance of the family. Few luxuries were seen on the table of Joseph and Mary, for they were among the poor and lowly.

Relation of Diet to Moral Development

(1890) C.T.B.H. 134

362. The power of Satan over the youth of this age is fearful. Unless the minds of our children are firmly balanced by religious principle, their morals will become corrupted by the vicious examples with which they come in contact. The greatest danger of the young is from a lack of self-control. Indulgent parents do not teach their children self-denial. The very food they place before them is such as to irritate the stomach. The excitement thus produced is communicated to the brain, and as a result the passions are aroused. It cannot be too often repeated, that whatever is taken into the stomach affects not only the body, but ultimately the mind as well. Gross and stimulating food fevers the blood, excites the nervous system, and too often dulls the moral perceptions, so that reason and conscience are overborne by the sensual impulses. It is difficult, and often well-nigh impossible, for one who is intemperate in diet to exercise patience and self-control. Hence the special importance of allowing children, whose characters are yet unformed, to have only such food as is healthful and unstimulating. It was in love that our heavenly Father sent the light of health reform to guard against the evils that result from unrestrained indulgence of appetite.

"Whether therefore ye eat, or drink, or whatsoever ye do, do all to the glory of God." Are parents doing this when they prepare food for the table, and call the family to partake of it? Do they place before their children that only which they know will make the very best blood, that which will keep the system in the least feverish condition, and will place it in the best relation to life and health? Or do they, regardless of the future good of their children, provide for them unhealthful, stimulating, irritating food?

(1870) 2T 365

363. But even health reformers can err in the quantity of food. They can eat immoderately of a healthful quality of food. Some in this house err in the quality. They have never taken their position upon health reform. They have chosen to eat and drink what they pleased and when they pleased. They are injuring their systems in this way. Not only this, but they are injuring their families by placing upon their tables a feverish diet, which will increase the animal passions of their children, and lead them to care but little for heavenly things. The parents are thus strengthening the animal, and lessening the spiritual powers of their children. What a heavy penalty will they have to pay in the end! And then they wonder that their children are so weak morally!

Corruption Among Children

(1870) 2T 359-362

364. We live in a corrupt age. It is a time when Satan seems to have almost perfect control over minds that are not fully consecrated to God. Therefore there is a very great responsibility resting upon parents and guardians who have children to bring up. Parents have taken the responsibility of bringing these children into existence; and now what is their duty? Is it to let them come up just as they may, and just as they will? Let me tell you, a weighty responsibility rests upon these parents. . . .

I have said that some of you are selfish. You have not understood what I have meant. You have studied what food would taste best. Taste and pleasure, instead of the glory of God, and a desire to advance in the divine life, and to perfect holiness in the fear of God, have ruled. You have consulted your own pleasure, your own appetite; and while you have been doing this, Satan has been gaining a march upon you, and as is generally the case, has frustrated your efforts every time.

Some of you fathers have taken your children to the physician to see what was the matter with them. I could have told you in two minutes what was the trouble. Your children are corrupt. Satan has obtained control of them. He has come right in past you, while you, who are as God to them, to guard them, were at ease, stupefied, and asleep. God has commanded you to bring them up in the fear and nurture of the Lord. But Satan has passed right in before you and has woven strong bands around them. And yet you sleep on. May Heaven pity you and your children, for every one of you needs His pity.

THINGS MIGHT HAVE BEEN DIFFERENT

Had you taken your position upon the health reform; had you added to your faith virtue, to virtue knowledge, and to knowledge temperance, things might have been different. But you have been only partially aroused by the iniquity and corruption that is in your houses. . . .

You should be teaching your children. You should be instructing them how to shun the vices and corruptions of this age. Instead of this, many are studying how to get something good to eat. You place upon your tables butter, eggs, and meat, and your children partake of them. They are fed with the very things that will excite their animal passions, and then you come to meeting and ask God to bless and save your children. How high do your prayers go? You have a work to do first. When you have done all for your children which God has left for you to do, then you can with confidence claim the special help that God has promised to give you.

You should study temperance in all things. You must study it in what you eat and in what you drink. And yet you say, "It is nobody's business what I eat, or what I drink, or what I place upon my table." It is somebody's business, unless you take your children and shut them up, or go into the wilderness where you will not be a burden upon others, and where your unruly, vicious children will not corrupt the society in which they mingle.

Teach Children How to Meet Temptation

[C.T.B.H. 63, 64] (1890) F.E. 152, 153

365. Set a guard over the appetite; teach your children by example as well as by precept to use a simple diet. Teach them to be industrious, not merely busy, but engaged in useful labor. Seek to arouse the moral sensibilities. Teach them that God has claims upon them, even from the early years of their childhood. Tell them that there are moral corruptions to be met on every hand, that they need to come to Jesus and give themselves to Him, body and spirit, and that in Him they will find strength to resist every temptation. Keep before their minds that they were not created merely to please themselves, but to be the Lord's agent for noble purposes. Teach them, when temptations urge into paths of selfish indulgences, when Satan is seeking to shut out God from their sight, to look to Jesus, pleading, "Save, Lord, that I be not overcome." Angels will gather about them in answer to their prayer, and lead them into safe paths.

Christ prayed for His disciples, not that they should be taken out of the world, but that they should be kept from evil,—that they might be kept from yielding to the temptations they would meet on every hand. This is a prayer that should be offered up by every father and mother. But should they thus plead with God in behalf of their children, and then leave them to do as they please? Should they pamper the appetite until it gets the mastery, and then expect to restrain the children? No; temperance and self-control should be taught from the very cradle up. Upon the mother must rest largely the responsibility of this work. The tenderest earthly tie is that between the mother and her child. The child is more readily impressed by the life and example of the mother than by that of the father, because of this stronger and more tender bond of union. Yet the mother's responsibility is a heavy one and should have the constant aid of the father.

[C.T.B.H. 79, 80] (1890) F.E. 143

366. It will pay you, mothers, to use the precious hours which are given you by God in forming the character of your children, and in teaching them to adhere strictly to the principles of temperance in eating and drinking. . . .

Satan sees that he cannot have so great power over minds when the appetite is kept under control as when it is indulged, and he is constantly working to lead men to indulgence. Under the influence of unhealthful food, the conscience becomes stupefied, the mind is darkened, and its susceptibility to impressions is impaired. But the guilt of the transgressor is not lessened because the conscience has been violated till it has become insensible.

(1909) 9T 160, 161

367. Fathers and mothers, watch unto prayer. Guard strictly against intemperance in every form. Teach your children the principles of true health reform. Teach them what things to avoid in order to preserve health. Already the wrath of God has begun to be visited upon the children of disobedience. What crimes, what sins, what iniquitous practices, are being revealed on every hand! As a people, we are to exercise great care in guarding our children against depraved associates.

[The country home; its relation to diet and morals—711]

Healthful Cookery

Quotations in Section XIV

Healthful Cookery

Poor Cooking a Sin

MS 95, 1901

368. It is a sin to place poorly prepared food on the table, because the matter of eating concerns the well-being of the entire system. The Lord desires His people to appreciate the necessity of having food prepared in such a way that it will not make sour stomachs, and in consequence, sour tempers. Let us remember that there is practical religion in a loaf of good bread.

A KNOWLEDGE OF COOKERY WORTH TEN TALENTS

Let not the work of cooking be looked upon as a sort of slavery. What would become of those in our world if all who are engaged in cooking should give up their work with the flimsy excuse that it is not sufficiently dignified? Cooking may be regarded as less desirable than some other lines of work, but in reality it is a science in value above all other sciences. Thus God regards the preparation of healthful food. He places a high estimate on those who do faithful service in preparing wholesome, palatable food. The one who understands the art of properly preparing food, and who uses this knowledge, is worthy of higher commendation than those engaged in any other line of work. This talent should be regarded as equal in value to ten talents; for its right use has much to do with keeping the human organism in health. Because so inseparably connected with life and health, it is the most valuable of all gifts.

Respect Due the Cook

(1870) 2T 370

369. I prize my seamstress, I value my copyist; but my cook, who knows well how to prepare the food to sustain life and nourish brain, bone, and muscle, fills the most important place among the helpers in my family.

(1890) C.T.B.H. 74

370. Some who learn to be seamstresses, typesetters, proofreaders, bookkeepers, or school teachers, consider themselves too aristocratic to associate with the cook.

These ideas have pervaded nearly all classes of society. The cook is made to feel that her occupation is one which places her low in the scale of social life, and that she must not expect to associate with the family on equal terms. Can you be surprised, then, that intelligent girls seek some other employment? Do you marvel that there are so few educated cooks? The only marvel is that there are so many who will submit to such treatment.

The cook fills an important place in the household. She is preparing food to be taken into the stomach, to form brain, bone, and muscle. The health of all members of the family depends largely upon her skill and intelligence. Household duties will never receive the attention they demand until those who faithfully perform them are held in proper respect.

(1873) 3T 156-158

371. There are very many girls who have married and have families, who have but little practical knowledge of the duties devolving upon a wife and mother. They can read and play upon an instrument of music; but they cannot cook. They cannot make good bread, which is very essential to the health of the family. . . . To cook well, to present healthful food upon the table in an inviting manner, requires intelligence and experience. The one who prepares the food that is to be placed in our stomachs, to be converted into blood to nourish the system, occupies a most important and elevated position. The position of copyist, dressmaker, or music teacher cannot equal in importance that of the cook.

Every Woman's Duty to Become a Skillful Cook

(1870) 2T 370

372. Our sisters often do not know how to cook. To such I would say, I would go to the very best cook that could be found in the country, and remain there, if necessary, for weeks, until I had become mistress of the art,—an intelli-

gent, skillful cook. I would pursue this course if I were forty years old. It is your duty to know how to cook, and it is your duty to teach your daughters to cook. When you are teaching them the art of cookery, you are building around them a barrier that will preserve them from the folly and vice which they may otherwise be tempted to engage in.

[C.T.B.H. 49] (1890) C.H. 117

373. In order to learn how to cook, women should study, and then patiently reduce what they learn to practice. People are suffering because they will not take the trouble to do this. I say to such, It is time for you to rouse your dormant energies, and inform yourselves. Do not think the time wasted which is devoted to obtaining a thorough knowledge and experience in the preparation of healthful, palatable food. No matter how long an experience you have had in cooking, if you still have the responsibilities of a family, it is your duty to learn how to care for them properly.

Let Men and Women Learn to Cook

[C.T.B.H. 56, 57] (1890) C.H. 155

374. Many who adopt the health reform complain that it does not agree with them; but after sitting at their tables I come to the conclusion that it is not the health reform that is at fault, but the poorly prepared food. I appeal to men and women to whom God has given intelligence: Learn how to cook. I make no mistake when I say "men," for they, as well as women, need to understand the simple, healthful preparation of food. Their business often takes them where they cannot obtain wholesome food. They may be called to remain days and even weeks in families that are entirely ignorant in this respect. Then, if they have the knowledge, they can use it to good purpose.

Study Health Journals

Letter 135, 1902

375. Those who do not know how to cook hygienically should learn to combine wholesome, nourishing articles of food in such a way as to make appetizing dishes. Let those

who desire to gain knowledge in this line subscribe for ou[r] health journals. They will find information on this poin[t] in them. . . .

Without continually exercising ingenuity, no one ca[n] excel in healthful cookery, but those whose hearts are ope[n] to impressions and suggestions from the Great Teacher wi[ll] learn many things, and will be able also to teach others; f[or] He will give them skill and understanding.

Encourage Development of Individual Talent

(1902) 7T 133

376. It is the Lord's design that in every place men an[d] women shall be encouraged to develop their talents by pre paring healthful foods from the natural products of the[ir] own section of the country. If they look to God, exercisin[g] their skill and ingenuity under the guidance of His Spir[it] they will learn how to prepare natural products into health ful foods. Thus they will be able to teach the poor how [to] provide themselves with foods that will take the place [of] flesh meat. Those thus helped can in turn instruct other[s] Such a work will yet be done with consecrated zeal an[d] energy. If it had been done before, there would today [be] many more people in the truth, and many more who coul[d] give instruction. Let us learn what our duty is, and the[n] do it. We are not to be dependent and helpless, waiting f[or] others to do the work that God has committed to us.

A Call for Cooking Schools

MS 95, 1901

377. Connected with our sanitariums and schools the[re] should be cooking schools, where instruction is given on th[e] proper preparation of food. In all our schools there shoul[d] be those who are fitted to educate the students, both youn[g] men and women, in the art of cooking. Women especiall[y] should learn how to cook.

R. & H., June 6, 1912

378. Good service can be done by teaching the peopl[e] how to prepare healthful food. This line of work is as esser[tial]

tial as any that can be taken up. More cooking schools should be established, and some should labor from house to house, giving instruction in the art of cooking wholesome foods.

[See "Cooking Schools" in Section XXV]

Health Reform and Good Cooking

[C.T.B.H. 119] (1890) C.H. 450, 451

379. One reason why many have become discouraged in practicing health reform is that they have not learned how to cook so that proper food, simply prepared, would supply the place of the diet to which they have been accustomed. They become disgusted with the poorly prepared dishes, and next we hear them say that they have tried the health reform, and cannot live in that way. Many attempt to follow out meager instructions in health reform, and make such sad work that it results in injury to digestion, and in discouragement to all concerned in the attempt. You profess to be health reformers, and for this very reason you should become good cooks. Those who can avail themselves of the advantages of properly conducted hygienic cooking schools, will find it a great benefit, both in their own practice and in teaching others.

Changing From a Meat Diet

(1868) 2T 63

380. We advise you to change your habits of living; but while you do this we caution you to move understandingly. I am acquainted with families who have changed from a meat diet to one that is impoverished. Their food is so poorly prepared that the stomach loathes it, and such have told me that the health reform did not agree with them; that they were decreasing in physical strength. Here is one reason why some have not been successful in their efforts to simplify their food. They have a poverty-stricken diet. Food is prepared without painstaking and there is a continual sameness. There should not be many kinds at any one meal, but all meals should not be composed of the same kinds of food without variation. Food should be prepared with simplicity, yet with a nicety which will invite the appetite. You should

keep grease out of your food. It defiles any preparation of food you may make. Eat largely of fruits and vegetables.

Letter 60a, 1896

381. The proper cooking of food is a most important accomplishment. Especially where meat is not made a principal article of food is good cooking an essential requirement. Something must be prepared to take the place of meat, and these substitutes for meat must be well prepared, so that meat will not be desired.

Letter 73a, 1896

382. It is the positive duty of physicians to educate, educate, educate, by pen and voice, all who have the responsibility of preparing food for the table.

Y.I., May 31, 1894

383. We need persons who will educate themselves to cook healthfully. Many know how to cook meats and vegetables in different forms, who yet do not understand how to prepare simple and appetizing dishes.

[Tasteless dishes—324, 327]
[Camp meeting demonstrations—763]
[The need for meat substitute pointed out in 1884—720]
[Skillful arrangement of bounties, an aid in health reform—710]
[Tact and discernment required in work of giving instruction in meatless cookery—816]

Poor Cooking a Cause of Disease

(1890) C.T.B.H. 156-158

384. For want of knowledge and skill in regard to cooking, many a wife and mother daily sets before her family ill-prepared food, which is steadily and surely impairing the digestive organs, and making a poor quality of blood; the result is, frequent attacks of inflammatory disease, and sometimes death. . . .

We can have a variety of good, wholesome food, cooked in a healthful manner, so that it will be palatable to all. It is of vital importance to know how to cook. Poor cooking produces disease and bad tempers; the system becomes deranged, and heavenly things cannot be discerned. There is more religion in good cooking than you have any idea of. When I have been away from home sometimes, I have known that the bread upon the table, as well as most of the other food, would hurt me; but I would be obliged to eat a little in order to sustain life. It is a sin in the sight of Heaven to have such food.

Appropriate Epitaphs

(1905) M.H. 302, 303

385. Scanty, ill-cooked food depraves the blood by weakening the blood-making organs. It deranges the system, and brings on disease, with its accompaniment of irritable nerves and bad tempers. The victims of poor cookery are numbered by thousands and tens of thousands. Over many graves might be written: "Died because of poor cooking;" "Died of an abused stomach."

SOULS LOST BECAUSE OF POOR COOKING

It is a sacred duty for those who cook to learn how to prepare healthful food. Many souls are lost as the result of poor cookery. It takes thought and care to make good bread; but there is more religion in a loaf of good bread than many think. There are few really good cooks. Young women think that it is menial to cook and do other kinds of housework; and for this reason, many girls who marry and have the care of families have little idea of the duties devolving upon a wife and mother.

NO MEAN SCIENCE

Cooking is no mean science and it is one of the most essential in practical life. It is a science that all women should learn, and it should be taught in a way to benefit the poorer classes. To make food appetizing and at the same time simple and nourishing, requires skill; but it can be done. Cooks should know how to prepare simple food in a simple and healthful manner, and so that it will be found more palatable, as well as more wholesome, because of its simplicity.

Every woman who is at the head of a family and yet does not understand the art of healthful cookery should determine to learn that which is so essential to the well-being of her household. In many places hygienic cooking schools afford opportunity for instruction in this line. She who has not the help of such facilities should put herself under the instruction of some good cook, and persevere in her efforts for improvement until she is mistress of the culinary art.

[Cooking a most valuable art because so closely connected with life—817]

Study Economy

MS 3, 1897

386. In every line of cooking the question that should be considered is, "How shall the food be prepared in the most natural and inexpensive manner?" And there should be careful study that the fragments of food left over from the table be not wasted. Study how, that in some way these fragments of food shall not be lost. This skill, economy, and tact is a fortune. In the warmer parts of the season, prepare less food. Use more dry substance. There are many poor families, who, although they have scarcely enough to eat, can often be enlightened as to why they are poor; there are so many jots and tittles wasted.

Lives Sacrificed to Fashionable Eating

(1890) C.T.B.H. 73

387. With many, the all-absorbing object of life—that which justifies any expenditure of labor—is to appear in the latest style. Education, health, and comfort are sacrificed at the shrine of fashion. Even in the table arrangements, fashion and show exert their baleful influence. The healthful preparation of food becomes a secondary matter. The serving of a great variety of dishes absorbs time, money, and taxing labor, without accomplishing any good. It may be fashionable to have half a dozen courses at a meal, but the custom is ruinous to health. It is a fashion that sensible men and women should condemn, by both precept and example. Do have a little regard for the life of your cook. "Is not the life more than meat, and the body than raiment?"

In these days, domestic duties claim almost the whole time of the housekeeper. How much better it would be for the health of the household, if the table preparations were more simple. Thousands of lives are sacrificed every year at this altar,—lives which might have been prolonged had it not been for this endless round of manufactured duties. Many a mother goes down to the grave, who, had her habits been simple, might have lived to be a blessing in the home, the church, and the world.

[Evils of the course system—218]

The Choice and Preparation of Foods Important

Letter 72, 1896

388. The large amount of cooking done is not at all necessary. Neither should there be any poverty-stricken diet either in quality or quantity.

(1870) 2T 367

389. It is important that the food should be prepared with care, that the appetite, when not perverted, can relish it. Because we from principle discard the use of meat, butter, mince pies, spices, lard, and that which irritates the stomach and destroys health, the idea should never be given that it is of but little consequence what we eat.

(1905) M.H. 300

390. It is wrong to eat merely to gratify the appetite, but no indifference should be manifested regarding the quality of the food, or the manner of its preparation. If the food eaten is not relished, the body will not be so well nourished. The food should be carefully chosen and prepared with intelligence and skill.

The Stereotyped Breakfast

Letter 19c, 1892

391. I would pay a higher price for a cook than for any other part of my work. . . . If that person is not apt and has no skill in cooking, you will see, as we have in our experience, the stereotyped breakfast,—porridge, as it is called,— we call it mush, baker's bread, and some kind of sauce, and that is all with the exception of a little milk. Now those after eating in this kind of way for months, knowing what will appear before them at every meal, come to dread the hour which should be interesting to them, as the dreaded pe-

riod of the day. I suppose you will not understand all this until you have experienced it. But I am really perplexed over this matter. Were I to act over the preparation in coming to this place, I would say, Give me an experienced cook, who has some inventive powers, to prepare simple dishes healthfully, and that will not disgust the appetite.

Study and Practice

(1868) 1T 681-685

392. Many do not feel that this [cooking] is a matter of duty, hence they do not try to prepare food properly. This can be done in a simple, healthful, and easy manner, without the use of lard, butter, or flesh meats. Skill must be united with simplicity. To do this, women must read, and then patiently reduce what they read to practice. Many are suffering because they will not take the trouble to do this. I say to such, It is time for you to rouse your dormant energies and read up. Learn how to cook with simplicity, and yet in a manner to secure the most palatable and healthful food.

Because it is wrong to cook merely to please the taste, or to suit the appetite, no one should entertain the idea that an impoverished diet is right. Many are debilitated with disease, and need a nourishing, plentiful, well-cooked diet. . . .

AN IMPORTANT BRANCH OF EDUCATION

It is a religious duty for those who cook to learn how to prepare healthful food in different ways, so that it may be eaten with enjoyment. Mothers should teach their children how to cook. What branch of the education of a young lady can be so important as this? The eating has to do with the life. Scanty, impoverished, ill-cooked food is constantly depraving the blood, by weakening the blood-making organs. It is highly essential that the art of cookery be considered one of the most important branches of education. There are but few good cooks. Young ladies consider that it is stooping to a menial office to become a cook. This is not the case. They do not view the subject from a right standpoint. Knowledge of how to prepare food healthfully, especially bread, is no mean science. . . .

Mothers neglect this branch in the education of their daughters. They take the burden of care and labor, and are fast wearing out, while the daughter is excused, to visit, to crochet, or study her own pleasure. This is mistaken love, mistaken kindness. The mother is doing an injury to her child, which frequently lasts her lifetime. At the age when she should be capable of bearing some of life's burdens, she is unqualified to do so. Such will not take care and burdens. They go light-loaded, excusing themselves from responsibilities, while the mother is pressed down under her burden of care, as a cart beneath sheaves. The daughter does not mean to be unkind, but she is careless and heedless, or she would notice the tired look, and mark the expression of pain upon the countenance of the mother, and would seek to do her part, to bear the heavier part of the burden, and relieve the mother, who must have freedom from care, or be brought upon a bed of suffering, and it may be, of death.

Why will mothers be so blind and negligent in the education of their daughters? I have been distressed, as I have visited different families, to see the mother bearing the heavy burdens, while the daughter, who manifested buoyancy of spirit, and had a good degree of health and vigor, felt no care, no burden. When there are large gatherings, and families are burdened with company, I have seen the mother bearing the burden, with the care of everything upon her, while the daughters are sitting down chatting with young friends, having a social visit. These things seem so wrong to me that I can hardly forbear speaking to the thoughtless youth, and telling them to go to work. Release your tired mother. Lead her to a seat in the parlor, and urge her to rest and enjoy the society of her friends.

But the daughters are not the ones to be blamed wholly in this matter. The mother is at fault. She has not patiently taught her daughters how to cook. She knows that they lack knowledge in the cooking department, and therefore feels no release from the labor. She must attend to everything that requires care, thought, and attention. Young ladies should be thoroughly instructed in cooking. Whatever may be their circumstances in life, here is knowledge which may be put to a practical use. It is a branch of education which has the most direct influence upon human life, especially the lives of those held most dear.

Many a wife and mother who has not had the right education, and lacks skill in the cooking department, is daily presenting her family with ill-prepared food, which is steadily and surely destroying the digestive organs, making a poor quality of blood, and frequently bringing on acute attacks of inflammatory disease, and causing premature death. . . .

ENCOURAGE THE LEARNERS

It is a religious duty for every Christian girl and woman to learn at once to make good, sweet, light bread from unbolted wheat flour. Mothers should take their daughters into the kitchen with them when very young, and teach them the art of cooking. The mother cannot expect her daughters to understand the mysteries of housekeeping without education. She should instruct them patiently, lovingly, and make the work as agreeable as she can by her cheerful countenance and encouraging words of approval. If they fail once, twice, or thrice, censure not. Already discouragement is doing its work, and tempting them to say, "It is of no use; I can't do it." This is not the time for censure. The will is becoming weakened. It needs the spur of encouraging, cheerful, hopeful words, as, "Never mind the mistakes you have made. You are but a learner, and must expect to make blunders. Try again. Put your mind on what you are doing. Be very careful, and you will certainly succeed."

Many mothers do not realize the importance of this branch of knowledge, and rather than have the trouble and care of instructing their children and bearing with their failings and errors while learning, they prefer to do all themselves. And when their daughters make a failure in their efforts, they send them away with, "It is no use, you can't do this or that. You perplex and trouble me more than you help me."

Thus the first efforts of the learners are repulsed, and the first failure so cools their interest and ardor to learn that they dread another trial, and will propose to sew, knit, clean house, anything but cook. Here the mother was greatly at fault. She should have patiently instructed them, that they might, by practice, obtain an experience which would remove the awkwardness and remedy the unskillful movements of the inexperienced worker.

Cooking Lessons More Essential Than Music

MS 95, 1901

393. Some are called to what are looked upon as humble duties—it may be, to cook. But the science of cooking is not a small matter. The skillful preparation of food is one of the most essential arts, standing above music teaching or dressmaking. By this I do not mean to discount music teaching or dressmaking, for they are essential. But more important still is the art of preparing food so that it is both healthful and appetizing. This art should be regarded as the most valuable of all the arts, because it is so closely connected with life. It should receive more attention; for in order to make good blood, the system requires good food. The foundation of that which keeps people in health is the medical missionary work of good cooking.

Often health reform is made health deform by the unpalatable preparation of food. The lack of knowledge regarding healthful cookery must be remedied before health reform is a success.

Good cooks are few. Many, many mothers need to take lessons in cooking, that they may set before the family well-prepared, neatly served food.

Before children take lessons on the organ or the piano they should be given lessons in cooking. The work of learning to cook need not exclude music, but to learn music is of less importance than to learn how to prepare food that is wholesome and appetizing.

(1870) 2T 538, 539

394. Your daughters may love music, and this may be all right; it may add to the happiness of the family; but the knowledge of music without the knowledge of cookery, is

not worth much. When your daughters have families of their own, an understanding of music and fancywork will not provide for the table a well-cooked dinner, prepared with nicety, so that they will not blush to place it before their most esteemed friends. Mothers, yours is a sacred work. May God help you to take it up with His glory in view, and work earnestly, patiently, and lovingly, for the present and future good of your children, having an eye single to the glory of God.

[Irregular eating and "picked up" meals when the family are alone—284]

Teach the Mysteries of Cooking

(1870) 2T 537, 538

395. Do not neglect to teach your children how to cook. In so doing, you impart to them principles which they must have in their religious education. In giving your children lessons in physiology, and teaching them how to cook with simplicity and yet with skill, you are laying the foundation for the most useful branches of education. Skill is required to make good light bread. There is religion in good cooking, and I question the religion of that class who are too ignorant and too careless to learn to cook. . . .

Poor cookery is slowly wearing away the life energies of thousands. It is dangerous to health and life to eat at some tables the heavy, sour bread, and the other food prepared in keeping with it. Mothers, instead of seeking to give your daughters a musical education, instruct them in these useful branches which have the closest connection with life and health. Teach them all the mysteries of cooking. Show them that this is a part of their education, and essential for them in order to become Christians. Unless the food is prepared in a wholesome, palatable manner, it cannot be converted into good blood, to build up the wasting tissues.

[An attempt to make sugar supply the place of good cooking —527]
[Influence of the table on temperance principle—351, 354]
[If digestion is taxed, an investigation is needed—445]
[Less cooking, more natural foods—466, 546]

Health Foods and Hygienic Restaurants

Quotations in Section XV

Health Foods and Hygienic Restaurants

From the Heavenly Provider

(1902) 7T 114

396. FROM the record of the Lord's miracles in providing wine at the wedding feast and in feeding the multitude, we may learn a lesson of the highest importance. The health-food business is one of the Lord's own instrumentalities to supply a necessity. The heavenly Provider of all foods will not leave His people in ignorance in regard to the preparation of the best foods for all times and occasions.

To Be Like the Manna

(1902) 7T 124, 126

397. During the past night many things have been opened before me. The manufacture and sale of health foods will require careful and prayerful consideration.

There are many minds in many places to whom the Lord will surely give knowledge of how to prepare foods that are healthful and palatable, if He sees that they will use this knowledge righteously. Animals are becoming more and more diseased, and it will not be long until animal food will be discarded by many besides Seventh-day Adventists. Foods that are healthful and life sustaining are to be prepared, so that men and women will not need to eat meat.

The Lord will teach many in all parts of the world to combine fruits, grains, and vegetables into foods that will sustain life and will not bring disease. Those who have never seen the recipes for making the health foods now on the market, will work intelligently, experimenting with the food productions of the earth, and will be given light regarding the use of these productions. The Lord will show them what to do.

He who gives skill and understanding to His people in one part of the world will give skill and understanding to His people in other parts of the world. It is His design that the food treasures of each country shall be so prepared that they can be used in the countries for which they are suited. As God gave manna from heaven to sustain the children of Israel, so He will now give His people in different places skill and wisdom to use the productions of these countries in preparing foods to take the place of meat.

Letter 25, 1902

398. The same God who gave the children of Israel manna from heaven lives and reigns. He will give skill and understanding in the preparation of health foods. He will guide His people in the preparation of wholesome food. He desires them to see what they can do in the preparation of such food, not only for their own families, which is their first responsibility, but for the help of the poor. They are to show Christlike liberality, realizing that they are representing God, and that all they have is His endowment.

Knowledge Divinely Imparted

MS 96, 1905

399. The Lord would have a knowledge of diet reform imparted to the people of God. It is an essential part of the education to be given in our schools. As the truth is presented in new places, lessons should be given in hygienic cookery. Teach the people how they may live without the use of flesh meats. Teach them the simplicity of living.

The Lord has been working, and is still working, to lead men to prepare from fruits and grains, foods more simple and less expensive than many of those that can now be obtained. Many cannot obtain these expensive food preparations, yet they need not necessarily live upon an impoverished diet. The same God who fed the thousands in the wilderness with bread from heaven will give to His people today a knowledge of how to provide food in a simple manner.

MS 156, 1901

400. When the message comes to those who have not heard the truth for this time, they see that a great reformation must take place in their diet. They see that they must put away flesh food, because it creates an appetite for liquor,

and fills the system with disease. By meat eating, the physical, mental, and moral powers are weakened. Man is built up from that which he eats. Animal passions bear sway as the result of meat eating, tobacco using, and liquor drinking. The Lord will give His people wisdom to prepare from that which the earth yields, foods that will take the place of flesh meat. Simple combinations of nuts and grains and fruits, manufactured with taste and skill, will commend themselves to unbelievers. But as a usual thing, too many nuts are used in the combinations made.

Simple, Easily Prepared, Healthful

MS 78, 1902

401. I must now give to my brethren the instruction that the Lord has given me in regard to the health food question. By many the health foods are looked upon as of man's devising, but they are of God's originating, as a blessing to His people. The health food work is the property of God, and is not to be made a financial speculation for personal gain. The light that God has given and will continue to give on the food question is to be to His people today what the manna was to the children of Israel. The manna fell from heaven, and the people were told to gather it, and prepare it to be eaten. So in the different countries of the world, light will be given to the Lord's people, and health foods suited to these countries will be prepared.

The members of every church are to cultivate the tact and ingenuity that God will give them. The Lord has skill and understanding for all who will use their ability in striving to learn how to combine the productions of the earth so as to make simple, easily prepared, healthful foods, which will take the place of flesh meats, so that people will have no excuse for eating flesh meat.

Those who are given a knowledge of how to prepare such foods must use their knowledge unselfishly. They are to help their poor brethren. They are to be producers as well as consumers.

It is God's purpose that health foods shall be manufactured in many places. Those who accept the truth are to learn how to prepare these simple foods. It is not the Lord's plan that the poor shall suffer for the necessaries of life. The Lord calls upon His people in the different countries to ask Him for wisdom, and then to use aright the wisdom He gives. We are not to settle down in hopelessness and discouragement. We are to do our best to enlighten others.

More Simple and Less Expensive

(1902) 7T 127, 128

402. In many respects, improvements can be made in the health foods sent out from our factories. The Lord will teach His servants how to make food preparations that are more simple and less expensive. There are many whom He will teach in this line if they will walk in His counsel, and in harmony with their brethren.

MS 75, 1906

403. Deal in foods that are much less costly, and which, prepared in a nutritious form, will answer every purpose. . . . Endeavor to produce less expensive preparations of the grains and fruits. All these are freely given us of God to supply our necessities. Health is not ensured by the use of expensive preparations. We can have just as good health while using the simple preparations from the fruits, grains, and the vegetables.

(1902) 7T 125, 126

404. It is our wisdom to prepare simple, inexpensive, healthful foods. Many of our people are poor, and healthful foods are to be provided that can be supplied at prices that the poor can afford to pay. It is the Lord's design that the poorest people in every place shall be supplied with inexpensive, healthful foods. In many places industries for the manufacture of these foods are to be established. That which is a blessing to the work in one place will be a blessing in another place where money is very much harder to obtain.

God is working in behalf of His people. He does not desire them to be without resources. He is bringing them back to the diet originally given to man. Their diet is to consist of the foods made from the materials He has provided.

The materials principally used in these foods will be fruits and grains and nuts, but various roots will also be used.

As Famine Increases, Foods Will Be Simplified

MS 14, 1901

405. The food question has not yet reached perfection. There is still much to learn in this line. The Lord desires the minds of His people all over the world to be in such a condition that they can receive His impressions regarding the combining of certain articles in the production of foods, which will be a necessity, but are not yet produced.

As famine and want and distress shall increase more and more in the world, the production of the health foods will be greatly simplified. Those who are engaged in this work should learn constantly of the Great Teacher, who loves His people, and keeps their good ever in view.

[Purpose of health foods in supplying the place of flesh meat, also milk and butter—583]

Christ's Lesson on Economy

Letter 27, 1902

406. There is much at stake in this work. The wholesome productions of the earth must be experimented upon in an effort to make wholesome, inexpensive foods.

The food business is to be made the subject of earnest prayer. Let the people ask God for wisdom to prepare wholesome foods. He who fed the five thousand with five loaves and two small fishes, will supply the needs of His children today. After Christ had performed this wonderful miracle, He gave a lesson on economy. After the hunger of the multitude had been satisfied, He said, "Gather up the fragments that remain, that nothing be lost." "And they took up the fragments that remained twelve baskets full."

Foods From Local Products in Different Lands

MS 40, 1902

407. To many in different places the Lord will give intelligence in regard to health foods. He can spread a table

in the wilderness. Health foods should be prepared by our churches who are trying to practice the principles of health reform. But as surely as they should do this, some would say that they were infringing on their rights. But who gave them the wisdom to prepare these foods?—The God of heaven. That same God will give wisdom to His people in the different countries to use the productions of these countries in preparing health foods. In simple, inexpensive ways, our people are to experiment with the fruits and grains and roots in the countries in which they live. In the different countries inexpensive health foods are to be manufactured for the benefit of the poor and for the benefit of the families of our own people.

The message that God has given me is that His people in foreign lands are not to depend for their supply of health foods on the importations of health foods from America. The freight and the duty make the cost of these foods so high that the poor, who are just as precious in the sight of God as the wealthy, cannot have the advantage of them.

Health foods are God's productions, and He will teach His people in missionary fields so to combine the productions of the earth, that simple, inexpensive, wholesome foods will be provided. If they will seek wisdom from God, He will teach them how to plan and devise to utilize these productions. I am instructed to say, Forbid them not.

Health Foods to Precede Advanced Phases of Health Reform

Letter 98, 1901

408. In the field in which you are working, there is much to be learned regarding the preparation of healthful foods. Foods that are perfectly healthful and yet inexpensive are to be made. To the poor the gospel of health is to be preached. In the manufacture of these foods, ways will be opened up whereby those who accept the truth and lose their work, will be able to earn a living. The productions which God has supplied are to be made up into healthful foods, which people can prepare for themselves. Then we can appropriately present the principles of health reform, and those

who hear will be convinced of the consistency of these principles, and will accept them. But until we can present health reform foods which are palatable, nourishing, and yet inexpensive, we are not at liberty to present the most advanced phases of health reform in diet.

[To encourage development of individual talents—376]

(1902) 7T 132

409. Wherever the truth is proclaimed, instruction should be given in the preparation of healthful foods. God desires that in every place the people should be taught to use wisely the products that can be easily obtained. Skillful teachers should show the people how to utilize to the very best advantage the products that they can raise or secure in their section of the country. Thus the poor, as well as those in better circumstances, can learn to live healthfully.

Nut Ingredients to Be Used Sparingly

Letter 188, 1901

410. The Lord would have people in all parts of the world become intelligent in regard to using the productions of the soil in every locality. The products of each locality are to be studied and carefully investigated, to see if they cannot be combined in such a way as to simplify the production of foods and lessen the cost of manufacture and transportation. Let all do their best under the Lord's supervision to accomplish this. There are many expensive articles of food that the genius of man can combine; and yet there is no real need of using the most expensive preparations.

Three years ago a letter came to me, saying, "I cannot eat the nut foods; my stomach cannot take care of them." Then there were several recipes presented before me; one was that there must be other ingredients combined with the nuts, which would harmonize with them, and not use such a large proportion. One-tenth to one-sixth part of nuts would be sufficient, according to combination. We tried this, and with success.

[See "Nuts and Nut Foods" in Section XXII]

SWEETENED CRACKERS

Other things were mentioned. One thing spoken of was sweetened crackers or biscuit. They are made because some one likes them, and then many obtain them who should not eat them. There are yet many improvements to be made, and God will work with all who will work with Him.

[See Sweet Breads, Cookies, Crackers—507, 508]

[Some so-called "health confections," not harmless—530]

(1902) 7T 126

411. Great care should be exercised by those who prepare recipes for our health journals. Some of the specially prepared foods now being made can be improved, and our plans regarding their use will have to be modified. Some have used the nut preparations too freely. Many have written to me, "I cannot use the nut foods; what shall I use in place of meat?" One night I seemed to be standing before a company of people, telling them that nuts are used too freely in their preparation of foods; that the system cannot take care of them when used as in some of the recipes given, and that, if used more sparingly, the results would be more satisfactory.

Hygienic Restaurant Service at Camp Meetings

(1902) 7T 41

412. At our camp meetings, arrangements should be made so that the poor can obtain wholesome, well-prepared food as cheaply as possible. There should also be a restaurant in which healthful dishes are prepared and served in an inviting manner. This will prove an education to many not of our faith. Let not this line of work be looked upon as separate from other lines of camp meeting work. Each line of God's work is closely united with every other line, and all are to advance in perfect harmony.

MS 79, 1900

413. In our cities interested workers will take hold of various lines of missionary effort. Hygienic restaurants will be established. But with what carefulness should this work be done ! Those working in these restaurants should be con-

stantly experimenting, that they may learn how to prepare palatable, healthful foods. Every hygienic restaurant should be a school for the workers connected with it. In the cities this line of work may be done on a much larger scale than in smaller places. But in every place where there is a church and a church school, instruction should be given in regard to the preparation of simple health foods for the use of those who wish to live in accordance with the principles of health reform. And in all our missionary fields a similar work can be done.

Our Restaurants to Stand for Principle

Letter 201, 1902

414. You will need to guard constantly against the introduction of this and that, which, though seemingly harmless, would lead to the sacrifice of principles that should ever be maintained in our restaurant work. . . . We must not expect that those who all their life have indulged appetite will understand how to prepare food that will be at once wholesome, simple, and appetizing. This is the science that every sanitarium and health restaurant is to teach. . . .

If the patronage of our restaurants lessens because we refuse to depart from right principles, then let it lessen. We must keep the way of the Lord, through evil report as well as good report.

I present these things to you in my letters to help you to cleave to the right and to discard that which we cannot bring into our sanitariums and restaurants without sacrificing principle.

Avoid Complex Combinations

Letter 271, 1905

415. In all the restaurants in our cities, there is danger that the combination of many foods in the dishes served shall be carried too far. The stomach suffers when so many kinds of food are placed in it at one meal. Simplicity is a part of health reform. There is danger that our work shall cease to merit the name which it has borne.

If we would work for the restoration of health, it is necessary to restrain the appetite, to eat slowly, and only a limited variety at one time. This instruction needs to be repeated frequently. It is not in harmony with the principles of health reform to have so many different dishes at one meal. We must never forget that it is the religious part of the work, the work of providing food for the soul, that is more essential than anything else.

The Mission of Hygienic Restaurants

(1902) 7T 55

416. It was presented to me that we should not rest satisfied because we have a vegetarian restaurant in Brooklyn, but that others should be established in other sections of the city. The people living in one part of Greater New York do not know what is going on in other parts of that great city. Men and women who eat at the restaurants established in different places will become conscious of an improvement in health. Their confidence once gained, they will be more ready to accept God's special message of truth.

Wherever medical missionary work is carried on in our large cities, cooking schools should be held; and wherever a strong educational missionary work is in progress, a hygienic restaurant of some sort should be established, which shall give a practical illustration of the proper selection and the healthful preparation of foods.

(1902) 7T 115

417. The Lord has a message for our cities, and this message we are to proclaim in our camp meetings and by other public efforts, and also through our publications. In addition to this, hygienic restaurants are to be established in the cities, and by them the message of temperance is to be proclaimed. Arrangements should be made to hold meetings in connection with our restaurants. Whenever possible, let a room be provided where the patrons can be invited to lectures on the science of health and Christian temperance, where they can receive instruction on the preparation of wholesome food and on other important subjects. In these meetings there should be prayer and singing and talks, not only on health and temperance topics, but also on other

appropriate Bible subjects. As the people are taught how to preserve physical health, many opportunities will be found to sow the seeds of the gospel of the kingdom.

Ultimate Aim of Health-Food Work

MS 10, 1906

418. When conducted in such a manner that the gospel of Christ is brought to the attention of the people, the health-food work can be profitably engaged in. But I lift my voice in warning against efforts that accomplish nothing more than the production of foods to supply the physical needs. It is a serious mistake to employ so much time, and so much of the talents of men and women, in manufacturing foods, while no special effort is made at the same time to supply the multitudes with the bread of life. Great dangers attend a work that has not for its object the revelation of the way of eternal life.

[For comprehensive study of health food and restaurant work see 7T 110-131; C.H. 471-496]

Sanitarium Dietary

Quotations in Section XVI

Sanitarium Dietary

Rational Care and Good Food

MS 50, 1905

419. INSTITUTIONS for the care of the sick are to be established, where those who are suffering from disease may be placed under the care of God-fearing medical missionaries, and be treated without drugs. To these institutions there will come those who have brought disease upon themselves by improper habits of eating and drinking, and a simple, wholesome, palatable diet is to be provided. There is to be no starvation diet. Wholesome articles of food are to be combined in such a way as to make appetizing dishes.

MS 44, 1896

420. We wish to build a sanitarium where maladies may be cured by nature's own provisions, and where the people may be taught how to treat themselves when sick; where they will learn to eat temperately of wholesome food, and be educated to refuse all narcotics,—tea, coffee, fermented wines, and stimulants of all kinds,—and to discard the flesh of dead animals.

Responsibility of Physicians, Dietitians, and Nurses

Letter 112, 1909

421. It is the duty of the physician to see that wholesome food is provided, and it should be prepared in a way that will not create disturbances in the human organism.

MS 93, 1901

422. Physicians should watch unto prayer, realizing that they stand in a position of great responsibility. They should prescribe for their patients the food best suited for them. This food should be prepared by one who realizes that he occupies a most important position, inasmuch as good food is required to make good blood.

(1905) M.H. 221

423. An important part of the nurse's duty is the care of
the patient's diet. The patient should not be allowed to suffer
or become unduly weakened through lack of nourishment,
nor should the enfeebled digestive powers be overtaxed.
Care should be taken so to prepare and serve the food that it
will be palatable, but wise judgment should be used in adapt-
ing it to the needs of the patient, both in quantity and quality.

Seek the Comfort and Good Will of the Patients

Letter 213, 1902

424. The patients are to be provided with an abundance
of wholesome, palatable food, prepared and served in so appetizing a way that they will have no temptation to desire flesh
meat. The meals may be made the means of an education
in health reform. Care is to be shown in regard to the combinations of food given to the patients. Knowledge in regard to proper food combinations is of great worth, and is
to be received as wisdom from God.

The hours for meals should be so arranged that the patients will feel that those in charge of the institution are
working for their comfort and health. Then, when they
leave the institution, they will not carry away with them
the leaven of prejudice. In no case is a course to be followed that will give the patients the impression that the
time of meals has been fixed by unalterable laws.

If, after dispensing with the third meal in the sanitarium,
you see by the results that this is keeping people away from
the institution, your duty is plain. We must remember that
while there are some who are better for eating only two
meals, there are others who eat lightly at each meal, and
who feel that they need something in the evening. Food
enough is to be eaten to give strength to sinew and muscle.
And we are to remember that it is from the food eaten that
the mind gains strength. Part of the medical missionary
work that our sanitarium workers are to do is to show the
value of wholesome food.

It is right that no tea, coffee, or flesh meat be served in our sanitariums. To many, this is a great change and a severe deprivation. To enforce other changes, such as a change in the number of meals a day, is likely, in the cases of some, to do more harm than good.

[See Number of Meals in Section IX, Regularity in Eating]

Require Only Necessary Changes in Habits and Customs

Letter 213, 1902

425. Those connected with this institution are to remember that God wants them to meet the patients where they are. We are to be the helping hand of God in presenting the great problems of the truth for this time; and we must not attempt to interfere unnecessarily with the habits and customs of those who are in the sanitarium as patients or guests. Many of these people come to this retired place to remain a few weeks only. To compel them, for so short a time, to change their hours for meals, is to subject them to great inconvenience. If you do this, you will find, after test and trial, that you have made a mistake. Learn what you can in regard to the habits of the patients, and do not require them to change these habits when by the change nothing special is gained.

The atmosphere of the institution should be cheerful and homelike, and as social as possible. Those who come for treatment should be made to feel at home. Abrupt changes in regard to meals will keep them in an unsettled state of mind. Feelings of discomfort will be the result of the interuption of their habits. Their minds will be disturbed, and this will bring about unnatural conditions, by which they will be robbed of the blessings that they might otherwise obtain. When it is necessary to change their habits, do this so carefully and so pleasantly that they will look upon the change as a blessing rather than a discomfort. . . .

Let your regulations be so consistent that they will appeal to the reason of those even who have not been educated to see all things clearly. As you strive to introduce the renovating, transforming principles of truth into the life practice of those who come to the sanitarium to gain improvement in health, let them see that no arbitrary exactions are laid on them. Give them no reason to feel that they are compelled to follow a course that they do not choose.

Make Dietetic Changes Gradually

Letter 331, 1904

426. In the night season I was talking with you both. I had some things to say to you on the diet question. I was talking freely with you, telling you that you would have to make changes in your ideas in regard to the diet to be given those who come to the sanitarium from the world. These people have lived improperly on rich food. They are suffering as a result of indulgence of appetite. A reform in their habits of eating and drinking is needed. But this reform cannot be made all at once. The change must be made gradually. The health foods set before them must be appetizing. All their lives, perhaps, they have had three meals a day, and have eaten rich food. It is an important matter to reach these people with the truths of health reform. But in order to lead them to adopt a sensible diet, you must set before them an abundant supply of wholesome, appetizing food. Changes must not be made so abruptly that they will be turned from health reform, instead of being led to it. The food served to them must be nicely prepared, and it must be richer than either you or I would eat. . . .

I write this because I am sure that the Lord means you to have tact in meeting the people where they are, in their darkness and self-indulgence. As far as I am concerned personally, I am decidedly in favor of a plain, simple diet. But it will not be best to put worldly, self-indulgent patients on a diet so strict that they will be turned from health reform. This will not convince them of the need of a change in their habits of eating and drinking. Tell them the facts. Educate them to see the need of a plain, simple diet, and make the change gradually. Give them time to respond to the treatment and the instruction given them. Work and pray, and lead them along as gently as possible.

I remember once at ———, when at the sanitarium there, I was urged to sit at the table with the patients, and eat with them, that we might become acquainted. I saw then that a decided mistake was being made in the preparation of the food. It was put together in such a way that it was tasteless, and there was not more than two thirds enough. I found it impossible to make a meal that would satisfy my appetite. I tried to bring about a different order of things, and I think that matters were helped.

EDUCATION TO ACCOMPANY REFORMS

In dealing with the patients in our sanitariums, we must reason from cause to effect. We must remember that the habits and practices of a lifetime cannot be changed in a moment. With an intelligent cook, and an abundant supply of wholesome food, reforms can be brought about that will work well. But it may take time to bring them about. A strenuous effort should not be made unless it is actually demanded. We must remember that food which would be appetizing to a health reformer might be very insipid to those who have been accustomed to highly seasoned food. Lectures should be given, explaining why reforms in diet are essential, and showing that the use of highly seasoned food causes inflammation of the delicate lining of the digestive organs. Let it be shown why we as a people have changed our habits of eating and drinking. Show why we discard tobacco and all intoxicating liquor. Lay down the principles of health reform clearly and plainly, and with this, let there be placed on the table an abundance of wholesome food, tastefully prepared; and the Lord will help you to make impressive the urgency of reform, and will lead them to see that this reform is for their highest good. They will miss the highly seasoned food to which they have been accustomed, but an effort must be made to give them food that is so wholesome and so appetizing that they will cease to miss the unwholesome dishes. Show them that the treatment given them will not benefit them unless they make the needed change in their habits of eating and drinking.

Letter 45, 1903

427. In all our sanitariums a liberal bill of fare should be arranged for the patients' dining room. I have not seen anything very extravagant in any of our medical institutions; but I have seen some tables that were decidedly lacking in a supply of good, inviting, palatable food. Often patients at such institutions, after remaining for a while, have decided that they were paying a large sum for room, board, and treatment, without receiving much in return, and have therefore left. Of course, complaints greatly to the discredit of the institution were soon in circulation.

TWO EXTREMES

There are two extremes, both of which we should avoid. May the Lord help every one connected with our medical institutions not to advocate a meager supply of food. The men and women of the world who come to our sanitariums often have perverted appetites. Radical changes cannot be made suddenly for all these. Some cannot at once be placed on as plain a health reform diet as would be acceptable in a private family. In a medical institution there are varied appetites to satisfy. Some require well-prepared vegetables to meet their peculiar needs. Others have not been able to use vegetables without suffering the consequence. The poor, sick dyspeptics need to be given many words of encouragement. Let the religious influence of a Christian home pervade the sanitarium. This will be conducive to the health of the patients. All these things have to be managed carefully and prayerfully. The Lord sees the difficulties to be adjusted, and He will be your helper. . . .

VARY THE BILL OF FARE

Yesterday I wrote to you some things that I hope will in no wise confuse you. I may have written too much in regard to the importance of having a liberal dietary in our sanitariums. I have been in several medical institutions where the supply of food was not as liberal as it should have been. As you well know, in providing for the sick we must not follow one set regimen, but must frequently vary the bill of fare, and prepare food in different ways. I believe that the Lord will give all of you good judgment in the preparation of food.

Letter 37, 1904

428. Those who come to our sanitariums for treatment should be provided with a liberal supply of well-cooked food. The food placed before them must necessarily be more varied in kind than would be necessary in a home family. Let the diet be such that a good impression will be made on the guests. This is a matter of great importance. The patronage of a sanitarium will be larger if a liberal supply of appetizing food is provided.

Again and again I have left the tables of our sanitarium hungry and unsatisfied. I have talked with those in charge of the institutions, and have told them that their diet needed to be more liberal and the food more appetizing. I told them to put their ingenuity to work to make the necessary change in the best way. I told them to remember that what would perhaps suit the taste of health reformers would not answer at all for those who have always eaten luxuries, as they are termed. Much may be learned from the meals prepared and served in a successfully conducted hygienic restaurant. . . .

AVOID EXTREMES

Unless you give much attention to this matter, your patronage will decrease instead of increasing. There is danger of going to extremes in diet reform.

Last night I was in my sleep talking with Doctor ———. I said to him: You must still exercise care in regard to extremes in diet. You must not go to the extremes either in your own case or in regard to the food provided for the helpers and patients at the sanitarium. The patients pay a good price for their board, and they should have liberal fare. Some may come to the sanitarium in a condition demanding stern denial of appetite and the simplest fare, but as their health improves, they should be liberally supplied with nourishing food.

You may be surprised at my writing this, but last night I was instructed that a change in the diet would make a great difference in your patronage. A more liberal diet is needed.

Letter 127, 1904

429. The danger of going to extremes in diet must be guarded against in the sanitarium. We cannot expect worldlings to accept at once that which our people have been years in learning. Even now there are many of our ministers who do not practice health reform, notwithstanding the light they have had. We cannot expect those who do not realize the need of abstemiousness in diet, who have had no practical experiences on this subject, to take at once the wide step between self-indulgence in eating and the most strenuous diet in health reform.

Those who come to the sanitarium must be provided with wholesome food, prepared in the most palatable way consistent with right principles. We cannot expect them to live just as we live. The change would be too great. And there are very few throughout our ranks who live so abstemiously as Doctor ——— has thought it wise to live. Changes must not be made abruptly, when the patients are not prepared for them.

The food placed before the patients should be such as to make a favorable impression on them. Eggs can be prepared in a variety of ways. Lemon pie should not be forbidden.

Too little thought and painstaking effort has been given to making the food tasty and nourishing. We do not want that the sanitarium shall be destitute of patients. We cannot convert men and women from the error of their ways unless we treat them wisely.

Get the best cook possible, and do not limit the food to that which would suit the taste of some who are rigid health reformers. Were the patients given this food only, they would become disgusted, because it would taste so insipid. It is not thus that souls are to be won to the truth in our sanitariums. Let the cautions that the Lord has given Brother and Sister ——— in regard to extremes in diet, be heeded. I was instructed that Doctor ——— must change his diet, and eat more nourishing food. It is possible to avoid rich cooking, and yet make the food palatable. I know that every extreme in diet that is brought into the sanitarium will hurt the reputation of the institution. . . .

There is a way of combining and preparing food that will make it both wholesome and nourishing. Those in charge of the cooking in our sanitariums should understand how to do this. The matter should be treated from a Bible standpoint. There is such a thing as robbing the body of nutrition. The preparation of the food in the best manner possible is to become a science.

[Further statements regarding extremes in sanitarium diet—324, 331]

Influence of Short Rations or Unpalatable Food

Letter 61, 1886

430. They must have . . . the best quality of all sorts of healthful food. Those who have been in the habit of indulging the appetite with every luxury, if they come to the retreat and find at their first meal a meager diet, the impression is made at once on their minds that the reports which they have heard concerning the Adventists living so poor and starving themselves to death, is true. One meal of short rations will do more to the discredit of the institution than all the influences in other directions that can be made to counteract it. If we ever expect to meet the people where they are and bring them up to a sensible health reform diet, we must not begin by setting before them a radical diet. There must be placed upon the table nicely cooked dishes, and an abundance of good, palatable food, else those who think so much of what they eat will think they will surely starve to death. We want to have good dishes nicely prepared.

Flesh Foods Not a Part of the Sanitarium Dietary

Letter 37, 1904

431. I have received instruction in regard to the use of flesh meat in our sanitariums. Flesh meat should be excluded from the diet, and its place should be supplied by wholesome, palatable food, prepared in such a way as to be appetizing.

Letter 45, 1903

432. Brother and Sister ———, I wish to present for your consideration a few points that have been revealed to me since first there arose the difficulties connected with the question of discarding flesh meat from the tables of our medical institutions. . . .

I have been plainly instructed by the Lord that flesh meat should not be placed before the patients in our sanitarium dining rooms. Light was given me that the patients could have flesh meat, if, after hearing the parlor lectures, they still urged us to give it to them; but that, in such cases, it must be eaten in their own rooms. All the helpers are to discard flesh meat. But, as stated before, if, after knowing that the flesh of animals cannot be placed on the dining room tables, a few patients urge that they must have meat, cheerfully give it to them in their rooms.

Accustomed, as many are, to the use of flesh meat, it is not surprising that they should expect to see it on the sanitarium table. You may find it unadvisable to publish the bill of fare, giving a list of the foods supplied at the table; for the absence of flesh meat from the dietary may seem a formidable obstacle to those who are thinking of becoming patrons of the sanitarium.

Let the food be palatably prepared and nicely served. More dishes will have to be prepared than would be necessary if flesh meat were served. Other things can be provided, so that meats can be discarded. Milk and cream can be used by some.

No Prescription for Flesh Food

MS 64, 1901

433. Instruction has been given me that physicians who use flesh meat and prescribe it for their patients, should not be employed in our institutions, because they fail decidedly in educating the patients to discard that which makes them sick. The physician who uses and prescribes meat does not reason from cause to effect, and instead of acting as a restorer, he leads the patient by his own example to indulge perverted appetite.

The physicians employed in our institutions should be reformers in this respect and in every other. Many of the patients are suffering because of errors in diet. They need to be shown the better way. But how can a meat-eating physician do this? By his wrong habits he trammels his work and cripples his usefulness.

Many of the patients in our sanitariums have reasoned out for themselves the question of meat eating, and desiring to preserve their mental and physical faculties from suffering, have left meat out of their dietary. Thus they have obtained relief from the ills which have tortured their lives. Many not of our faith have become health reformers because, from a selfish standpoint, they saw the consistency of doing this. Many have conscientiously taken their position on health reform in diet and dress. Will Seventh-day Adventists continue to follow unhealthful practices? Will they not heed the injunction, "Whether therefore ye eat, or drink, or whatsoever ye do, do all to the glory of God"?

Caution in Prescribing No Flesh Foods

Letter 54, 1896

434. The light that God has given upon the subject of disease and its causes, needs to be dwelt upon largely; for it is the wrong habits of indulgence of appetite, and careless, reckless inattention to proper care for the body that tell upon people. Habits of cleanliness, care in regard to that which is introduced into the mouth, should be observed.

You are to make no prescriptions that flesh meats shall never be used, but you are to educate the mind, and let the light shine in. Let the individual conscience be awakened in regard to self-preservation and self-purity from every perverted appetite. . . .

This meat-eating question needs to be guarded. When one changes from the stimulating diet of meat eating to the fruit-and-vegetable diet, there will always be at first a sense of weakness and of lack of vitality, and many urge this as an argument for the necessity of a meat diet. But this result is the very argument that should be used in discarding a meat diet.

The change should not be urged to be made abruptly, especially for those who are taxed with continuous labor. Let the conscience be educated, the will energized, and the change can be made much more readily and willingly.

The consumptives who are going steadily down to the grave should not make particular changes in this respect, but care should be exercised to obtain the meat of as healthy animals as can be found.

Persons with tumors running their life away should not be burdened with the question as to whether they should leave meat eating or not. Be careful to make no stringent resolution in regard to this matter. It will not help the case to force changes, but will do injury to the nonmeat-eating principles. Give lectures in the parlor. Educate the mind, but force no one; for such reformation made under a press is worthless. . . .

There needs to be presented to all students and physicians, and by them to others, that the whole animal creation is more or less diseased. Diseased meat is not rare, but common. Every phase of disease is brought into the human system through subsisting upon the flesh of dead animals. The feebleness and weakness in consequence of a change from a meat diet will soon be overcome, and physicians ought to understand that they should not make the stimulus of meat eating essential for health and strength. All who leave it alone intelligently, after becoming accustomed to the change, will have health of sinews and muscles.

Letter 231, 1905

435. Doctor ———— asked me if, under any circumstances, I would advise the drinking of chicken broth, if one were sick and could not take anything else into the stomach. I said, "There are persons dying of consumption who, if they ask for chicken broth, should have it. But I would be very careful." The example should not injure a sanitarium or make excuse for others to think their case required the same diet. I asked Doctor ———— if she had such a case in the sanitarium. She said, "No; but I have a sister in the

sanitarium at ———, who is very weak. She has weak sinking spells, but cooked chicken she can eat." I said, "It would be best to remove her from the sanitarium. . . . The light given me is that if the sister you mention would brace up and cultivate her taste for wholesome food, all these sinking spells would pass away."

She has cultivated her imagination; the enemy has taken advantage of her weakness of body; and her mind is not braced to bear up against the hardships of everyday life. It is good, sanctified mind cure she needs, an increase of faith, and active service for Christ. She needs also the exercise of her muscles in outside practical labor. Physical exercise will be to her one of the greatest blessings of her life. She need not be an invalid, but a wholesome-minded, healthy woman, prepared to act her part nobly and well.

All the treatment that may be given to this sister will be of little advantage unless she acts her part. She needs to strengthen muscle and nerve by physical labor. She need not be an invalid, but can do good, earnest labor.

[Recognition of emergency conditions—699, 700]

"Do Not Let It Appear"

Letter 84, 1898

436. I met the doctors and Brother ———, and talked with them for about two hours, and I freed my soul. I told them that they had been tempted, and that they were yielding to temptation. In order to secure patronage, they would set a meat table, and then they would be tempted to go farther, to use tea and coffee and drugs. . . . I said, There will be temptation through the ones whose appetite for meat has been gratified, and if such ones have connection with the Health Home, they will present temptations to sacrifice principle. There must not be the first introduction of meat eating. Then there will not need to be an expulsion of meat, because it will never have appeared on the table. . . . The argument had been used, that they might use meat upon the table until they could educate in regard to its disuse. But as new patients were continually coming, the same excuse would establish meat eating. No; do not let it appear

on the table once. Then your lectures in regard to the meat question will correspond with the message you should bear.

Serving Tea, Coffee, and Flesh Meat in Patients' Rooms

Letter 213, 1902

437. In our sanitariums . . . no tea, coffee, or flesh meat is to be served, unless it is in some special case, where the patient particularly desires it, and then, these articles of food should be served to him in his room.

Tea, Coffee, and Flesh Meat Not to Be Prescribed

(1896) E. from U.T. 4, 5

438. Physicians are not employed to prescribe a flesh diet for patients, for it is this kind of diet that has made them sick. Seek the Lord. When you find Him, you will be meek and lowly of heart. Individually, you will not subsist upon the flesh of dead animals, neither will you put one morsel in the mouths of your children. You will not prescribe flesh, tea, or coffee for your patients, but will give talks in the parlor showing the necessity of a simple diet. You will cut away injurious things from your bill of fare.

To have the physicians of our institutions educating by precept and example, those under their care to use a meat diet, after years of instruction from the Lord, disqualifies them to be superintendents of our health institutes. The Lord does not give light on health reform that it may be disregarded by those who are in positions of influence and authority. The Lord means just what He says, and He is to be honored in what He says. Light is to be given upon these subjects. It is the diet question that needs close investigation, and prescriptions should be made in accordance with health principles.

[See Progressive Dietetic Reform in Seventh-day Adventist Institutions—720-725]

Liquor Not to Be Served

(1902) 7T 95

439. We are not building sanitariums for hotels. Receive into our sanitariums only those who desire to conform to

right principles, those who will accept the foods that we can conscientiously place before them. Should we allow patients to have intoxicating liquor in their rooms, or should we serve them with meat, we could not give them the help they should receive in coming to our sanitariums. We must let it be known that from principle we exclude such articles from our sanitariums and hygienic restaurants. Do we not desire to see our fellow beings freed from disease and infirmity, and in the enjoyment of health and strength? Then let us be as true to principle as the needle to the pole.

Dishes Inviting Appetite

Letter 54, 1907

440. We cannot mold the minds of worldlings to health reform principles all at once; therefore we must not set down too stringent rules in regard to the diet of the patients. When worldly patients come to the sanitarium, they have to make a great change in their dietary; and that they may feel the change as little as possible, the very best cookery in healthful lines should be brought in, the most palatable and inviting dishes placed upon the table. . . .

Those who pay for board and treatment should have their food prepared in the most palatable form. The reason for this is obvious. When the patients are deprived of flesh foods, the system feels the change. There is a feeling of letting down, and they will demand a liberality in their diet. Dishes should be prepared that will invite the appetite, and will be pleasing to the sight.

Foods for Invalids

Letter 171, 1903

441. A liberal diet should be provided for the patients, but care should be taken in the preparation and combination of food for the sick. The table of a sanitarium cannot be set exactly the same as the table of a restaurant. It makes a great difference whether the food is to be placed before healthy men, who can digest almost anything in the line of food, or before invalids.

There is danger of providing too limited a diet for people who have come directly from a diet so abundant as to encourage gluttony. The fare should be liberal. But at the same time, it should be simple. I know that food can be prepared simply, and yet be so palatable as to be enjoyed even by those who have been accustomed to a richer fare.

Let fruit be placed on the table in abundance. I am glad that you are able to provide for the sanitarium table, fruit fresh from your own orchards. This is indeed a great advantage.

[Not every one can use vegetables—516]

The Education of the Sanitarium Table

Letter 71, 1896

442. In the preparation of the food, the golden rays of light are to be kept shining, teaching those who sit at the table how to live. This education is also to be given to those who visit the Health Retreat, that they may carry from it reformatory principles.

Letter 73, 1905

443. The preparation of food for sanitarium patients needs close and careful attention. Some of the patients come from homes in which the tables are daily loaded with rich food, and every effort should be made to set before them food that is both appetizing and wholesome.

TO RECOMMEND HEALTH REFORM

The Lord would have the institution with which you are connected one of the most satisfying and enjoyable places in the world. I want you to show special care in providing for the patients a diet that will not endanger health, and at the same time will recommend our principles of health reform. This can be done, and being done, it will make a favorable impression on the minds of the patients. It will be an education to them, showing them the advantage of hygienic living above their own way of living. And when they leave the institution, they will carry with them a report that will influence others to go there.

The Helpers' Table

Letter 54, 1896

444. You have too little care and feel too lightly the burden of providing an orderly, ample repast for your workers. They are the ones who need an abundance of fresh wholesome provision. They are constantly taxed; their vitality must be preserved. Their principles should be educated. They, of all in the sanitarium, should be abundantly furnished with the best and most wholesome, strength-giving food. The table of your helpers should be furnished, not with meat, but with an abundant supply of good fruit, grains, and vegetables, prepared in a nice, wholesome way. Your neglect to do this has increased your income at altogether too great an expense to the strength and souls of your workers. This has not pleased the Lord. The influence of the entire fare does not recommend your principles to those that sit at the helpers' table.

The Cook, a Medical Missionary

Letter 100, 1903

445. Obtain the best help in the cooking that you can. If food is prepared in such a way that it is a tax on the digestive organs, be sure that investigation is needed. Food can be prepared in such a way as to be both wholesome and palatable.

MS 93, 1901

446. The cook in a sanitarium should be a thorough health reformer. A man is not converted unless his appetite and diet correspond with his profession of faith.

The cook in a sanitarium should be a well-trained medical missionary. He should be a capable person, able to experiment for himself. He should not confine himself to recipes. The Lord loves us, and He does not want us to do ourselves harm by following unhealthful recipes.

At every sanitarium there will be some who will complain about the food, saying that it does not suit them. They need to be educated in regard to the evils of unhealthful diet. How can the brain be clear while the stomach is suffering?

Letter 37, 1901

447. There should be in our sanitarium a cook who thoroughly understands the work, one who has good judgment, who can experiment, who will not introduce into the food those things which should be avoided.

Letter 331, 1904

448. Have you a cook who can prepare dishes that the patients cannot help but see are an improvement on the diet to which they have been accustomed? The one who does the cooking in a sanitarium should be able to make wholesome, appetizing food combinations, and these food combinations must necessarily be somewhat richer than you or I would eat.

MS 88, 1901

449. The one who holds the position as cook has a most responsible place. He should be trained in habits of economy and should realize that no food is to be wasted. Christ said, "Gather up the fragments, that nothing be lost." Let those who are engaged in any department, heed this instruction. Economy is to be learned by the educators and taught to the helpers not only by precept, but by example.

SECTION XVII

Diet a Rational Remedy

Quotations in Section XVII

Diet a Rational Remedy

Nature's Remedial Agencies

MS 86, 1897

450. It is important to become familiar with the benefit of dieting in case of sickness. All should understand what to do [for] themselves.

(1885) 5T 443

451. There are many ways of practicing the healing art; but there is only one way that Heaven approves. God's remedies are the simple agencies of nature, that will not tax or debilitate the system through their powerful properties. Pure air and water, cleanliness, a proper diet, purity of life, and a firm trust in God, are remedies for the want of which thousands are dying; yet these remedies are going out of date because their skillful use requires work that the people do not appreciate. Fresh air, exercise, pure water, and clean, sweet premises, are within the reach of all, with but little expense; but drugs are expensive, both in the outlay of means, and the effect produced upon the system.

(1905) M.H. 127

452. Pure air, sunlight, abstemiousness, rest, exercise, proper diet, the use of water, trust in divine power,—these are the true remedies. Every person should have a knowledge of nature's remedial agencies and how to apply them. It is essential both to understand the principles involved in the treatment of the sick and to have a practical training that will enable one rightly to use this knowledge.

The use of natural remedies requires an amount of care and effort that many are not willing to give. Nature's process of healing and upbuilding is gradual, and to the impatient it seems slow. The surrender of hurtful indulgences requires sacrifice. But in the end it will be found that nature, untrammeled, does her work wisely and well. Those who persevere in obedience to her laws will reap the reward in health of body and health of mind.

(1890) C.T.B.H. 160

453. Physicians often advise invalids to visit foreign countries, to go to some mineral spring, or to traverse the ocean, in order to regain health; when, in nine cases out of ten, if they would eat temperately, and engage in healthful exercise with a cheerful spirit, they would regain health and save time and money. Exercise, and a free, abundant use of the air and sunlight—blessings which heaven has bestowed upon all—would in many cases give life and strength to the emaciated invalid.

Some Things We Can Do for Ourselves

Letter 35, 1890

454. In regard to that which we can do for ourselves, there is a point that requires careful, thoughtful consideration.

I must become acquainted with myself, I must be a learner always as to how to take care of this building, the body God has given me, that I may preserve it in the very best condition of health. I must eat those things which will be for my very best good physically, and I must take special care to have my clothing such as will conduce to a healthful circulation of the blood. I must not deprive myself of exercise and air. I must get all the sunlight that it is possible for me to obtain. I must have wisdom to be a faithful guardian of my body.

I should do a very unwise thing to enter a cool room when in a perspiration; I should show myself an unwise steward to allow myself to sit in a draft, and thus expose myself so as to take cold. I should be unwise to sit with cold feet and limbs, and thus drive back the blood from the extremities to the brain or internal organs. I should always protect my feet in damp weather. I should eat regularly of the most healthful food which will make the best quality of blood, and I should not work intemperately if it is in my power to avoid doing so. And when I violate the laws God has established in my being, I am to repent and reform, and place myself in the most favorable condition under the doctors God has provided,—pure air, pure water, and the healing, precious sunlight.

Water can be used in many ways to relieve suffering. Drafts of clear, hot water taken before eating (half a quart, more or less), will never do any harm, but will rather be productive of good.

Faith and Correct Eating and Drinking

Letter 5, 1904

455. Let those who are sick do all in their power, by correct practice in eating, drinking, and dressing, and by taking judicious exercise, to secure the recovery of health. Let the patients who come to our sanitariums be taught to cooperate with God in seeking health. "Ye are God's husbandry, ye are God's building." God made nerve and muscle in order that they might be used. It is the inaction of the human machinery that brings suffering and disease.

(1867) 1T 561

456. Those who treat the sick should move forward in their important work with strong reliance upon God for His blessing to attend the means which He has graciously provided, and to which He has in mercy called our attention as a people, such as pure air, cleanliness, healthful diet, proper periods of labor and repose, and the use of water.

Rational Remedies in Sanitariums

Letter 79, 1905

457. The light given me was that a sanitarium should be established, and that in it drug medication should be discarded, and simple, rational methods of treatment employed for the healing of disease. In this institution people were to be taught how to dress, breathe, and eat properly—how to prevent sickness by proper habits of living.

MS 49, 1908

458. In our sanitariums, we advocate the use of simple remedies. We discourage the use of drugs, for they poison the current of the blood. In these institutions sensible instruction should be given how to eat, how to drink, how to dress, and how to live so that the health may be preserved.

Letter 73a, 1896

459. The question of health reform is not agitated as it must and will be. A simple diet, and the entire absence of drugs, leaving nature free to recuperate the wasted energies of the body, would make our sanitariums far more effectual in restoring the sick to health.

A Remedial Diet

(1864) Sp. Gifts IV, 133-135

460. Indulging in eating too frequently and in too large quantities, overtaxes the digestive organs and produces a feverish state of the system. The blood becomes impure, and then diseases of various kinds occur. A physician is sent for, who prescribes some drug which gives present relief, but which does not cure the disease. It may change the form of disease, but the real evil is increased tenfold. Nature was doing her best to rid the system of an accumulation of impurities, and could she have been left to herself, aided by the common blessings of Heaven, such as pure air and pure water, a speedy and safe cure would have been effected.

The sufferers in such cases can do for themselves that which others cannot do as well for them. They should commence to relieve nature of the load they have forced upon her. They should remove the cause. Fast a short time, and give the stomach chance for rest. Reduce the feverish state of the system by a careful and understanding application of water. These efforts will help nature in her struggles to free the system of impurities. But generally the persons who suffer pain become impatient. They are not willing to use self-denial, and suffer a little from hunger. . . .

The use of water can accomplish but little, if the patient does not feel the necessity of also strictly attending to his diet.

Many are living in violation of the laws of health, and are ignorant of the relation their habits of eating, drinking, and working sustain to their health. They will not arouse to their true condition until nature protests against the abuses she is suffering, by aches and pains in the system.

If, even then, the sufferers would only commence the work right, and would resort to the simple means they have neglected,—the use of water and proper diet,—nature would have just the help she requires, and which she ought to have had long before. If this course is pursued, the patient will generally recover without being debilitated.

(1905) M.H. 235

461. Intemperate eating is often the cause of sickness, and what nature most needs is to be relieved of the undue burden that has been placed upon her. In many cases of sickness, the very best remedy is for the patient to fast for a meal or two, that the overworked organs of digestion may have an opportunity to rest. A fruit diet for a few days has often brought great relief to brain workers. Many times a short period of entire abstinence from food, followed by simple, moderate eating, has led to recovery through nature's own recuperative effort. An abstemious diet for a month or two would convince many sufferers that the path of self-denial is the path to health.

Strict Temperance a Remedy for Disease

(1905) M.H. 114

462. When a physician sees a patient suffering from disease caused by improper eating and drinking or other wrong habits, yet neglects to tell him of this, he is doing his fellow being an injury. Drunkards, maniacs, those who are given over to licentiousness, all appeal to the physician to declare clearly and distinctly that suffering results from sin. Those who understand the principles of life should be in earnest in striving to counteract the causes of disease. Seeing the continual conflict with pain, laboring constantly to alleviate suffering, how can the physician hold his peace? Is he benevolent and merciful if he does not teach strict temperance as a remedy for disease?

The Best Food Needed

MS 93, 1901

463. Physicians should watch unto prayer, realizing that they stand in a position of great responsibility. They should

prescribe for their patients the food best suited for them. This food should be prepared by one who realizes that he occupies a most important position, inasmuch as good food is required to make good blood.

[Olives as laxative—614, 615]
[Remedial value of eggs—628, 629, 631]

Fruits, Cereals, and Vegetables

Quotations in Section XVIII

Fruits, Cereals, and Vegetables

PART I—FRUITS

A Blessing in Fresh Fruits

Letter 157, 1900

464. I AM so thankful to God that when Adam lost his Eden home, the Lord did not cut off the supply of fruit.

(1902) 7T 126

465. The Lord desires those living in countries where fresh fruit can be obtained during a large part of the year, to awake to the blessing they have in this fruit. The more we depend upon the fresh fruit just as it is plucked from the tree, the greater will be the blessing.

(1902) 7T 134

466. It would be well for us to do less cooking and to eat more fruit in its natural state. Let us teach the people to eat freely of the fresh grapes, apples, peaches, pears, berries, and all other kinds of fruit that can be obtained. Let these be prepared for winter use by canning, using glass, as far as possible, instead of tin.

[Fruit is excellent food, saves much cooking—546]

(1870) 2T 373

467. For a dyspeptic stomach, you may place upon your tables fruits of different kinds, but not too many at one meal.

MS 43, 1908

468. Fruit we would especially recommend as a health-giving agency. But even fruit should not be eaten after a full meal of other foods.

Letter 12, 1887

469. Nicely prepared vegetables and fruits in their season will be beneficial, if they are of the best quality, not showing the slightest sign of decay, but are sound and unaffected by any disease or decay. More die by eating decayed fruit and decayed vegetables which ferment in the stomach and result in blood poisoning, than we have any idea of.

309

Letter 103, 1896

470. A plain, simple, but liberal supply of fruit is the best food that can be placed before those who are preparing for the work of God.

[Fruits and grains, food for those preparing for translation—488, 515]

A Part of an Adequate Diet

(1905) M.H. 296

471. Grains, fruits, nuts, and vegetables constitute the diet chosen for us by our Creator. These foods prepared in as simple and natural a manner as possible, are the most healthful and nourishing. They impart a strength, a power of endurance, and a vigor of intellect, that are not afforded by a more complex and stimulating diet.

[Fruits, grains, vegetables with milk and cream, the most healthful diet—487]

[Vegetables on E. G. White's table—Appendix I:4, 8, 15]

MS 27, 1906

472. In grains, fruits, vegetables, and nuts are to be found all the food elements that we need. If we will come to the Lord in simplicity of mind, He will teach us how to prepare wholesome food free from the taint of flesh meat.

[Fruit a part of the adequate diet—483, 486, 513]

[Nature's ample supply of fruits, nuts, and grains—485]

[Fruit a constituent of health foods—399, 400, 403, 404, 407, 810]

A Temporary Fruit Diet

(1905) M.H. 235

473. Intemperate eating is often the cause of sickness, and what nature most needs is to be relieved of the undue burden that has been placed upon her. In many cases of sickness, the very best remedy is for the patient to fast for a meal or two, that the overworked organs of digestion may have an opportunity to rest. A fruit diet for a few days has often brought great relief to brain workers. Many times a short period of entire abstinence from food, followed by simple, moderate eating, has led to recovery through nature's own recuperative effort. An abstemious diet for a month or two would convince many sufferers that the path of self-denial is the path to health.

Replacing Injurious Articles

Letter 145, 1904

474. In our medical institutions clear instruction should be given in regard to temperance. The patients should be shown the evil of intoxicating liquor, and the blessing of total abstinence. They should be asked to discard the things that have ruined their health, and the place of these things should be supplied with an abundance of fruit. Oranges, lemons, prunes, peaches, and many other varieties can be obtained; for the Lord's world is productive, if painstaking effort is put forth.

(1905) M.H. 305

475. Do not eat largely of salt, avoid the use of pickles and spiced foods, eat an abundance of fruit, and the irritation that calls for so much drink at mealtime will largely disappear.

[To take the place of flesh meat—149, 312, 320, 492, 514, 649, 795]

[To take place of desserts—546]

[Not relished by those accustomed to rich and highly seasoned foods—563]

[To take the place of much porridge eating—490, 499]

Canning and Drying

(1905) M.H. 299

476. Wherever fruit can be grown in abundance, a liberal supply should be prepared for winter, by canning or drying. Small fruits, such as currants, gooseberries, strawberries, raspberries, and blackberries, can be grown to advantage in many places where they are but little used, and their cultivation is neglected.

For household canning, glass, rather than tin cans, should be used whenever possible. It is especially necessary that the fruit for canning should be in good condition. Use little sugar, and cook the fruit only long enough to ensure its preservation. Thus prepared, it is an excellent substitute for fresh fruit.

Wherever dried fruits, such as raisins, prunes, apples, pears, peaches, and apricots, are obtainable at moderate prices, it will be found that they can be used as staple articles of diet much more freely than is customary, with the best results to the health and vigor of all classes of workers.

Letter 195, 1905

477. Applesauce, put up in glass, is wholesome and palatable. Pears and cherries, if they can be obtained, make very nice sauce for winter use.

Letter 5, 1870

478. If you can get apples, you are in a good condition as far as fruit is concerned, if you have nothing else. . . . I do not think such large varieties of fruit are essential, yet they should be carefully gathered and preserved in their season for use when there are no apples to be had. Apples are superior to any fruit for a standby that grows.

Fresh From Orchard and Garden

MS 114, 1902

479. There is another advantage to be gained by carrying on the cultivation of fruit in connection with our sanitariums. Thus fruit absolutely free from decay, and fresh from the trees, can be obtained for table use.

MS 13, 1911

480. Families and institutions should learn to do more in the cultivation and improvement of land. If people only knew the value of the products of the ground, which the earth brings forth in their season, more diligent efforts would be made to cultivate the soil. All should be acquainted with the special value of fruits and vegetables fresh from the orchard and garden. As the number of patients and students increases, more land will be needed. Grapevines could be planted, thus making it possible for the institution to produce its grapes. The orange orchard that is on the place would be an advantage.

[Importance of raising fruit and vegetables for the table—519]
[Fruit and vegetables at same meal—188, 190, 722]
[Use of fruit on E. G. White's table—Appendix I:4, 9, 15, 22, 23]
[Fruit in sanitarium dietary—441]
[Use of fruit on the helpers' table—444, 651]
[Fruit in the camp meeting diet—124, 765]
[To be included in a simple diet for visitors—129]
[A part of a wholesome, palatable diet—204, 503]
[Tomatoes recommended by E. G. White—Appendix I:16, 22, 23]

PART II—GRAINS

In a Diet of the Creator's Choice

(1905) M.H. 296

481. Grains, fruits, nuts, and vegetables constitute the
diet chosen for us by our Creator. These foods, prepared
in as simple and natural a manner as possible, are the most
healthful and nourishing. They impart a strength, a power
of endurance, and a vigor of intellect, that are not afforded
by a more complex and stimulating diet.

[For context see 111]

(1905) M.H. 313

482. Those who eat flesh are but eating grains and vegetables at second hand; for the animal receives from these
things the nutrition that produces growth. The life that
was in the grains and vegetables passes into the eater. We
receive it by eating the flesh of the animal. How much
better to get it direct, by eating the food that God provided
for our use!

[The people to be brought back to diet of fruits, vegetables,
and grains—515]

A Part of an Adequate Diet

(1905) M.H. 316

483. It is a mistake to suppose that muscular strength
depends on the use of animal food. The needs of the system
can be better supplied, and more vigorous health can be enjoyed, without its use. The grains, with fruits, nuts, and
vegetables, contain all the nutritive properties necessary to
make good blood.

MS 27, 1906

484. In grains, fruits, vegetables, and nuts are to be
found all the food elements that we need. If we will come
to the Lord in simplicity of mind, He will teach us how to
prepare wholesome food free from the taint of flesh meat.

[Contain necessary nutritive properties—513]

Abundantly Supplied

(1905) M.H. 297

485. Nature's abundant supply of fruits, nuts, and grains
is ample, and year by year the products of all lands are more

generally distributed to all, by the increased facilities for
transportation. As a result, many articles of food which a
few years ago were regarded as expensive luxuries, are now
within the reach of all as foods for everyday use.

(1905) M.H. 299

486. If we plan wisely, that which is most conducive to
health can be secured in almost every land. The various
preparations of rice, wheat, corn, and oats are sent abroad
everywhere, also beans, peas, and lentils. These, with na
tive or imported fruits, and the variety of vegetables that
grow in each locality, give an opportunity to select a dietary
that is complete without the use of flesh meats.

[Grains one of nature's abundant luxuries—503]

Properly Prepared

[C.T.B.H. 47] (1890) C.H. 115

487. Fruits, grains, and vegetables, prepared in a simple
way, free from spice and grease of all kinds, make, with milk
or cream, the most healthful diet. They impart nourishment
to the body, and give a power of endurance and a vigor of
intellect that are not produced by a stimulating diet.

[For context see 137]

(1869) 2T 352

488. Grains and fruits prepared free from grease, and in
as natural a condition as possible, should be the food for the
tables of all who claim to be preparing for translation to
heaven.

[To educate ourselves to subsist on fruits, grains, and
vegetables—514]

[Grains a constituent of health foods—399, 400, 403, 404, 407,
810]

Porridge

(1905) M.H. 301

489. Grains used for porridge or "mush" should have sev
eral hours' cooking. But soft or liquid foods are less whole
some than dry foods, which require thorough mastication

Y.I., May 31, 1894

490. Some honestly think that a proper dietary consists
chiefly of porridge. To eat largely of porridge would no

nsure health to the digestive organs; for it is too much like
quid.   Encourage the eating of fruit and vegetables and
read.

[Too much porridge eating a mistake—499]

Graham Gruel

(1871) 2T 603

491. You can make graham gruel. If the graham flour
 too coarse, sift it, and while the gruel is hot, add milk.
'his will make a most palatable and healthful dish for the
ampground.

To Take the Place of Flesh Meat

(1905) M.H. 316, 317

492. When flesh food is discarded, its place should be
upplied with a variety of grains, nuts, vegetables, and
'uits, that will be both nourishing and appetizing. . . . The
lace of meat should be supplied with wholesome foods that
re inexpensive.

[Taking the place of flesh meat—765, 795]
[Flesh meat not needed where there are fruits, grains, and
uts—138]
[To be included in a simple diet for visitors—129]
[Use of grains at helpers' table—444, 651]
[On E. G. White's table—Appendix I:15-23]
[Sanitarium patients to be taught use of—767]

PART III—BREAD

The Staff of Life

MS 34, 1899

493. Religion will lead mothers to make bread of the
ery best quality. . . . Bread should be thoroughly baked,
iside and out. The health of the stomach demands that it
e light and dry. Bread is the real staff of life, and there-
ore every cook should excel in making it.

Religion in a Good Loaf

[C.T.B.H. 49] (1890) C.H. 117

494. Some do not feel it is a religious duty to prepare
od properly; hence they do not try to learn how. They

let the bread sour before baking, and the saleratus added to remedy the cook's carelessness makes it totally unfit for the human stomach. It requires thought and care to make good bread. But there is more religion in a good loaf of bread than many think.

(1868) 1T 684

495. It is a religious duty for every Christian girl and woman to learn at once to make good, sweet, light bread from unbolted wheat flour. Mothers should take their daughters into the kitchen with them when very young, and teach them the art of cooking.

[Knowledge of breadmaking indispensable--822]

Use of Soda in Bread

(1905) M.H. 300-302

496. The use of soda or baking powder in breadmaking is harmful and unnecessary. Soda causes inflammation of the stomach and often poisons the entire system. Many housewives think that they cannot make good bread without soda, but this is an error. If they would take the trouble to learn better methods, their bread would be more wholesome, and, to a natural taste, it would be more palatable.

[Use of saleratus in bread—See "Soda and Baking Powder," 565, 569]

USING MILK IN YEAST BREAD

In the making of raised or yeast bread, milk should not be used in the place of water. The use of milk is an additional expense, and it makes the bread much less wholesome. Milk bread does not keep sweet so long after baking as does that made with water, and it ferments more readily in the stomach.

HOT YEAST BREAD

Bread should be light and sweet. Not the least taint of sourness should be tolerated. The loaves should be small and so thoroughly baked that, as far as possible, the yeast germs shall be destroyed. When hot, or new, raised bread of any kind is difficult of digestion. It should never appear on the table. This rule does not, however, apply to unleav-

:ned bread. Fresh rolls made of wheaten meal, without
:east or leaven, and baked in a well-heated oven, are both
vholesome and palatable. . . .

ZWIEBACK

Zwieback, or twice-baked bread, is one of the most easily
ligested and most palatable of foods. Let ordinary raised
read be cut in slices and dried in a warm oven till the last
race of moisture disappears. Then let it be browned
slightly all the way through. In a dry place this bread can
)e kept much longer than ordinary bread, and if reheated
)efore using, it will be as fresh as when new.

[Zwieback good for the evening meal—273]
[Zwieback in diet of E. G. White—Appendix I:22]

Old Bread Preferable to Fresh

Letter 142, 1900

497. Bread which is two or three days old is more
aealthful than new bread. Bread dried in the oven is one
)f the most wholesome articles of diet.

The Evils of Sour Bread

(1868) 1T 681-684

498. We frequently find graham bread heavy, sour, and
)ut partially baked. This is for want of interest to learn,
and care to perform the important duty of cook. Sometimes
ve find gem cakes, or soft biscuit, dried, not baked, and
)ther things after the same order. And then cooks will tell
you they can do very well in the old style of cooking, but to
ell the truth, their families do not like graham bread; that
hey would starve to live in this way.

I have said to myself, I do not wonder at it. It is your
nanner of preparing food that makes it so unpalatable. To
:at such food would certainly give one the dyspepsia. These
)oor cooks, and those who have to eat their food, will gravely
ell you that the health reform does not agree with them.

The stomach has not power to convert poor, heavy, sour
)read into good food; but this poor bread will convert a
aealthy stomach into a diseased one. Those who eat such

food know that they are failing in strength. Is there not a cause? Some of these persons call themselves health reformers, but they are not. They do not know how to cook. They prepare cakes, potatoes, and graham bread, but there is the same round, with scarcely a variation, and the system is not strengthened. They seem to think the time wasted which is devoted to obtaining a thorough experience in the preparation of healthful, palatable food. . . .

In many families we find dyspeptics, and frequently the reason of this is the poor bread. The mistress of the house decides that it must not be thrown away, and they eat it. Is this the way to dispose of poor bread? Will you put it into the stomach to be converted into blood? Has the stomach power to make sour bread sweet? heavy bread light? moldy bread fresh? . . .

Many a wife and mother who has not had the right education and lacks skill in the cooking department, is daily presenting her family with ill-prepared food which is steadily and surely destroying the digestive organs, making poor quality of blood, and frequently bringing on acute attacks of inflammatory disease and causing premature death. Many have been brought to their death by eating heavy sour bread. An instance was related to me of a hired girl who made a batch of sour, heavy bread. In order to get rid of it and conceal the matter, she threw it to a couple of very large hogs. Next morning the man of the house found his swine dead, and upon examining the trough, found pieces of this heavy bread. He made inquiries, and the girl acknowledged what she had done. She had not a thought of the effect of such bread upon the swine. If heavy, sour bread will kill swine, which can devour rattlesnakes, and almost every detestable thing, what effect will it have upon that tender organ, the human stomach?

The Advantage of Using Bread and Other Hard Food

MS 3, 1897

499. Great care should be taken when the change is made from a flesh meat to a vegetarian diet, to supply the table with wisely prepared, well-cooked articles of food. So much

orridge eating is a mistake. The dry food that requires
astication is far preferable. The health food preparations
re a blessing in this respect. Good brown bread and rolls,
repared in a simple manner, yet with painstaking effort,
ill be healthful. Bread should never have the slightest
int of sourness. It should be cooked until it is thoroughly
one. Thus all softness and stickiness will be avoided.

For those who can use them, good vegetables, prepared
a a healthful manner, are better than soft mushes or por-
idge. Fruits used with thoroughly cooked bread two or
aree days old will be more healthful than fresh bread.
his, with slow and thorough mastication, will furnish all
aat the system requires.

[Good bread in place of rich foods—312]

Hot Biscuits

(Written 1884) E. from U.T. 2

500. Hot biscuits and flesh meats are entirely out of har-
ony with health reform principles.

Letter 72, 1896

501. Hot soda biscuits are often spread with butter, and
aten as a choice diet; but the enfeebled digestive organs
annot but feel the abuse placed upon them.

Letter 3, 1884

502. We have been going back to Egypt rather than on to
anaan. Shall we not reverse the order of things? Shall
e not have plain, wholesome food on our tables? Shall we
ot dispense with hot biscuits, which only cause dyspepsia?

[A cause of dyspepsia—720]

Gems and Rolls

R. & H., May 8, 1883

503. Hot biscuit raised with soda or baking powder
ould never appear upon our tables. Such compounds are
nfit to enter the stomach. Hot raised bread of any kind is
ifficult of digestion. Graham gems, which are both whole-
me and palatable, may be made from the unbolted flour,

mixed with pure cold water and milk. But it is difficult t
teach our people simplicity. When we recommend graha
gems, our friends says, "Oh, yes, we know how to mak
them." We are much disappointed when they appear raise
with baking powder or with sour milk and soda. Thes
give no evidence of reform. The unbolted flour, mixed wit
pure soft water and milk, makes the best gems we have eve
tasted. If the water is hard, use more sweet milk, or ad
an egg to the batter. Gems should be thoroughly baked in
well-heated oven, with a steady fire.

To make rolls, use soft water and milk, or a little crean
make a stiff dough and knead it as for crackers. Bake o
the grate of the oven. These are sweet and delicious. The
require thorough mastication, which is a benefit to both th
teeth and the stomach. They make good blood, and impar
strength. With such bread, and the abundant fruits, vege
tables, and grains with which our country abounds, r
greater luxuries should be desired.

Whole-Wheat Bread Better Than White

(1868) 2T 68

504. Fine-flour bread cannot impart to the system th
nourishment that you will find in the unbolted-wheat brea
The common use of bolted-wheat bread cannot keep the sy
tem in a healthy condition. You both have inactive liver
The use of fine flour aggravates the difficulties under whic
you are laboring.

(1905) M.H. 300

505. For use in breadmaking, the superfine white flour
not the best. Its use is neither healthful nor economic
Fine-flour bread is lacking in nutritive elements to be foun
in bread made from the whole wheat. It is a frequent cau
of constipation and other unhealthful conditions.

[Unbolted or graham flour the best for the body—171, 49
499, 503]
[Grains to be used in natural state—481]
[Graham bread in camp meeting diet—124]
[A religious duty to know how to make good bread fro
unbolted wheat flour—392]

Grains in Bread May Be Varied

Letter 91, 1898

506. All wheat flour is not best for a continuous diet. A mixture of wheat, oatmeal, and rye would be more nutritious than the wheat with the nutrifying properties separated from it.

Sweet Breads

Letter 363, 1907

507. Sweet breads and cookies we seldom have on our table. The less of sweet foods that are eaten, the better; these cause disturbances in the stomach, and produce impatience and irritability in those who accustom themselves to their use.

Letter 37, 1901

508. It is well to leave sugar out of the crackers that are made. Some enjoy best the sweetest crackers, but these are an injury to the digestive organs.

[Sweetened crackers—410]
[Bread not relished by those accustomed to rich and highly seasoned food—563]

PART IV—VEGETABLES

Fresh Vegetables, Simply Prepared

MS 13, 1911

509. All should be acquainted with the special value of fruits and vegetables fresh from the orchard and garden.

[Encourage the eating of vegetables—490]
[No greater luxury—503]

[C.T.B.H. 47] (1890) C.H. 115

510. Fruits, grains, and vegetables, prepared in a simple way, free from spice and grease of all kinds, make, with milk and cream, the most healthful diet. They impart nourishment to the body, and give a power of endurance and a vigor of intellect that are not produced by a stimulating diet.

[Fruits, grains, and vegetables good food for visitors—129]
[Danger of using decayed vegetables—469]
[Defiled by use of grease in preparation—320]
[In the diet of the Creator's choice—471]
[A constituent of health foods—403, 404, 407, 810]

11

MS 3, 1897

511. For those who can use them, good vegetables, prepared in a healthful manner, are better than soft mushes or porridge.

(1909) 9T 162

512. Vegetables should be made palatable with a little milk or cream, or something equivalent.

A Part of a Complete Diet

Letter 72, 1896

513. The simple grains, fruits of the trees, vegetables, have all the nutritive properties necessary to make good blood. This a flesh diet cannot do.

[In the adequate diet—483, 484, 486]

Plenty of Vegetables

Letter 3, 1884

514. We are built up from that which we eat. Shall we strengthen the animal passions by eating animal food? In the place of educating the taste to love this gross diet, it is high time that we were educating ourselves to subsist upon fruits, grains, and vegetables. . . . A variety of simple dishes, perfectly healthful and nourishing, may be provided, aside from meat. Hearty men must have plenty of vegetables, fruits, and grains.

[For the helpers' table—444, 651]
[To take the place of flesh meat—492, 649, 765, 795]
[To take the place of rich foods—312]
[Not relished by those accustomed to transgressing nature's laws—204, 563]
[Flesh diet vegetables secondhand—482]

Letter 72, 1896

515. The Lord intends to bring His people back to live upon simple fruits, vegetables, and grains.

Some Cannot Use Vegetables

Letter 45, 1903

516. In a medical institution there are varied appetites to satisfy. Some require well-prepared vegetables to meet their

peculiar needs.   Others have not been able to use vegetables without suffering the consequence.

Potatoes, Irish and Sweet

Letter 322, 1905

517. We do not think fried potatoes are healthful, for there is more or less grease or butter used in preparing them. Good baked or boiled potatoes served with cream and a sprinkling of salt are the most healthful. The remnants of Irish and sweet potatoes are prepared with a little cream and salt and rebaked, and not fried; they are excellent.

Beans a Wholesome Dish

(1871) 2T 603

518. Another very simple yet wholesome dish, is beans boiled or baked. Dilute a portion of them with water, add milk or cream, and make a broth.

Growing and Preserving Vegetables

Letter 5, 1904

519. Many do not see the importance of having land to cultivate, and of raising fruit and vegetables, that their tables may be supplied with these things. I am instructed to say to every family and every church, God will bless you when you work out your own salvation with fear and trembling, fearing lest, by unwise treatment of the body, you will mar the Lord's plan for you.

[All should be acquainted with value of fruits and vegetables fresh from the orchard and garden—480]

Letter 195, 1905

520. Provision should be made for obtaining a supply of dried sweet corn. Pumpkins can be dried, and used to advantage during the winter in making pies.

Greens and Tomatoes in the Diet of Ellen G. White

Letter 31, 1901

521. You speak in regard to my diet. I have not become so wedded to one thing as not to be able to eat anything else. But as far as material for greens is concerned, you need have

no concern; for to my certain knowledge there are in the section of country where you live many kinds of vegetable productions which I can use as greens. I shall be able to obtain the leaves of the yellow dock, the young dandelion, and mustard. There will be a far more bountiful supply there, and of a superior quality, than we could obtain in Australia. And if there was nothing else, there are the grain productions.

Letter 10, 1902

522. My appetite left me some time before I went to the East. But now it has returned; and I am very hungry when mealtime comes. My thistle greens, nicely cooked, and seasoned with sterilized cream and lemon juice, are very appetizing. I have vermicelli-tomato soup one meal and greens the next. I have begun again to eat potato meal. My food all tastes good. I am like a fever patient who has been half-starved, and I am in danger of overeating.

Letter 70, 1900

523. The tomatoes you sent were very nice and very palatable. I find that tomatoes are the best article of diet for me to use.

[See also Appendix I:16, 22, 23]

Letter 363, 1907

524. Of corn and peas we have raised enough for ourselves and our neighbors. The sweet corn we dry for winter use; then when we need it we grind it in a mill and cook it. It makes most palatable soups and other dishes. . . .

In their season we have grapes in abundance, also prunes and apples, and some cherries, peaches, pears, and olives, which we prepare ourselves. We also grow a large quantity of tomatoes. I never make excuses for the food that is on my table. I do not think God is pleased to have us do so. Our visitors eat as we do, and appear to enjoy our bill of fare.

[Corn used by E. G. White—Appendix I:22, 23]
[Caution regarding using with fruit—188, 190]
[Caution regarding using vegetables with desserts—189, 722]
[In diet of E. G. White—Appendix I:4, 8, 15]

SECTION XIX

Desserts

Quotations in Section XIX

Desserts

PART I—SUGAR

MS 93, 1901

525. SUGAR is not good for the stomach. It causes fermentation, and this clouds the brain and brings peevishness into the disposition.

(1905) M.H. 302

526. Far too much sugar is ordinarily used in food. Cakes, sweet puddings, pastries, jellies, jams, are active causes of indigestion. Especially harmful are the custards and puddings in which milk, eggs, and sugar are the chief ingredients. The free use of milk and sugar taken together should be avoided.

[See milk and sugar—533, 536]
[Use only a little in fruit canning—476]
[A little sugar permissible—550]

(1870) 2T 369, 370

527. Sugar clogs the system. It hinders the working of the living machine.

There was one case in Montcalm County, Michigan, to which I will refer. The individual was a noble man. He stood six feet, and was of fine appearance. I was called to visit him in his sickness. I had previously conversed with him in regard to his manner of living. "I do not like the looks of your eyes," said I. He was eating large quantities of sugar. I asked him why he did this. He said that he had left off meat, and did not know what would supply its place as well as sugar. His food did not satisfy him, simply because his wife did not know how to cook.

Some of you send your daughters, who have nearly grown to womanhood, to school to learn the sciences before they know how to cook, when this should be made of the first importance. Here was a woman who did not know how to cook; she had not learned how to prepare healthful food. The wife and mother was deficient in this important branch of education; and as the result, poorly cooked food not being sufficient to sustain the demands of the system, sugar was eaten immoderately, which brought on a diseased condition of the entire system. This man's life was sacrificed unnecessarily to bad cooking.

When I went to see the sick man, I tried to tell them as well as I could how to manage, and soon he began slowly to improve. But he imprudently exercised his strength when not able, ate a small amount not of the right quality, and was taken down again. This time there was no help for him. His system appeared to be a living mass of corruption. He died a victim to poor cooking. He tried to make sugar supply the place of good cooking, and it only made matters worse.

I frequently sit down to the tables of the brethren and sisters, and see that they use a great amount of milk and sugar. These clog the system, irritate the digestive organs, and affect the brain. Anything that hinders the active motion of the living machinery, affects the brain very directly. And from the light given me, sugar, when largely used, is more injurious than meat. These changes should be made cautiously, and the subject should be treated in a manner not calculated to disgust and prejudice those whom we would teach and help.

[Sweet breads and crackers—410, 507, 508]

R. & H., Jan. 7, 1902

528. We should not be prevailed upon to take anything into the mouth that will bring the body into an unhealthy condition, no matter how much we like it. Why?—Because we are God's property. You have a crown to win, a heaven to gain, and a hell to shun. Then for Christ's sake, I ask you, Will you have the light shine before you in clear and distinct rays, and then turn away from it and say, "I love this, and I love that"? God calls upon every one of you to begin to plan, to cooperate with God in His great care and love, to elevate, ennoble, and sanctify the whole soul, body, and spirit, that we may be workers together with God. . . .

It is better to let sweet things alone. Let alone those sweet dessert dishes that are placed on the table. You do not need them. You want a clear mind to think after God's order.

[See Part III—pie, cake, pastry, and puddings]
[Candy not to be given infants—346]

Sale of Knickknacks on the Campground

Letter 25a, 1889

529. Years ago I had a testimony of reproof for the managers in our camp meetings bringing upon the ground and selling to our people cheese and other hurtful things, and presenting candies for sale when I was laboring to instruct the young and old to put the money they had expended for candy in the missionary box and thus teach their children self-denial.

MS 87, 1908

530. Light has been given me in regard to the foods provided at our camp meetings. Foods are sometimes brought onto the campground which are not in keeping with the principles of health reform.

If we are to walk in the light God has given us, we must educate our people, old and young, to dispense with these foods that are eaten merely for the indulgence of appetite. Our children should be taught to deny themselves of such unnecessary things as candies, gum, ice cream, and other knickknacks, that they may put the money saved by their self-denial into the self-denial box, of which there should be one in every home. By this means large and small sums would be saved for the cause of God.

Not a few of our people need instruction in regard to the principles of health reform. There are various confections that have been invented by manufacturers of health foods, and recommended as perfectly harmless; but I have a different testimony to bear concerning them. They are not truly healthful, and their use should not be encouraged. We need to keep more strictly to a simple diet of fruits, nuts, grains, and vegetables.

Let not foods or confectionery be brought upon our campground that will counterwork the light given our people on health reform. Let us not gloss over the temptation to indulge appetite, by saying that the money received from the sale of such things is to be used to meet the expenses of a good work. All such temptation to self-indulgence should be firmly resisted. Let us not persuade ourselves to do that which is unprofitable to the individual under the pretext that good will come of it. Let us individually learn what it means to be self-denying, yet healthful, active missionaries.

Sugar in Ellen G. White's Diet

Letter 5, 1870

531. Everything is plain yet wholesome because it is not merely thrown together in a haphazard manner. We have no sugar on our table. Our sauce which is our dependence is apples, baked or stewed, sweetened as is required before being put upon the table.

Letter 1, 1873

532. We have always used a little milk and some sugar. This we have never denounced, either in our writings or in our preaching. We believe cattle will become so much diseased that these things will yet be discarded, but the time has not yet come for sugar and milk to be wholly abolished from our tables.

PART II—MILK AND SUGAR

(1870) 2T 368, 369

533. Now in regard to milk and sugar: I know of persons who have become frightened at the health reform, and said they would have nothing to do with it, because it has spoken against a free use of these things. Changes should be made with great care; and we should move cautiously and wisely. We want to take that course which will recommend itself to the intelligent men and women of the land. Large quantities of milk and sugar eaten together are injurious. They impart impurities to the system. Animals from which milk is obtained are not always healthy. They may be diseased. A cow may be apparently well in the morning and die before night. Then she was diseased in the morning, and her milk was diseased, but you did not know it. The animal creation is diseased. Flesh meats are diseased. Could we know that animals were in perfect health, I would recommend that people eat flesh meats sooner than large quantities of milk and sugar. It would

not do the injury that milk and sugar do. Sugar clogs the system. It hinders the working of the living machine.

(1870) 2T 370

534. I frequently sit down to the tables of the brethren and sisters, and see that they use a great amount of milk and sugar. These clog the system, irritate the digestive organs, and affect the brain.

[For context see 527]

[C.T.B.H. 57] (1890) C.H. 154

535. Some use milk and a large amount of sugar on mush, thinking that they are carrying out health reform. But the sugar and milk combined are liable to cause fermentation in the stomach, and are thus harmful.

(1905) M.H. 302

536. Especially harmful are the custards and puddings in which milk, eggs, and sugar are the chief ingredients. The free use of milk and sugar taken together should be avoided.

[Ice cream—530, 540]
[Cake eaten with milk or cream—552]

PART III—PIE, CAKE, PASTRY, PUDDINGS

[Spec. Test. on Education, October, 1893] F.E. 227

537. The desserts which take so much time to prepare, are, many of them, detrimental to health.

A Temptation to Overindulgence

Letter 73a, 1896

538. At too many tables, when the stomach has received all that it requires to properly carry on its work of nourishing the system, another course, consisting of pies, puddings, and highly flavored sauces, is placed upon the table. . . . Many, though they have already eaten enough, will overstep the bounds, and eat the tempting dessert, which, however, proves anything but good for them. . . . If the extras which are provided for dessert were dispensed with altogether, it would be a blessing.

(1864) Sp. Gifts IV, 130

539. Because it is the fashion, in harmony with morbid appetite, rich cake, pies, and puddings, and every hurtful thing, are crowded into the stomach. The table must be loaded down with a variety, or the depraved appetite cannot be satisfied. In the morning, these slaves to appetite often have impure breath, and a furred tongue. They do not enjoy health, and wonder why they suffer with pains, headaches, and various ills.

(1865) H. to L., ch. 1, p. 53

540. The human family have indulged an increasing desire for rich food, until it has become a fashion to crowd all the delicacies possible into the stomach. Especially at parties of pleasure is the appetite indulged with but little restraint. Rich dinners and late suppers are partaken of, consisting of highly seasoned meats with rich gravies, rich cakes, pies, ice cream, etc.

(1865) H. to L., ch. 1, p. 54

541. Because it is fashion, many who are poor and dependent upon their daily labor, will be to the expense of preparing different kinds of rich cakes, preserves, pies, and a variety of fashionable food for visitors, which only injure those who partake of them; when, at the same time, they need the amount thus expended, to purchase clothing for themselves and children. This time occupied in cooking food to gratify the taste at the expense of the stomach, should be devoted to the moral and religious instruction of their children.

[For context see 128]
[Rich foods create desire for stimulants—203]

Not a Part of a Healthful, Nourishing Diet

Y.I., May 31, 1894

542. Many understand how to make different kinds of cakes, but cake is not the best food to be placed upon the table. Sweet cakes, sweet puddings, and custards will disorder the digestive organs; and why should we tempt those who surround the table by placing such articles before them?

(1870) 2T 400

543. Flesh meats and rich cakes and pies prepared with spices of any kind, are not the most healthful and nourishing diet.

Letter 91, 1898

544. The desserts that are taken in the form of custards are liable to do more harm than good. Fruit, if it can be obtained, is the best article of food.

(1905) M.H. 302

545. Far too much sugar is ordinarily used in food. Cakes, sweet puddings, pastries, jellies, jams, are active causes of indigestion. Especially harmful are the custards and puddings in which milk, eggs, and sugar are the chief ingredients. The free use of milk and sugar taken together should be avoided.

Letter 135, 1902

546. Let those who advocate health reform strive earnestly to make it all that they claim it is. Let them discard everything detrimental to health. Use simple, wholesome food. Fruit is excellent, and saves much cooking. Discard rich pastries, cakes, desserts, and other dishes prepared to tempt the appetite. Eat fewer kinds of food at one meal, and eat with thanksgiving.

Simple Desserts Not Forbidden

Letter 17, 1895

547. Plain, simple pie may serve as dessert, but when one eats two or three pieces merely to gratify an inordinate appetite, he unfits himself for the service of God. Some, after partaking largely of other food, will take dessert, not because they need it, but because it tastes good. If they are asked to take a second piece, the temptation is too great to be resisted, and two or three pieces of pie are added to the load placed upon the already overworked stomach. He who will do this has never educated himself to practice self-denial. The victim of appetite is so wedded to his own way that he cannot see the injury he is doing to himself.

(1870) 2T 383, 384

548. Then, when she needed extra clothing and extra food, and that of a simple yet nutritious quality, it was not allowed her. Her system craved material to convert into blood; but he would not provide it. A moderate amount of milk and sugar, a little salt, white bread raised with yeast for a change, graham flour prepared in a variety of ways by other hands than her, plain cake with raisins, rice pudding with raisins, prunes, and figs, occasionally, and many other dishes I might mention, would have answered the demand of appetite.

Letter 127, 1904

549. The food placed before the patients should be such as to make a favorable impression on them. Eggs can be prepared in a variety of ways. Lemon pie should not be forbidden.

[Lemon pie used by E. G. White—Appendix I:22]

Letter 53, 1898

550. The dessert should be placed on the table and served with the rest of the food; for often, after the stomach has been given all it should have, the dessert is brought on, and is just that much too much.

For Clear Minds and Strong Bodies

Letter 10, 1891

551. I wish we were all health reformers. I am opposed to the use of pastries. These mixtures are unhealthful; no one can have good digestive powers and a clear brain who will eat largely of sweet cookies and cream cake and all kinds of pies, and partake of a great variety of food at one meal. When we do this, and then take cold, the whole system is so clogged and enfeebled that it has no power of resistance, no strength to combat disease. I would prefer a meat diet to the sweet cakes and pastries so generally used.

Letter 142, 1900

552. Let health reformers remember that they may do harm by publishing recipes which do not recommend health reform. Great care is to be shown in furnishing recipes for

custards and pastry. If for dessert sweet cake is eaten with milk or cream, fermentation will be created in the stomach, and then the weak points of the human organism will tell the story. The brain will be affected by the disturbance in the stomach. This may be easily cured if people will study from cause to effect, cutting out of their diet that which injures the digestive organs and causes pain in the head. By unwise eating, men and women are unfitted for the work they might do without injury to themselves if they would eat simply.

(1871) 2T 602

553. I am convinced that none need to make themselves sick preparing for camp meeting, if they observe the laws of health in their cooking. If they make no cake or pies, but cook simple graham bread, and depend on fruit, canned or dried, they need not get sick in preparing for the meeting, and they need not be sick while at the meeting.

R. & H., Jan. 7, 1902

554. It is better to let sweet things alone. Let alone those sweet dessert dishes that are placed on the table. You do not need them. You want a clear mind to think after God's order. We should now come into line with health reform principles.

[Cakes, pies, ices, served at rich dinners and late suppers —233]

[Preparations for fashionable gatherings—128]

[Educating the appetite to accept a plain diet—245]

[Fasting a help in overcoming perverted appetite—312]

[Though mince pies, spices, etc., are discarded, food should be prepared with care—389]

[Cakes or pies not to be included in preparations for camp meeting—57, 74]

[Rich food and desserts not served in White home—Appendix I:4, 13]

[The less condiments and desserts, the better—193]

[Rich desserts served with vegetables—722]

[Rich pastry deranges the stomach and excites the nerves —356]

[Detrimental effects of desserts in diet of children—288, 350, 355, 360]

[Rich food not best for sedentary workers—225]

[Making a covenant with God to discontinue the use of rich foods—41]

SECTION XX

Condiments, Etc.

Quotations in Section XX

Condiments, Etc.

PART I—SPICES AND CONDIMENTS

Letter 142, 1900

555. CONDIMENTS, so frequently used by those of the world, are ruinous to the digestion.

(1905) M.H. 325

556. Under the head of stimulants and narcotics is classed a great variety of articles that, altogether, used as food or drink, irritate the stomach, poison the blood, and excite the nerves. Their use is a positive evil. Men seek the excitement of stimulants, because, for the time, the results are agreeable. But there is always a reaction. The use of unnatural stimulants always tends to excess, and it is an active agent in promoting physical degeneration and decay.

In this fast age, the less exciting the food, the better. Condiments are injurious in their nature. Mustard, pepper, spices, pickles, and other things of a like character, irritate the stomach and make the blood feverish and impure. The inflamed condition of the drunkard's stomach is often pictured as illustrating the effect of alcoholic liquors. A similarly inflamed condition is produced by the use of irritating condiments. Soon ordinary food does not satisfy the appetite. The system feels a want, a craving, for something more stimulating.

(1896) E. from U.T. 6

557. Condiments and spices used in the preparation of food for the table aid in digestion in the same way that tea, coffee, and liquor are supposed to help the laboring man perform his tasks. After the immediate effects are gone, they drop as correspondingly below par as they were elevated above par by these stimulating substances. The system is weakened. The blood is contaminated, and inflammation is the sure result.

Spices Irritate the Stomach and Cause Unnatural Cravings

R. & H., Nov. 6, 1883

558. Our tables should bear only the most wholesome food, free from every irritating substance. The appetite for

liquor is encouraged by the preparation of food with condiments and spices. These cause a feverish state of the system, and drink is demanded to allay the irritation. On my frequent journeys across the continent, I do not patronize restaurants, dining cars, or hotels, for the simple reason that I cannot eat the food there provided. The dishes are highly seasoned with salt and pepper, creating an almost intolerable thirst. . . . They would irritate and inflame the delicate coating of the stomach. . . . Such is the food that is commonly served upon fashionable tables, and given to the children. Its effect is to cause nervousness and to create thirst which water does not quench. . . . Food should be prepared in as simple a manner as possible, free from condiments and spices, and even from an undue amount of salt.

[Spiced foods create desire for beverages with meals—570]

Letter 53, 1898

559. Some have so indulged their taste, that unless they have the very article of food it calls for, they find no pleasure in eating. If condiments and spiced foods are placed before them, they make the stomach work by applying this fiery whip; for it has been so treated that it will not acknowledge unstimulating food.

(1890) C.T.B.H. 17

560. Luxurious dishes are placed before the children,— spiced foods, rich gravies, cakes, and pastries. This highly seasoned food irritates the stomach, and causes a craving for still stronger stimulants. Not only is the appetite tempted with unsuitable food, of which the children are allowed to eat freely at their meals, but they are permitted to eat between meals; and by the time they are twelve or fourteen years of age, they are often confirmed dyspeptics.

You have perhaps seen a picture of the stomach of one who is addicted to strong drink. A similar condition is produced under the irritating influence of fiery spices. With the stomach in such a state, there is a craving for something more to meet the demands of the appetite, something stronger, and still stronger.

[For context see 355]

Their Use a Cause of Faintness

(1864) Sp. Gifts IV, 129

561. There is a class who profess to believe the truth, who do not use tobacco, snuff, tea, or coffee, yet they are guilty of gratifying the appetite in a different manner. They crave highly seasoned meats, with rich gravies, and their appetite has become so perverted that they cannot be satisfied with even meat, unless prepared in a manner most injurious. The stomach is fevered, the digestive organs are taxed, and yet the stomach labors hard to dispose of the load forced upon it. After the stomach has performed its task, it becomes exhausted, which causes faintness. Here many are deceived, and think that it is the want of food which produces such feelings, and without giving the stomach time to rest, they take more food, which for the time removes the faintness. And the more the appetite is indulged, the more will be its clamors for gratification.

[C.T.B.H. 47] (1890) C.H. 114

562. Spices at first irritate the tender coating of the stomach, but finally destroy the natural sensitiveness of this delicate membrane. The blood becomes fevered, the animal propensities are aroused, while the moral and intellectual powers are weakened, and become servants to the baser passions. The mother should study to set a simple yet nutritious diet before her family.

(1864) Sp. Gifts IV, 130

563. Persons who have indulged their appetite to eat freely of meat, highly seasoned gravies, and various kinds of rich cakes and preserves, cannot immediately relish a plain, wholesome, nutritious diet. Their taste is so perverted they have not appetite for a wholesome diet of fruits, plain bread, and vegetables. They need not expect to relish at first food so different from that in which they have been indulging.

MS 33, 1909

564. With all the precious light that has continually been given to us in the health publications, we cannot afford to live careless, heedless lives, eating and drinking as we please,

and indulging in the use of stimulants, narcotics, and condiments. Let us take into consideration the fact that we have souls to save or to lose, and that it is of vital consequence how we relate ourselves to the question of temperance. It is of great importance that individually we act well our part, and have an intelligent understanding of what we should eat and drink, and how we should live to preserve health. All are being proved to see whether we will accept the principles of health reform or follow a course of self-indulgence.

[Temperance reformers should awaken to evils from use of condiments—747]

[Though mince pies, spices, etc., are discarded, the food should be prepared with care—389]

[Time wasted preparing foods seasoned with spices, which ruin health, sour the temper, and becloud the reason—234]

[Spices and condiments allowed to children—348, 351, 354, 360]

[Highly seasoned food encourages overeating and produces feverish conditions—351]

[Free use of pickles and condiments by a nervous, irritable child—574]

[Cannot be converted into good blood—576]

[Refusal of dainty dishes and rich condiments, etc., proves workers to be practical health reformers—227]

[Animal passions excited by spiced foods—348]

[Foods taken to camp meeting should be free from all spices and grease—124]

[Spices not used in the White home—Appendix I:4]

[Spiced foods and condiments excite nerves and enfeeble intellect—356]

[The blessing of a diet free from spices—119]

[Simple foods, without spices, are best—487]

[Those craving condiments to be enlightened—779]

PART II—SODA AND BAKING POWDER

(1905) M.H. 300, 301

565. The use of soda or baking powder in breadmaking is harmful and unnecessary. Soda causes inflammation of the stomach, and often poisons the entire system. Many housewives think that they cannot make good bread without soda, but this is an error. If they would take the trouble to learn better methods, their bread would be more wholesome, and, to a natural taste, it would be more palatable.

R. & H., May 8, 1883

566. Hot biscuit raised with soda or baking powder should never appear upon our tables. Such compounds are unfit to enter the stomach. Hot raised bread of any kind is difficult of digestion.

Graham gems which are both wholesome and palatable may be made from the unbolted flour, mixed with pure cold water and milk. But it is difficult to teach our people simplicity. When we recommend graham gems, our friends say, "Oh, yes, we know how to make them." We are much disappointed when they appear, raised with baking powder or with sour milk and soda. These give no evidence of reform. The unbolted flour, mixed with pure soft water and milk, makes the best gems we ever tasted. If the water is hard, use more sweet milk, or add an egg to the batter. Gems should be thoroughly baked in a well-heated oven, with a steady fire.

Health Reformer, August, 1873

567. In my travels, I see entire families suffering with sickness in consequence of poor cooking. Sweet, nice, healthful bread is seldom seen upon their tables. Yellow, saleratus biscuits and heavy, clammy bread are breaking down the digestive organs of tens of thousands.

[C.T.B.H. 49] (1890) C.H. 117

568. Some do not feel that it is a religious duty to prepare food properly; hence they do not try to learn how. They let the bread sour before baking, and the saleratus added to remedy the cook's carelessness, makes it totally unfit for the human stomach.

(1870) 2T 537

569. We see sallow complexions, and groaning dyspeptics wherever we go. When we sit at the tables, and eat the food cooked in the same manner as it has been for months, and perhaps years, I wonder that these persons are alive. Bread and biscuit are yellow with saleratus. This resort to saleratus was to save a little care; in consequence of forgetfulness, the bread is often allowed to sour before baking, and to remedy the evil a large portion of saleratus is added,

which only makes it totally unfit for the human stomach. Saleratus in any form should not be introduced into the stomach; for the effect is fearful. It eats the coatings of the stomach, causes inflammation, and frequently poisons the entire system. Some plead, "I cannot make good bread or gems unless I use soda or saleratus." You surely can if you become a scholar and will learn. Is not the health of your family of sufficient value to inspire you with ambition to learn how to cook and how to eat?

PART III—SALT

(1905) M.H. 305

570. Do not eat largely of salt, avoid the use of pickles and spiced foods, eat an abundance of fruit, and the irritation that calls for so much drink at mealtime will largely disappear.

(1909) 9T 162

571. Food should be prepared in such a way that it will be appetizing as well as nourishing. It should not be robbed of that which the system needs. I use some salt, and always have, because salt, instead of being deleterious, is actually essential for the blood.

Letter 37, 1901

572. At one time Doctor ———— tried to teach our family to cook according to health reform, as he viewed it, without salt or anything else to season the food. Well, I determined to try it, but I became so reduced in strength that I had to make a change; and a different policy was entered upon with great success. I tell you this because I know that you are in positive danger. Food should be prepared in such a way that it will be nourishing. It should not be robbed of that which the system needs. . . .

I use some salt, and always have, because from the light given me by God, this article, in the place of being deleterious, is actually essential for the blood. The whys and wherefores of this I know not, but I give you the instruction as it is given me.

[Some salt should be used—548]
[Avoid an undue amount of salt—558]
[Some salt used by E. G. White—Appendix I:4]

PART IV—PICKLES AND VINEGAR

(1905) M.H. 325

573. In this fast age, the less exciting the food, the better. Condiments are injurious in their nature. Mustard, pepper, spices, pickles, and other things of a like character irritate the stomach and make the blood feverish and impure.

[C.T.B.H. 61, 62] (1890) F.E. 150, 151

574. I was seated once at the table with several children under twelve years of age. Meat was plentifully served, and then a delicate, nervous girl called for pickles. A bottle of chowchow, fiery with mustard and pungent with spices, was handed her, from which she helped herself freely. The child was proverbial for her nervousness and irritability of temper, and these fiery condiments were well calculated to produce such a condition.

(1870) 2T 368

575. The mince pies and the pickles, which should never find a place in any human stomach, will give a miserable quality of blood.

(1870) 2T 383

576. The blood-making organs cannot convert spices, mince pies, pickles, and diseased flesh meats into good blood.
[For context see 336]

(1905) M.H. 305

577. Do not eat largely of salt, avoid the use of pickles and spiced foods, eat an abundance of fruit, and the irritation that calls for so much drink at mealtime will largely disappear.
[Pickles irritate the stomach and make blood impure—556]

Vinegar

Letter 9, 1887

578. The salads are prepared with oil and vinegar, fermentation takes place in the stomach, and the food does not digest, but decays or putrefies; as a consequence, the blood is not nourished, but becomes filled with impurities, and liver and kidney difficulties appear.
[Personal experience in conquering the vinegar habit—Appendix I:6]

SECTION XXI

Fats

Quotations in Section XXI

Fats

PART I—BUTTER

Progressive Reform

(1902) 7T 135

579. LET the diet reform be progressive. Let the people be taught how to prepare food without the use of milk or butter. Tell them that the time will soon come when there will be no safety in using eggs, milk, cream, or butter, because disease in animals is increasing in proportion to the increase of wickedness among men. The time is near when, because of the iniquity of the fallen race, the whole animal creation will groan under the diseases that curse our earth.

God will give His people ability and tact to prepare wholesome food without these things. Let our people discard all unwholesome recipes.

[Health educational efforts of James and Ellen White in which "positive testimony" was borne against "tea, coffee, flesh meats, butter, spices," etc., in 1871—803]

(1905) M.H. 302

580. Butter is less harmful when eaten on cold bread than when used in cooking; but, as a rule, it is better to dispense with it altogether.

[Hot soda biscuits and butter—501]

Replacing With Olives, Cream, Nuts, and Health Foods

(1902) 7T 134

581. Olives may be so prepared as to be eaten with good results at every meal. The advantages sought by the use of butter may be obtained by the eating of properly prepared olives. The oil in the olives relieves constipation, and for consumptives, and for those who have inflamed, irritated stomachs, it is better than any drug. As a food it is better than any oil coming secondhand from animals.

(1905) M.H. 298

582. When properly prepared, olives, like nuts, supply the place of butter and flesh meats. The oil, as eaten in the olive, is far preferable to animal oil or fat. It serves as a laxative. Its use will be found beneficial to consumptives, and it is healing to an inflamed, irritated stomach.

Union Conference Record (Australasian), Jan. 1, 1900

583. The health food business is in need of means and of the active cooperation of our people, that it may accomplish the work it ought to do. Its purpose is to supply the people with food which will take the place of flesh meat, and also milk and butter, which, on account of the diseases of cattle, are becoming more and more objectionable.

[Replacing with cream—586, 610]

Not Best for Children

(1873) 3T 136

584. Children are allowed to eat flesh meats, spices, butter, cheese, pork, rich pastry, and condiments generally. They are also allowed to eat irregularly and between meals of unhealthful food. These things do their work of deranging the stomach, exciting the nerves to unnatural action, and enfeebling the intellect. Parents do not realize that they are sowing the seed which will bring forth disease and death.

[Butter a stimulant—61]
[Free use of butter by children—288, 356, 364]
[Discarding butter from principle—389]

Free Use Obstructs Digestion

Letter 37, 1901

585. Butter should not be placed on the table; for if it is, some will use it too freely, and it will obstruct digestion. But for yourself, you should occasionally use a little butter on cold bread, if this will make the food more appetizing. This would do you far less harm than to confine yourself to preparations of food that are not palatable.

When the Purest Butter Cannot Be Obtained

Letter 45, 1903

586. I eat but two meals a day, and still follow the light given me thirty-five years ago. I use no meat. As for myself, I have settled the butter question. I do not use it. This question should easily be settled in every place where the purest article cannot be obtained. We have two good milch cows, a Jersey and a Holstein. We use cream, and all are satisfied with this.

[Use of cream in place of butter in White home—Appendix I:20, 23]

[Use of butter in the White home—Appendix I:4]

[Butter not on White table, but used in cooking—Appendix I:14]

[Butter not on table in White home, and not used by E. G. White—Appendix I:5, 8, 9, 16, 20, 21, 22, 23]

Not to Be Classed With Flesh Meat

(1902) 7T 135

587. Milk, eggs, and butter should not be classed with flesh meat. In some cases the use of eggs is beneficial. The time has not come to say that the use of milk and eggs should be wholly discarded. There are poor families whose diet consists largely of bread and milk. They have little fruit, and cannot afford to purchase the nut foods. In teaching health reform, as in all other gospel work, we are to meet the people where they are. Until we can teach them how to prepare health reform foods that are palatable, nourishing, and yet inexpensive, we are not at liberty to present the most advanced propositions regarding health reform diet.

Allow Others Their Convictions

[Letter 331, 1904] M.M. 269

588. We must remember that there are a great many different minds in the world, and we cannot expect every one to see exactly as we do in regard to all questions of diet. Minds do not run in exactly the same channel. I do not eat butter, but there are members of my family who do. It is not placed on my table; but I make no disturbance because some members of my family choose to eat it occasionally.

Many of our conscientious brethren have butter on their tables, and I feel under no obligation to force them to do otherwise. These things should never be allowed to cause disturbance among brethren. I cannot see the need of butter, where there is abundance of fruit and of sterilized cream.

Those who love and serve God should be allowed to follow their own convictions. We may not feel justified in doing as they do, but we should not allow differences of opinion to create disunion.

Letter 104, 1901

589. I cannot see but that you are trying your best to live out the principles of health reform. Study economy in everything, but do not withhold from the diet food which the system needs. With regard to the nut foods, there are many who cannot eat them. If your husband enjoys dairy butter, let him eat it until he is convinced that this is not best for his health.

Caution Against Extremes

Letter 98, 1901

590. There is danger that in presenting the principles of health reform some will be in favor of bringing in changes that would be for the worse instead of for the better. Health reform must not be urged in a radical manner. As the situation now is, we cannot say that milk and eggs and butter should be entirely discarded. We must be careful to make no innovations, because under the influence of extreme teaching there are conscientious souls who will surely go to extremes. Their physical appearance will injure the cause of health reform; for few know how to properly supply the place of that which they discard.

(1909) 9T 162

591. While warnings have been given regarding the dangers of disease through butter, and the evil of the free use of eggs by small children, yet we should not consider it a violation of principle to use eggs from hens that are well cared for and suitably fed. Eggs contain properties that are remedial agencies in counteracting certain poisons.

Some, in abstaining from milk, eggs, and butter, have failed to supply the system with proper nourishment, and as a consequence have become weak and unable to work. Thus health reform is brought into disrepute. The work that we have tried to build up solidly is confused with strange things that God has not required, and the energies of the church are crippled. But God will interfere to prevent the results of these too-strenuous ideas. The gospel is to harmonize the sinful race. It is to bring the rich and poor together at the feet of Jesus.

Letter 37, 1901

592. The poor say, when health reform is presented to them, "What shall we eat? We cannot afford to buy the nut foods." As I preach the gospel to the poor, I am instructed to tell them to eat that food which is most nourishing. I cannot say to them, "You must not eat eggs or milk or cream. You must use no butter in the preparation of food." The gospel must be preached to the poor, and the time has not yet come to prescribe the strictest diet. . . .

GOD WILL GUIDE

But I wish to say that when the time comes that it is no longer safe to use milk, cream, butter, and eggs, God will reveal this. No extremes in health reform are to be advocated. The question of using milk and butter and eggs will work out its own problem. At present we have no burden on this line. Let your moderation be known unto all men.

PART II—LARD AND GREASE *

(1868) 1T 681

593. Many do not feel that this is a matter of duty, hence they do not try to prepare food properly. This can be done in a simple, healthful, and easy manner, without the use of

---

*Grease is defined by Webster as "animal fat, especially when soft: any fatty, oily, or unctuous substance."

Ellen White stated that olives, properly prepared, may be eaten with benefit at every meal, the oil in them providing a substitute for animal oil and butter. (See MH 298; 7T 134.) This seems to indicate that a limited amount of fat, particularly from vegetable sources, is part of a healthy dietary.

lard, butter, or flesh meats. Skill must be united with simplicity. To do this, women must read, and then patiently reduce what they read to practice.

[Lard discarded from principle—317]

[C.T.B.H. 47] (1890) C.H. 115

594. Fruits, grains, and vegetables, prepared in a simple way, free from spice and grease of all kinds, make, with milk or cream, the most healthful diet.

(1868) 2T 63

595. Food should be prepared with simplicity, yet with a nicety which will invite the appetite. You should keep grease out of your food. It defiles any preparation of food you may make.

[C.T.B.H. 46, 47] (1890) C.H. 114

596. Many a mother sets a table that is a snare to her family. Flesh meats, butter, cheese, rich pastry, spiced foods, and condiments are freely partaken of by both old and young. These things do their work in deranging the stomach, exciting the nerves, and enfeebling the intellect. The blood-making organs cannot convert such things into good blood. The grease cooked in the food renders it difficult of digestion.

Letter 322, 1905

597. We do not think fried potatoes are healthful, for there is more or less grease or butter used in preparing them. Good baked or boiled potatoes, served with cream and a sprinkling of salt, are the most healthful. The remnants of Irish and sweet potatoes are prepared with a little cream and salt and rebaked, and not fried; they are excellent.

Letter 297, 1904

598. Let all who sit down at your table see upon it well-cooked, hygienic, palatable food. Be very careful in regard to your eating and drinking, Brother ——, so that you will not continue to have a diseased body. Eat regularly, and eat only food that is free from grease.

(1868) 2T 45

599. A plain diet, free from spices and flesh meats and grease of all kinds, would prove a blessing to you, and would

save your wife a great amount of suffering, grief, and despondency.

(1869) 2T 352

600. Grains and fruits prepared free from grease, and in as natural a condition as possible, should be the food for the tables of all who claim to be preparing for translation to heaven.

[Lard not used in White home—Appendix I:4]
[Camp meeting food to be simple and free from grease—124]
[Greasy mixtures not used in the White home—Appendix I:21]

PART III—MILK AND CREAM

Part of a Nourishing, Palatable Diet

[C.T.B.H. 47] (1890) C.H. 114, 115

601. God has furnished man with abundant means for the gratification of an unperverted appetite. He has spread before him the products of the earth,—a bountiful variety of food that is palatable to the taste, and nutritious to the system. Of these our benevolent heavenly Father says we may freely eat. Fruits, grains, and vegetables, prepared in a simple way, free from spice and grease of all kinds, make, with milk or cream, the most healthful diet. They impart nourishment to the body, and give a power of endurance and a vigor of intellect that are not produced by a stimulating diet.

(1909) 9T 162

602. Food should be prepared in such a way that it will be appetizing as well as nourishing. It should not be robbed of that which the system needs. I use some salt, and always have, because salt, instead of being deleterious, is actually essential for the blood. Vegetables should be made palatable with a little milk or cream, or something equivalent. . . .

Some, in abstaining from milk, eggs, and butter, have failed to supply the system with proper nourishment, and as a consequence have become weak and unable to work. Thus health reform is brought into disrepute. . . .

The time will come when we may have to discard some of the articles of diet we now use, such as milk and cream and eggs; but it is not necessary to bring upon ourselves perplexity by premature and extreme restrictions. Wait until the circumstances demand it, and the Lord prepares the way for it.

The Danger of Unsafe Milk

(1902) 7T 135

603. Milk, eggs, and butter should not be classed with flesh meat. In some cases the use of eggs is beneficial. The time has not come to say that the use of milk and eggs should be wholly discarded. There are poor families whose diet consists largely of bread and milk. They have little fruit, and cannot afford to purchase the nut foods. In teaching health reform, as in all other gospel work, we are to meet the people where they are. Until we can teach them how to prepare health reform foods that are palatable, nourishing, and yet inexpensive, we are not at liberty to present the most advanced propositions regarding health reform diet.

Let the diet reform be progressive. Let the people be taught how to prepare food without the use of milk or butter. Tell them that the time will soon come when there will be no safety in using eggs, milk, cream, or butter, because disease in animals is increasing in proportion to the increase of wickedness among men. The time is near when, because of the iniquity of the fallen race, the whole animal creation will groan under the diseases that curse our earth.

[Not to be wholly discarded by those especially needing milk—625]

[People to be taught how to cook without milk—807]

Letter 1, 1873

604. We have always used a little milk and some sugar. This we have never denounced, either in our writings or in our preaching. We believe cattle will become so much diseased that these things will yet be discarded, but the time has not yet come for sugar and milk to be wholly abolished from our tables.

[Use of milk and sugar together, see "Milk and Sugar," Section XX]

(1870) 2T 369

605. Animals from which milk is obtained are not always healthy. They may be diseased. A cow may be apparently

well in the morning, and die before night. Then she was diseased in the morning, and her milk was diseased, but you did not know it. The animal creation is diseased.

Union Conference Record (Australasian), July 28, 1899

606. The light given me is that it will not be very long before we shall have to give up any animal food. Even milk will have to be discarded. Disease is accumulating rapidly. The curse of God is upon the earth, because man has cursed it.

Sterilization of Milk

(1905) M.H. 302

607. If milk is used, it should be thoroughly sterilized; with this precaution, there is less danger of contracting disease from its use.

Letter 39, 1901

608. The time may come when it will not be safe to use milk. But if the cows are healthy and the milk thoroughly cooked, there is no necessity of creating a time of trouble beforehand.

A Substitute for Butter

Letter 45, 1903

609. I eat but two meals a day, and still follow the light given me thirty-five years ago. I use no meat. As for myself, I have settled the butter question. I do not use it. This question should easily be settled in every place where the purest article cannot be obtained. We have good milch cows, a Jersey and a Holstein. We use cream, and all are satisfied with this.

[Letter 331, 1904] M.M. 269

610. I cannot see the need of butter where there is abundance of fruit and of sterilized cream.

[For context see 588]

Letter 5, 1870

611. We place no butter upon our table. Our vegetables are generally cooked with milk or cream and made very palatable. . . . We think a moderate amount of milk from a healthy cow not objectionable.

[Milk and cream used in the White home—Appendix I:4, 13, 14, 16, 22]

[Use of milk and cream in the preparation of food—517, 518, 522]

[Recommended for camp meeting diet—491]

The Strictest Diet Not Best

Letter 37, 1901

612. We are to be brought into connection with the masses. Should health reform be taught them in its most extreme form, harm would be done. We ask them to leave off eating meat and drinking tea and coffee. That is well. But some say that milk also should be given up. This is a subject that needs to be carefully handled. There are poor families whose diet consists of bread and milk, and, if they can get it, a little fruit. All flesh food should be discarded, but vegetables should be made palatable with a little milk or cream or something equivalent. The poor say, when health reform is presented to them, "What shall we eat? We cannot afford to buy the nut foods." As I preach the gospel to the poor, I am instructed to tell them to eat that food which is most nourishing. I cannot say to them, "You must not eat eggs or milk or cream. You must use no butter in the preparation of food." The gospel must be preached to the poor, and the time has not yet come to prescribe the strictest diet.

The time will come when we may have to discard some of the articles of diet we now use, such as milk and cream and eggs, but my message is that you must not bring yourself to a time of trouble beforehand, and thus afflict yourself with death. Wait till the Lord prepares the way before you....

I assure you that your ideas in regard to diet for the sick are not advisable. The change is too great. While I would discard flesh meat as injurious, something less objectionable may be used, and this is found in eggs. Do not remove milk from the table or forbid its being used in the cooking of food. The milk should be procured from healthy cows, and should be sterilized. . . .

The time will come when milk cannot be used as freely as it is now used; but the present is not the time to discard it. . . .

But I wish to say that when the time comes that it is no longer safe to use milk, cream, butter, and eggs, God will reveal this. No extremes in health reform are to be advocated. The question of using milk and butter and eggs will work out its own problem. At present we have no burden on this line. Let your moderation be known unto all men.

[Health foods to take place of milk and butter—583]

God Will Provide

Letter 151, 1901

613. We see that cattle are becoming greatly diseased, the earth itself is corrupted, and we know that the time will come when it will not be best to use milk and eggs. But that time has not yet come. We know that when it does come, the Lord will provide. The question is asked, meaning much to all concerned, Will God set a table in the wilderness? I think the answer may be made, Yea, God will provide food for His people.

In all parts of the world provision will be made to supply the place of milk and eggs. And the Lord will let us know when the time comes to give up these articles. He desires all to feel that they have a gracious heavenly Father who will instruct them in all things. The Lord will give dietetic art and skill to His people in all parts of the world, teaching them how to use for the sustenance of life the products of the earth.

[Use of milk in breadmaking—496]
[Use of milk in whole-wheat rolls—503]

PART IV—OLIVES AND OLIVE OIL

(1905) M.H. 298

614. When properly prepared, olives, like nuts, supply the place of butter and flesh meats. The oil, as eaten in the olive, is far preferable to animal oil or fat. It serves as a laxative. Its use will be found beneficial to consumptives, and it is healing to an inflamed, irritated stomach.

(1902) 7T 134

615. Olives may be so prepared as to be eaten with good results at every meal. The advantages sought by the use of

butter may be obtained by the eating of properly prepared olives. The oil in the olives relieves constipation; and for consumptives, and for those who have inflamed, irritated stomachs, it is better than any drug. As a food it is better than any oil coming secondhand from animals.

Letter 14, 1901

616. The oil in olives is a remedy for constipation and kidney diseases.

Proteins

Quotations in Section XXII

Proteins

PART I—NUTS AND NUT FOODS

Part of an Adequate Diet

(1905) M.H. 296

617. GRAINS, fruits, nuts, and vegetables constitute the diet chosen for us by our Creator. These foods, prepared in as simple and natural a manner as possible, are the most healthful and nourishing. They impart a strength, a power of endurance, and a vigor of intellect, that are not afforded by a more complex and stimulating diet.

MS 27, 1906

618. In grains, fruit, vegetables, and nuts are to be found all the food elements that we need. If we will come to the Lord in simplicity of mind, He will teach us how to prepare wholesome food free from the taint of flesh meat.

[In the adequate diet—483]
[In the diet provided by God—404]
[Sanitarium patients to be taught to use—767]

Nut Foods to Be Carefully Prepared and Inexpensive

(1905) M.H. 297, 298

619. God has given us an ample variety of healthful foods, and each person should choose from it the things that experience and sound judgment prove to be best suited to his own necessities.

Nature's abundant supply of fruits, nuts, and grains is ample, and year by year the products of all lands are more generally distributed to all, by the increased facilities for transportation. . . .

Nuts and nut foods are coming largely into use to take the place of flesh meats. With nuts may be combined grains, fruits, and some roots, to make foods that are healthful and nourishing. Care should be taken, however, not to use too large a proportion of nuts. Those who realize ill effects from the use of nut foods may find the difficulty removed by attending to this precaution.

[Grains, nuts, vegetables, and fruit as substitutes for flesh food—492]

Letter 177, 1901

620. Much time should be spent in learning how to prepare nut foods. But care should be taken not to reduce the bill of fare to a few articles, using little else than the nut foods. The majority of our people cannot obtain the nut preparations; few know how to prepare them properly for use, even if they could buy them.

Letter 14, 1901

621. The foods used should correspond to the climate. Some foods suitable for one country would not do at all in another place. And the nut foods should be made as inexpensive as possible, so that they can be procured by the poor.

Proportion of Nuts to Other Ingredients

Letter 135, 1902

622. Careful attention should be given to the proper use of nut foods. Some kinds of nuts are not so wholesome as others. Do not reduce the bill of fare to a few articles composed largely of nut foods. These foods should not be used too freely. If they were used more sparingly by some, the results would be more satisfactory. As combined in large proportions with other articles in some of the recipes given, they make the food so rich that the system cannot properly assimilate it.

(1902) 7T 134

623. I have been instructed that the nut foods are often used unwisely, that too large a proportion of nuts is used, that some nuts are not as wholesome as others. Almonds are preferable to peanuts; but peanuts, in limited quantities, may be used in connection with grains to make nourishing and digestible food.

Letter 188, 1901

624. Three years ago a letter came to me saying, "I cannot eat the nut foods; my stomach cannot take care of them." Then there were several recipes presented before

me; one was that there must be other ingredients combined
with the nuts, which would harmonize with them, and not
use such a large proportion of nuts. One-tenth to one-
sixth part of nuts would be sufficient, varied according to
combinations. We tried this, and with success.

[Too large a proportion of nuts used—400, 411]
[Not all can use the nut foods—589]
[Use of nut foods in the White home—Appendix I:16]

PART II—EGGS

Use of Eggs Will Become More and More Unsafe

(1905) M.H. 320, 321

625. Those who live in new countries or in poverty-
stricken districts where fruits and nuts are scarce, should
not be urged to exclude milk and eggs from their dietary. It
is true that persons in full flesh and in whom the animal passions are strong need to avoid the use of stimulating foods.
Especially in families of children who are given to sensual
habits, eggs should not be used. But in the case of persons
whose blood-making organs are feeble,—especially if other
foods to supply the needed elements cannot be obtained,—
milk and eggs should not be wholly discarded. Great care
should be taken, however, to obtain milk from healthy
cows and eggs from healthy fowls, that are well fed and well
cared for; and the eggs should be so cooked as to be most
easily digested.

The diet reform should be progressive. As disease in
animals increases, the use of milk and eggs will become more
and more unsafe. An effort should be made to supply their
place with other things that are healthful and inexpensive.
The people everywhere should be taught how to cook without milk and eggs, so far as possible, and yet have their
food wholesome and palatable.

Not to Be Classed With Flesh Meat

(1902) 7T 135

626. Milk, eggs, and butter should not be classed with
flesh meat. In some cases the use of eggs is beneficial. The

time has not come to say that the use of milk and eggs should be wholly discarded. . . .

Let the diet reform be progressive. Let the people be taught how to prepare food without the use of milk or butter. Tell them that the time will soon come when there will be no safety in using eggs, milk, cream, or butter, because disease in animals is increasing in proportion to the increase of wickedness among men. The time is near when, because of the iniquity of the fallen race, the whole animal creation will groan under the diseases that curse our earth. God will give His people ability and tact to prepare wholesome food without these things. Let our people discard all unwholesome recipes.

Exciting to Children

(1870) 2T 362

627. You should be teaching your children. You should be instructing them how to shun the vices and corruptions of this age. Instead of this, many are studying how to get something good to eat. You place upon your tables butter, eggs, and meat, and your children partake of them. They are fed with the very things that will excite their animal passions, and then you come to meeting and ask God to bless and save your children. How high do your prayers go? You have a work to do first. When you have done all for your children which God has left for you to do, then you can with confidence claim the special help that God has promised to give you.

Properties in Eggs Are Remedial Agencies; Guard Against Extremes

Letter 37, 1901

628. Do not go to extremes in regard to the health reform. Some of our people are very careless in regard to health reform. But because some are far behind, you must not, in order to be an example to them, be an extremist. You must not deprive yourself of that class of food which makes good blood. Your devotion to true principles is leading you to submit yourself to a diet which is giving you an experience that will not recommend health reform. This

is your danger. When you see that you are becoming weak physically, it is essential for you to make changes, and at once. Put into your diet something you have left out. It is your duty to do this. Get eggs of healthy fowls. Use these eggs cooked or raw. Drop them uncooked into the best unfermented wine you can find. This will supply that which is necessary to your system. Do not for a moment suppose that it will not be right to do this. . . .

The time will come when milk cannot be used as freely as it is now used; but the present is not the time to discard it. And eggs contain properties which are remedial agencies in counteracting poisons. . . .

IN SANITARIUM DIETARY

While I would discard flesh meat as injurious, something less objectionable may be used, and this is found in eggs. Do not remove milk from the table or forbid its being used in the cooking of food. The milk used should be procured from healthy cows, and should be sterilized. . . .

But I wish to say that when the time comes that it is no longer safe to use milk, cream, butter, and eggs, God will reveal this. No extremes in health reform are to be advocated. The question of using milk and butter and eggs will work out its own problem. At present we have no burden on this line. Let your moderation be known unto all men.

[For context see 324]

Letter 37, 1904

629. When a letter came to me from Cooranbong, saying that Doctor ——— was dying, I was that night instructed that he must have a change of diet. A raw egg, taken two or three times a day, would give the nourishment that he greatly needed.

Letter 127, 1904

630. Those who come to the sanitarium must be provided with wholesome food prepared in the most palatable way consistent with right principles. We cannot expect them to live just as we live. . . . The food placed before the patients should be such as to make a favorable impression on them. Eggs can be prepared in a variety of ways.

Failure to Replace Food Elements

(1909) 9T 162

631. While warnings have been given regarding the dangers of disease through butter, and the evil of the free use of eggs by small children, yet we should not consider it a violation of principle to use eggs from hens that are well cared for and suitably fed. Eggs contain properties that are remedial agencies in counteracting certain poisons.

Some, in abstaining from milk, eggs, and butter, have failed to supply the system with proper nourishment, and as a consequence have become weak and unable to work. Thus health reform is brought into disrepute. The work that we have tried to build up solidly is confused with strange things that God has not required, and the energies of the church are crippled. But God will interfere to prevent the results of these too-strenuous ideas. The gospel is to harmonize the sinful race. It is to bring the rich and poor together at the feet of Jesus.

The time will come when we may have to discard some of the articles of diet we now use, such as milk and cream and eggs; but it is not necessary to bring upon ourselves perplexity by premature and extreme restrictions. Wait until the circumstances demand it, and the Lord prepares the way for it.

[For context see 327]

PART III—CHEESE
Unfit for Food

(1868) 2T 68

632. Cheese should never be introduced into the stomach.

(1905) M.H. 302

633. Butter is less harmful when eaten on cold bread than when used in cooking; but, as a rule, it is better to dispense with it altogether. Cheese* is still more objectionable; it is wholly unfit for food.

[C.T.B.H. 46, 47] (1890) C.H. 114

634. Many a mother sets a table that is a snare to her family. Flesh meats, butter, cheese, rich pastry, spiced

---

*Translated "Strong, sharp cheese," with Ellen White's approval, in the German-language edition.

foods, and condiments are freely partaken of by both old and young. These things do their work in deranging the stomach, exciting the nerves, and enfeebling the intellect. The blood-making organs cannot convert such things into good blood. The grease cooked in the food renders it difficult of digestion. The effect of cheese is deleterious.

(1873) 3T 136

635. Children are allowed to eat flesh meats, spices, butter, cheese, pork, rich pastry, and condiments generally. They are also allowed to eat irregularly and between meals of unhealthful food. These things do their work of deranging the stomach, exciting the nerves to unnatural action, and enfeebling the intellect. Parents do not realize that they are sowing the seed which will bring forth disease and death.

R. & H., July 19, 1870

636. When we commenced the camp meeting in Nora, Illinois, I felt it my duty to make some remarks in reference to their eating. I related the unfortunate experience of some at Marion, and told them I charged it to unnecessary preparations made for the meeting, and also eating the unnecessary preparations while at the meeting. Some brought cheese to the meeting, and ate it; although new, it was altogether too strong for the stomach, and should never be introduced into it.

Letter 40, 1893

637. It was decided that at a certain camp meeting, cheese should not be sold to those on the ground; but on coming to the ground, Doctor Kellogg found to his surprise that a large quantity of cheese had been purchased for sale at the grocery. He and some others objected to this, but those in charge of the grocery said that the cheese had been bought with the consent of Brother ———, and that they could not afford to lose the money invested in it. Upon this, Doctor Kellogg asked the price of the cheese, and bought the whole of it from them. *He had traced the matter from cause to effect, and knew that some foods generally thought to be wholesome, were very injurious.*

[Selling cheese on campground—529]

Practice of Mrs. White

Letter 1, 1873

638. In regard to cheese, I am now quite sure we have not purchased or placed on our table cheese for years. We never think of making cheese an article of diet, much less of buying it.

[Cheese not used by E. G. White—Appendix I:21]

Flesh Meats (Proteins Continued)

Quotations in Section XXIII

Flesh Meats (Proteins Continued)

Flesh Diet—An Aftermath of Sin

(1864) Sp. Gifts IV, 120, 121

639. GOD gave our first parents the food He designed that the race should eat. It was contrary to His plan to have the life of any creature taken. There was to be no death in Eden. The fruit of the trees in the garden, was the food man's wants required. God gave man no permission to eat animal food until after the flood. Everything had been destroyed upon which man could subsist, and therefore the Lord in their necessity gave Noah permission to eat of the clean animals which he had taken with him into the ark. But animal food was not the most healthful article of food for man.

The people who lived before the flood ate animal food and gratified their lusts until their cup of iniquity was full, and God cleansed the earth of its moral pollution by a flood. Then the third dreadful curse rested upon the earth. The first curse was pronounced upon the posterity of Adam and upon the earth, because of disobedience. The second curse came upon the ground after Cain slew his brother Abel. The third most dreadful curse from God came upon the earth at the flood.

After the flood the people ate largely of animal food. God saw that the ways of man were corrupt, and that he was disposed to exalt himself proudly against his Creator and to follow the inclinations of his own heart. And He permitted that long-lived race to eat animal food to shorten their sinful lives. Soon after the flood the race began to rapidly decrease in size, and in length of years.

Antediluvian Depravity

(1865) H. to L., ch. 1, p. 52

640. The inhabitants of the Old World were intemperate in eating and drinking. They would have flesh meats, although God had given them no permission to eat animal food. They ate and drank to excess, and their depraved

appetites knew no bounds. They gave themselves up to abominable idolatry. They became violent and ferocious, and so corrupt that God could bear with them no longer. Their cup of iniquity was full, and God cleansed the earth of its moral pollution by a flood. As men multiplied upon the face of the earth after the flood, they forgot God, and corrupted their ways before Him. Intemperance in every form increased to a great extent.

Israel's Failure and Spiritual Loss

(1905) M.H. 311, 312

641. The diet appointed man in the beginning did not include animal food. Not till after the flood, when every green thing on the earth had been destroyed, did man receive permission to eat flesh.

In choosing man's food in Eden, the Lord showed what was the best diet; in the choice made for Israel, He taught the same lesson. He brought the Israelites out of Egypt, and undertook their training, that they might be a people for His own possession. Through them He desired to bless and teach the world. He provided them with the food best adapted for this purpose, not flesh, but manna, "the bread of heaven." It was only because of their discontent and their murmurings for the fleshpots of Egypt that animal food was granted them, and this only for a short time. Its use brought disease and death to thousands. Yet the restriction to a nonflesh diet was never heartily accepted. It continued to be the cause of discontent and murmuring, open or secret, and it was not made permanent.

Upon their settlement in Canaan, the Israelites were permitted the use of animal food, but under careful restrictions, which tended to lessen the evil results. The use of swine's flesh was prohibited, as also of other animals and of birds and fish whose flesh was pronounced unclean. Of the meats permitted, the eating of the fat and the blood was strictly forbidden.

Only such animals could be used for food as were in good condition. No creature that was torn, that had died of itself or from which the blood had not been carefully drained, could be used as food.

By departing from the plan divinely appointed for their diet, the Israelites suffered great loss. They desired a flesh diet, and they reaped its results. They did not reach God's ideal of character or fulfill His purpose. The Lord "gave them their request, but sent leanness into their soul." They valued the earthly above the spiritual, and the sacred preeminence which was His purpose for them they did not attain.

Nonflesh Diet to Modify the Disposition

MS 38, 1898

642. The Lord plainly told His people that every blessing would come to them if they would keep His commandments, and be a peculiar people. He warned them through Moses in the wilderness, specifying that health would be the reward of obedience. The state of the mind has largely to do with the health of the body, and especially with the health of the digestive organs. As a general thing, the Lord did not provide His people with flesh meat in the desert, because He knew that the use of this diet would create disease and insubordination. In order to modify the disposition, and bring the higher powers of the mind into active exercise, He removed from them the flesh of dead animals. He gave them angels' food, manna from heaven.

Rebellion and Its Punishment

(1864) Sp. Gifts IV, 15-18

643. God continued to feed the Hebrew host with the bread rained from heaven; but they were not satisfied. Their depraved appetites craved meat, which God in His wisdom had withheld, in a great measure, from them. . . . Satan, the author of disease and misery, will approach God's people where he can have the greatest success. He has controlled the appetite in a great measure from the time of his successful experiment with Eve, in leading her to eat the forbidden fruit. He came with his temptations first to the mixed multitude, the believing Egyptians, and stirred them up to seditious murmurings. They would not be content with the

healthful food which God had provided for them. Their depraved appetites craved a greater variety, especially flesh meats.

This murmuring soon infected nearly the whole body of the people. At first, God did not gratify their lustful appetites, but caused His judgments to come upon them, and consumed the most guilty by lightning from heaven. Yet this, instead of humbling them, only seemed to increase their murmurings. When Moses heard the people weeping in the door of their tents, and complaining throughout their families, he was displeased. He presented before the Lord the difficulties of his situation, and the unsubmissive spirit of the Israelites, and the position in which God had placed him to the people,—that of a nursing father, who should make the sufferings of the people his own. . . .

The Lord directed Moses to gather before him seventy of the elders, whom he knew to be the elders of the people. They were not to be those only in advanced years, but men of dignity, sound judgment, and experience, who were qualified to be judges, or officers. "And bring them unto the tabernacle of the congregation, that they may stand there with thee. And I will come down and talk with thee there; and I will take of the spirit which is upon thee, and will put it upon them, and they shall bear the burden of the people with thee, that thou bear it not thyself alone.

"And say thou unto the people, Sanctify yourselves against tomorrow, and ye shall eat flesh; for ye have wept in the ears of the Lord. saying, Who shall give us flesh to eat? for it was well with us in Egypt; therefore, the Lord will give you flesh, and ye shall eat. Ye shall not eat one day, nor two days, nor five days, neither ten days, nor twenty days; but even a whole month, until it come out at your nostrils, and it be loathsome unto you; because that ye have despised the Lord which is among you, and have wept before Him, saying, Why came we forth out of Egypt?

"And Moses said, The people among whom I am, are six hundred thousand footmen; and Thou hast said, I will give them flesh, that they may eat a whole month. Shall the

locks and herds be slain for them, to suffice them? or shall
ll the fish of the sea be gathered together for them, to
uffice them? And the Lord said unto Moses, Is the Lord's
and waxed short? thou shalt see now whether My word
hall come to pass unto thee or not." . . .

"And there went forth a wind from the Lord, and
rought quails from the sea, and let them fall by the camp,
s it were a day's journey on this side, and as it were a day's
ourney on the other side, round about the camp, and, as it
vere, two cubits high upon the face of the earth. And the
eople stood up all that day, and all that night, and all the
ext day, and they gathered the quails. He that gathered
east gathered ten homers, and they spread them all abroad
or themselves round about the camp.

"And while the flesh was yet between their teeth, the
vrath of the Lord was kindled against the people, and the
_ord smote the people with a very great plague."

In this instance the Lord gave the people that which was
ot for their best good, because they would have it. They
vould not submit to receive from the Lord those things
vhich would prove for their good. They gave themselves
ip to seditious murmurings against Moses, and against the
_ord, because they did not receive those things which would
rove an injury to them. Their depraved appetites con-
rolled them, and God gave them flesh meats, as they desired,
nd He let them suffer the results of gratifying their lustful
ppetites. Burning fevers cut down very large numbers of
he people. Those who had been most guilty in their mur-
nurings were slain as soon as they tasted the meat for which
hey had lusted. If they had submitted to have the Lord
elect their food for them, and had been thankful and satis-
ied for food which they could eat freely of without injury,
hey would not have lost the favor of God, and then been
unished for their rebellious murmurings by great numbers
f them being slain.

God's Purpose for Israel

(1890) C.T.B.H. 118, 119

644. When God led the children of Israel out of Egypt, it
vas His purpose to establish them in the land of Canaan a

pure, happy, healthy people. Let us look at the means b
which He would accomplish this. He subjected them to
course of discipline, which, had it been cheerfully followee
would have resulted in good, both to themselves and to thei
posterity. He removed flesh food from them in a grea
measure. He had granted them flesh in answer to their clam
ors, just before reaching Sinai, but it was furnished for onl
one day. God might have provided flesh as easily as manna
but a restriction was placed upon the people for their goo
It was His purpose to supply them with food better suited t
their wants than the feverish diet to which many of ther
had been accustomed in Egypt. The perverted appetite wa
to be brought into a more healthy state, that they migl
enjoy the food originally provided for man,—the fruits o
the earth, which God gave to Adam and Eve in Eden.

Had they been willing to deny appetite in obedience t
His restrictions, feebleness and disease would have been ur
known among them. Their descendants would have pos
sessed physical and mental strength. They would have ha
clear perceptions of truth and duty, keen discrimination, an
sound judgment. But they were unwilling to submit t
God's requirements, and they failed to reach the standar
He had set for them, and to receive the blessings that migl
have been theirs. They murmured at God's restriction
and lusted after the fleshpots of Egypt. God let them hav
flesh, but it proved a curse to them.

An Ensample for Us

1 Cor. 10:6, 11

645. "Now these things were our examples, to the inter
we should not lust after evil things, as they also lusted
"Now all these things happened unto them for ensamples
and they are written for our admonition, upon whom th
ends of the world are come."

(1873) 3T 171, 172

646. The church in general at Battle Creek have not sus
tained the Institute by their example. They have not hor
ored the light of health reform by carrying it out in the

amilies. The sickness that has visited many families in
Battle Creek need not have been, if they had followed the
ight God has given them. Like ancient Israel, they have
disregarded the light, and could see no more necessity of
estricting their appetite than did ancient Israel. The children of Israel would have flesh meats, and said, as many now
ay, We shall die without meat. God gave rebellious Israel
flesh, but His curse was with it. Thousands of them died
while the meat they desired was between their teeth. We
have the example of ancient Israel, and the warning for us
not to do as they did. Their history of unbelief and rebellion
s left on record as a special warning that we should not
ollow their example of murmuring at God's requirements.
How can we pass on so indifferently, choosing our own
course, following the sight of our own eyes, and departing
farther and farther from God, as did the Hebrews? God
cannot do great things for His people because of their hard-
ess of heart and sinful unbelief.

God is no respecter of persons; but in every generation
they that fear the Lord and work righteousness are accepted
of Him; while those who are murmuring, unbelieving, and
rebellious, will not have His favor or the blessings promised
o those who love the truth and walk in it. Those who have
the light and do not follow it, but disregard the requirements
of God, will find that their blessings will be changed into
curses, and their mercies into judgments. God would have
s learn humility and obedience as we read the history of
ancient Israel, who were His chosen and peculiar people,
but who brought their own destruction by following their
own ways.

(1900) 6T 372

647. Our habits of eating and drinking show whether
we are of the world or among the number whom the Lord by
His mighty cleaver of truth has separated from the world.
These are His peculiar people, zealous of good works. God
has spoken in His word. In the case of Daniel and his three
companions, there are sermons upon health reform. God has
spoken in the history of the children of Israel, from whom
or their good He sought to withhold a flesh diet. He fed

them with bread from heaven; "man did eat angels' food.
But they encouraged their earthly appetite; and the mor
they centered their thoughts upon the fleshpots of Egypt
the more they hated the food which God gave them to kee
them in health physically, mentally, and morally. The
longed for the fleshpots, and in this they did just as many i
our own time have done.

[Further statements regarding the use of flesh meat by th
antediluvians and the Israelites—231, 233]

Back to the Original Diet

[C.T.B.H. 119] (1890) C.H. 450

648. Again and again I have been shown that God i
trying to lead us back, step by step, to His original design,–
that man should subsist upon the natural products of th
earth.

MS 115, 1903

649. Vegetables, fruits, and grains should compose ou
diet. Not an ounce of flesh meat should enter our stomach
The eating of flesh is unnatural. We are to return to God
original purpose in the creation of man.

(1905) M.H. 317

650. Is it not time that all should aim to dispense wit
flesh foods? How can those who are seeking to becom
pure, refined, and holy, that they may have the companior
ship of heavenly angels, continue to use as food anythin
that has so harmful an effect on soul and body? How ca
they take the life of God's creatures that they may consum
the flesh as a luxury? Let them, rather, return to the whole
some and delicious food given to man in the beginning, an
themselves practice, and teach their children to practic
mercy toward the dumb creatures that God has made an
has placed under our dominion.

Preparing for Translation

(1890) C.T.B.H. 119

651. Among those who are waiting for the coming of th
Lord, meat eating will eventually be done away; flesh wi

cease to form a part of their diet. We should ever keep this end in view, and endeavor to work steadily toward it. I cannot think that in the practice of flesh eating we are in harmony with the light which God has been pleased to give us. All who are connected with our health institutions especially should be educating themselves to subsist on fruits, grains, and vegetables. If we move from principle in these things, if we as Christian reformers educate our own taste, and bring our diet to God's plan, then we may exert an influence upon others in this matter, which will be pleasing to God.

[C.T.B.H. 48] (1890) C.H. 116

652. It is not the chief end of man to gratify his appetite. There are physical wants to be supplied; but because of this is it necessary that man shall be controlled by appetite? Will the people who are seeking to become holy, pure, refined, that they may be introduced into the society of heavenly angels, continue to take the life of God's creatures, and enjoy their flesh as a luxury? From what the Lord has shown me, this order of things will be changed, and God's peculiar people will exercise temperance in all things.

(1909) 9T 153, 154

653. Those who have received instruction regarding the evils of the use of flesh foods, tea, and coffee, and rich and unhealthful food preparations, and who are determined to make a covenant with God by sacrifice, will not continue to indulge their appetite for food that they know to be unhealthful. God demands that the appetite be cleansed, and that self-denial be practiced in regard to those things which are not good. This is a work that will have to be done before His people can stand before Him a perfected people.

MS 71, 1908

654. It is for their own good that the Lord counsels the remnant church to discard the use of flesh meats, tea, and coffee, and other harmful foods. There are plenty of other things on which we can subsist that are wholesome and good.

Perfecting Holiness

[R. & H., May 27, 1902] C.H. 575, 576

655. Greater reforms should be seen among the peopl
who claim to be looking for the soon appearing of Christ
Health reform is to do among our people a work which i
has not yet done. There are those who ought to be awak
to the danger of meat eating, who are still eating the flesl
of animals, thus endangering the physical, mental, and spir
itual health. Many who are now only half converted on
the question of meat eating will go from God's people to
walk no more with them.

In all our work we must obey the laws which God ha
given, that the physical and spiritual energies may work i
harmony. Men may have a form of godliness, they may
even preach the gospel, and yet be unpurified and unsancti
fied. Ministers should be strictly temperate in their eating
and drinking, lest they make crooked paths for their feet
turning the lame—those weak in the faith—out of the way
If, while proclaiming the most solemn and important mes
sage God has ever given, men war against the truth by
indulging wrong habits of eating and drinking, they take
all the force from the message they bear.

Those who indulge in meat eating, tea drinking, and
gluttony are sowing seeds for a harvest of pain and death
The unhealthful food placed in the stomach strengthens the
appetites that war against the soul, developing the lowe
propensities. A diet of flesh meat tends to develop animal
ism. A development of animalism lessens spirituality
rendering the mind incapable of understanding truth.

The word of God plainly warns us that unless we abstair
from fleshly lusts, the physical nature will be brought into
conflict with the spiritual nature. Lustful eating war
against health and peace. Thus a warfare is institute
between the higher and the lower attributes of the mar
The lower propensities, strong and active, oppress the soul
The highest interests of the being are imperiled by the
indulgence of appetites unsanctioned by Heaven.

Letter 48, 1902

656. Those who claim to believe the truth are to guard carefully the powers of body and mind, so that God and His cause will not be in any way dishonored by their words or actions. The habits and practices are to be brought into subjection to the will of God. We are to give careful attention to our diet. It has been clearly presented to me that God's people are to take a firm stand against meat eating. Would God for thirty years give His people the message that if they desire to have pure blood and clear minds, they must give up the use of flesh meat, if He did not want them to heed this message? By the use of flesh meats the animal nature is strengthened and the spiritual nature weakened.

(1905) M.H. 315

657. The moral evils of a flesh diet are not less marked than are the physical ills. Flesh food is injurious to health, and whatever affects the body has a corresponding effect on the mind and the soul. Think of the cruelty to animals that meat eating involves, and its effect on those who inflict and those who behold it. How it destroys the tenderness with which we should regard these creatures of God!

MS 22, 1887

658. The common use of the flesh of dead animals has had a deteriorating influence upon the morals, as well as the physical constitution. Ill health in a variety of forms, if effect could be traced to the cause, would reveal the sure result of flesh eating.

Pacific Union Recorder, Oct. 9, 1902

659. Those who use flesh meat disregard all the warnings that God has given concerning this question. They have no evidence that they are walking in safe paths. They have not the slightest excuse for eating the flesh of dead animals. God's curse is resting upon the animal creation. Many times when meat is eaten, it decays in the stomach, and creates disease. Cancers, tumors, and pulmonary diseases are largely caused by meat eating.

MS 3, 1897

660. Oh, if every one could discern these matters as they have been presented to me, those who are now so careless, so indifferent in regard to their character building; those who plead for indulgence in a flesh meat diet, would never open their lips in justification of an appetite for the flesh of dead animals. Such a diet contaminates the blood in their veins and stimulates the lower animal passions. It enfeebles keen perception and vigor of thought to the understanding of God and the truth, and a knowledge of themselves.

Meat Eating Especially Dangerous Now

(1905) M.H. 313

661. Flesh was never the best food; but its use is now doubly objectionable, since disease in animals is so rapidly increasing.

(1900) 7T 124

662. Animals are becoming more and more diseased, and it will not be long until animal food will be discarded by many besides Seventh-day Adventists. Foods that are healthful and life sustaining are to be prepared, so that men and women will not need to eat meat.

MS 133, 1902

663. When will those who know the truth take their stand on the side of right principles for time and for eternity? When will they be true to the principles of health reform? When will they learn that it is dangerous to use flesh meat? I am instructed to say that if ever meat eating were safe, it is not safe now.

Union Conference Record (Australasian), July 28, 1899

664. The light given me is that it will not be very long before we shall have to give up using any animal food. Even milk will have to be discarded. Disease is accumulating rapidly. The curse of God is upon the earth, because man has cursed it. The habits and practices of men have brought the earth into such a condition that some other food than animal

food must be substituted for the human family. We do not need flesh food at all. God can give us something else.

(1870) 2T 404, 405

665. Could you know just the nature of the meat you eat, could you see the animals when living from which the flesh is taken when dead, you would turn with loathing from your flesh meats. The very animals whose flesh you eat, are frequently so diseased that, if left alone, they would die of themselves; but while the breath of life is in them, they are killed and brought to market. You take directly into your system humors and poison of the worst kind, and yet you realize it not.

Animal Suffering and Its Effects

(1905) M.H. 314

666. Often animals are taken to market and sold for food, when they are so diseased that their owners fear to keep them longer. And some of the processes of fattening them for market produce disease. Shut away from the light and pure air, breathing the atmosphere of filthy stables, perhaps fattening on decaying food, the entire body soon becomes contaminated with foul matter.

Animals are often transported long distances and subjected to great suffering in reaching a market. Taken from the green pastures and traveling for weary miles over the hot, dusty roads, or crowded into filthy cars, feverish and exhausted, often for many hours deprived of food and water, the poor creatures are driven to their death, that human beings may feast on the carcasses.

(1864) Sp. Gifts IV, 147, 148

667. Many die of disease caused wholly by meat eating; yet the world does not seem to be the wiser. Animals are frequently killed that have been driven quite a distance for the slaughter. Their blood has become heated. They are full of flesh, and have been deprived of healthy exercise, and when they have to travel far, they become surfeited and exhausted, and in that condition are killed for market. Their blood is highly inflamed, and those who eat of their meat, eat

poison. Some are not immediately affected, while others are attacked with severe pain, and die from fever, cholera, or some unknown disease.

Very many animals are sold for the city market known to be diseased by those who have sold them, and those who buy them are not always ignorant of the matter. Especially in larger cities this is practiced to a great extent, and meat eaters know not that they are eating diseased animals.

Some animals that are brought to the slaughter seem to realize by instinct what is to take place, and they become furious, and literally mad. They are killed while in that state, and their flesh is prepared for market. Their meat is poison, and has produced, in those who have eaten it, cramps, convulsions, apoplexy, and sudden death. Yet the cause of all this suffering is not attributed to the meat.

Some animals are inhumanly treated while being brought to the slaughter. They are literally tortured, and after they have endured many hours of extreme suffering, are butchered. Swine have been prepared for market even while the plague was upon them, and their poisonous flesh has spread contagious diseases, and great mortality has followed.

Physical Results of a Flesh Diet Increase Liability to Disease and Sudden Death

(1868) 2T 64

668. The liability to take disease is increased tenfold by meat eating.

Letter 83, 1901

669. Worldly physicians cannot account for the rapid increase of disease among the human family. But we know that much of this suffering is caused by the eating of dead flesh.

(1896) E. from U.T. 8

670. The animals are diseased, and by partaking of their flesh, we plant the seeds of disease in our own tissue and blood. Then when exposed to the changes in a malarious atmosphere, these are more sensibly felt; also when we are

exposed to prevailing epidemics and contagious diseases, the system is not in a condition to resist the disease.

(1868) 2T 61

671. You have flesh, but it is not good material. You are worse off for this amount of flesh. If you should each come down to a more spare diet, which would take from you twenty-five or thirty pounds of your gross flesh, you would be much less liable to disease. The eating of flesh meats has made a poor quality of blood and flesh. Your systems are in a state of inflammation, prepared to take on disease. You are liable to acute attacks of disease, and to sudden death, because you do not possess the strength of constitution to rally and resist disease. There will come a time when the strength and health you have flattered yourself you possessed will prove to be weakness.

Diseased Blood

(1896) E. from U.T. 4

672. I have felt urged by the Spirit of God to set before several the fact that their suffering and ill health was caused by a disregard of the light given them upon health reform. I have shown them that their meat diet, which was supposed to be essential, was not necessary, and that, as they were composed of what they ate, brain, bone, and muscle were in an unwholesome condition, because they lived on the flesh of dead animals; that their blood was being corrupted by this improper diet; that the flesh which they ate was diseased, and their entire system was becoming gross and corrupted.

(1870) 2T 368

673. Flesh meats will depreciate the blood. Cook meat with spices, and eat it with rich cakes and pies, and you have a bad quality of blood. The system is too heavily taxed in disposing of this kind of food. The mince pies and the pickles, which should never find a place in any human stomach, will give a miserable quality of blood. And a poor quality of food, cooked in an improper manner, and insufficient in quantity, cannot make good blood. Flesh meats and rich food, and an impoverished diet, will produce the same results.

(1896) E. from U.T. 7

674. Cancers, tumors, and all inflammatory diseases are largely caused by meat eating.

From the light God has given me, the prevalence of cancer and tumors is largely due to gross living on dead flesh.

Cancer, Tuberculosis, Tumors

MS 3, 1897

675. The meat diet is the serious question. Shall human beings live on the flesh of dead animals? The answer, from the light that God has given is, No, decidedly No. Health reform institutions should educate on this question. Physicians who claim to understand the human organism ought not to encourage their patients to subsist on the flesh of dead animals. They should point out the increase of disease in the animal kingdom. The testimony of examiners is that very few animals are free from disease, and that the practice of eating largely of meat is contracting diseases of all kinds,— cancers, tumors, scrofula, tuberculosis, and numbers of other like affections.

(1905) M.H. 313

676. Those who use flesh foods little know what they are eating. Often if they could see the animals when living and know the quality of the meat they eat, they would turn from it with loathing. People are continually eating flesh that is filled with tuberculosis and cancerous germs. Tuberculosis, cancer, and other fatal diseases are thus communicated.

(1875) 3T 563

677. The tables of many professed Christian women are daily set with a variety of dishes which irritate the stomach and produce a feverish condition of the system. Flesh meats constitute the principle article of food upon the tables of some families, until their blood is filled with cancerous and scrofulous humors. Their bodies are composed of what they eat. But when suffering and disease come upon them, it is considered an affliction of Providence.

Decreases Mental Vigor

[C.T.B.H. 47] (1890) C.H. 115

678. Those who use flesh meats freely, do not always have an unclouded brain and an active intellect, because the use of the flesh of animals tends to cause a grossness of body, and to benumb the finer sensibilities of the mind.

General Conference Bulletin, April 12, 1901

679. God wants the perceptive faculties of His people to be clear and capable of hard work. But if you are living on a flesh diet, you need not expect that your mind will be fruitful. The thoughts must be cleansed; then the blessing of God will rest upon His people.

(1868) 2T 62, 63

680. It is impossible for those who make free use of flesh meats to have an unclouded brain and an active intellect.

(1896) E. from U.T. 4

681. There is an alarming lethargy shown on the subject of unconscious sensualism. It is customary to eat the flesh of dead animals. This stimulates the lower passions of the human organism.

E. from U.T. 7

682. A meat diet changes the disposition and strengthens animalism. We are composed of what we eat, and eating much flesh will diminish intellectual activity. Students would accomplish much more in their studies if they never tasted meat. When the animal part of the human agent is strengthened by meat eating, the intellectual powers diminish proportionately. A religious life can be more successfully gained and maintained if meat is discarded, for this diet stimulates into intense activity lustful propensities, and enfeebles the moral and spiritual nature. "The flesh warreth against the spirit, and the spirit against the flesh."

Strengthens the Baser Passions

(1869) 2T 352

683. If ever there was a time when the diet should be of the most simple kind, it is now. Meat should not be placed

before our children. Its influence is to excite and strengthen the lower passions, and has a tendency to deaden the moral powers.

MS 50, 1904

684. I was instructed that the use of flesh meat has a tendency to animalize the nature, and to rob men and women of the love and sympathy which they should feel for every one. We are built up from that which we eat, and those whose diet is largely composed of animal food are brought into a condition where they allow the lower passions to assume control of the high powers of the being. . . .

We do not mark out any precise line to be followed in diet. There are many kinds of wholesome food. But we do say that flesh meat is not the right food for God's people. It animalizes human beings. In a country such as this, where there are fruits, grains, and nuts in abundance, how can one think that he must eat the flesh of dead animals?

Letter 200, 1903

685. If things were as they should be in the households that make up our churches, we might do double service for the Lord. The light given me is that a most decided message must be borne in regard to health reform. Those who use flesh meat strengthen the lower propensities and prepare the way for disease to fasten upon them.

(1868) 2T 60, 61

686. Your family have partaken largely of flesh meats, and the animal propensities have been strengthened, while the intellectual have been weakened. We are composed of what we eat, and if we subsist largely upon the flesh of dead animals, we shall partake of their nature. You have encouraged the grosser part of your organization, while the more refined has been weakened.

General Conference Bulletin, April 12, 1901

687. We want the pervading truth of God's word to get hold of every one of our people before this conference is over. We want them to understand that the flesh of animals is not the proper food for them to eat. Such a diet cultivates the animal passions in them and in their children. God wants us

to educate our children in right habits of eating, dressing, and working. He wants us to do what we can to repair the broken-down machinery.

[Effect on children of meat and rich foods—348, 350, 356, 357, 361, 578, 621, 711]

The Safest Course

(1868) 2T 64

688. The intellectual, the moral, and the physical powers are depreciated by the habitual use of flesh meats. Meat eating deranges the system, beclouds the intellect, and blunts the moral sensibilities. We say to you, dear brother and sister, your safest course is to let meat alone.

The Cause Not Recognized

(1905) M.H. 315

689. The effects of a flesh diet may not be immediately realized; but this is no evidence that it is not harmful. Few can be made to believe that it is the meat they have eaten which has poisoned their blood and caused their suffering.

(1896) E. from U.T. 8

690. I have the subject presented to me in different aspects. The mortality caused by meat eating is not discerned; if it were, we would hear no more arguments and excuses in favor of the indulgence of the appetite for dead flesh. We have plenty of good things to satisfy hunger without bringing corpses upon our table to compose our bill of fare.

[C.T.B.H. 48] (1890) C.H. 115

691. Many die of diseases wholly due to meat eating, when the real cause is scarcely suspected by themselves or others. Some do not immediately feel its effects, but this is no evidence that it does not hurt them. It may be doing its work surely upon the system, yet for the time being the victim may realize nothing of it.

(1868) 2T 61

692. You have repeatedly said in defense of your indulgence of meat eating, "However injurious it may be to

others, it does not injure me, for I have used it all my life."
But you know not how well you might have been if you had
abstained from the use of flesh meats.

The Swine Especially Condemned

(1868) 2T 96

693. God has given you light and knowledge, which you
have professed to believe came direct from Him, instructing
you to deny appetite. You know that the use of swine's flesh
is contrary to His express command, given not because He
wished to especially show His authority, but because it
would be injurious to those who should eat it. Its use would
cause the blood to become impure, so that scrofula and other
humors would corrupt the system, and the whole organism
would suffer. Especially would the fine, sensitive nerves of
the brain become enfeebled and so beclouded that sacred
things would not be discerned, but be placed upon the low
level with common things.

(1905) M.H. 313, 314

694. The tissues of the swine swarm with parasites. Of
the swine, God said, "It is unclean unto you; ye shall not eat
of their flesh, nor touch their dead carcass." This command
was given because swine's flesh is unfit for food. Swine are
scavengers, and this is the only use they were intended to
serve. Never, under any circumstances, was their flesh to be
eaten by human beings.

(1865) H. to L., ch. 1, p. 58

695. Pork, although one of the most common articles of
diet, is one of the most injurious. God did not prohibit the
Hebrews from eating swine's flesh merely to show His
authority, but because it was not a proper article of food for
man. It would fill the system with scrofula, and especially in
that warm climate produced leprosy, and disease of various
kinds. Its influence upon the system in that climate was far
more injurious than in a colder climate. But God never designed the swine to be eaten under any circumstances. The
heathen used pork as an article of food, and American people
have used pork freely as an important article of diet. Swine's

flesh would not be palatable to the taste in its natural state. It is made agreeable to the appetite by high seasoning, which makes a very bad thing worse. Swine's flesh above all other flesh meats, produces a bad state of the blood. Those who eat freely of pork can but be diseased. Those who have much outdoor exercise do not realize the bad effects of pork eating, as those do whose life is mostly indoors, and whose habits are sedentary, and whose labor is mental.

But it is not the physical health alone which is injured by pork eating. The mind is affected, and the finer sensibilities are blunted by the use of this gross article of food. It is impossible for the flesh of any living creatures to be healthy when filth is their natural element, and when they will feed upon every detestable thing. The flesh of swine is composed of what they eat. If human beings eat their flesh, their blood and their flesh will be corrupted by impurities conveyed to them through the swine.

The eating of pork has produced scrofula, leprosy, and cancerous humors. Pork eating is still causing the most intense suffering to the human race.

[Daniel's attitude toward swine's flesh—34]

Animal Fat and Blood

(1868) 2T 61

696. As a family, you are far from being free from disease. You have used the fat of animals which God in His word expressly forbids: "It shall be a perpetual statute for your generations throughout all your dwellings, that ye eat neither fat nor blood." "Moreover, ye shall eat no manner of blood, whether it be of fowl or of beast, in any of your dwellings. Whatsoever soul it be that eateth any manner of blood, even that soul shall be cut off from his people."

Letter 102, 1896

697. The meat is served reeking with fat, because it suits the perverted taste. Both the blood and the fat of animals are consumed as a luxury. But the Lord gave special directions that these should not be eaten. Why? Because their use would make a diseased current of blood in the human

system. The disregard for the Lord's special directions has brought a variety of difficulties and diseases upon human beings. . . . If they introduce into their systems that which cannot make good flesh and blood, they must endure the results of their disregard of God's word.

Fish Often Contaminated

(1905) M.H. 314, 315

698. In many places fish become so contaminated by the filth on which they feed as to be a cause of disease. This is especially the case where the fish come in contact with the sewage of large cities. The fish that are fed on the contents of the drains may pass into distant waters, and may be caught where the water is pure and fresh. Thus when used as food they bring disease and death on those who do not suspect the danger.

Recognition of Emergency Conditions

(1890) C.T.B.H. 117, 118

699. Where plenty of good milk and fruit can be obtained there is rarely any excuse for eating animal food; it is not necessary to take the life of any of God's creatures to supply our ordinary needs. In certain cases of illness or exhaustion it may be thought best to use some meat, but great care should be taken to secure the flesh of healthy animals. It has come to be a very serious question whether it is safe to use flesh food at all in this age of the world. It would be better never to eat meat than to use the flesh of animals that are not healthy. When I could not obtain the food I needed, I have sometimes eaten a little meat; but I am becoming more and more afraid of it.

[Ellen G. White at times compelled to eat a little meat— Appendix I:10]

Y.I., May 31, 1894

700. Some honestly think that a proper dietary consists chiefly of porridge. To eat largely of porridge would not ensure health to the digestive organs; for it is too much like liquid. Encourage the eating of fruit and vegetables and bread. A meat diet is not the most wholesome of diets, and

yet I would not take the position that meat should be discarded by every one. Those who have feeble digestive organs can often use meat, when they cannot eat vegetables, fruit, or porridge. If we would preserve the best health, we should avoid eating vegetables and fruit at the same meal. If the stomach is feeble, there will be distress, the brain will be confused, and unable to put forth mental effort. Have fruit at one meal and vegetables at the next. . . .

Sweet cakes, sweet puddings, and custards will disorder the digestive organs; and why should we tempt those who surround the table by placing such articles before them? The more largely flesh composes the diet of teachers and pupils, the less susceptible will be the mind to comprehend spiritual things. The animal propensities are strengthened, and the fine sensibilities of the mind are blunted. Diligent study is not the principal cause of the breaking down of the mental powers. The main cause is improper diet, irregular meals, and a lack of physical exercise. Irregular hours for eating and sleeping sap the brain forces.

[Not prepared in 1884 to do away entirely with meat eating in our institutions, although the step would be eventually taken —720]

[Undiseased flesh meat preferable to free use of milk and sugar—527, 533]

[Physicians to educate away from, but not to make prescriptions forbidding use of flesh meat—434, 438]

[Possible unwise changes from flesh diet of those dying of consumption—435]

[Flesh foods not to be condemned when adequate nonflesh diet is not available—796]

[Flesh food not the right food for God's people in countries where fruits, grains, and nuts are available in abundance—719]

[Flesh served to patients in sanitariums in their rooms—437]

A Nonflesh Diet Adequate

R. & H., May 8, 1883

701. Meat is not essential for health or strength, else the Lord made a mistake when He provided food for Adam and Eve before their fall. All the elements of nutrition are contained in the fruits, vegetables, and grains.

(1905) M.H. 316

702. It is a mistake to suppose that muscular strength depends on the use of animal food. The needs of the system can be better supplied, and more vigorous health can be enjoyed, without its use. The grains, with fruits, nuts, and vegetables, contain all the nutritive properties necessary to make good blood. These elements are not so well or so fully supplied by a flesh diet. Had the use of flesh been essential to health and strength, animal food would have been included in the diet appointed man in the beginning.

[Meat not advised in the case of impoverished diet—319]

Why Use Secondhand Food?

Letter 72, 1896

703. The diet of the animals is vegetables and grains. Must the vegetables be animalized, must they be incorporated into the system of animals, before we get them? Must we obtain our vegetable diet by eating the flesh of dead creatures? God provided fruit in its natural state for our first parents. He gave to Adam charge of the garden, to dress it, and to care for it, saying, "To you it shall be for meat." One animal was not to destroy another animal for food.

(1905) M.H. 313

704. Those who eat flesh are but eating grains and vegetables at second hand; for the animal receives from these things the nutrition that produces growth. The life that was in the grains and vegetables passes into the eater. We receive it by eating the flesh of the animal. How much better to get it direct by eating the food that God provided for our use!

Meat a Typical Stimulant

(1905) M.H. 316

705. When the use of flesh food is discontinued, there is often a sense of weakness, a lack of vigor. Many urge this as evidence that flesh food is essential; but it is because foods of this class are stimulating, because they fever the blood and excite the nerves, that they are so missed. Some will find it

as difficult to leave off flesh eating as it is for the drunkard to give up his dram; but they will be the better for the change.

[See also 61]

(1903) Ed. 203

706. Flesh food also is harmful. Its naturally stimulating effect should be a sufficient argument against its use; and the almost universally diseased condition of animals makes it doubly objectionable. It tends to irritate the nerves and to excite the passions, thus giving the balance of power to the lower propensities.

Letter 73a, 1896

707. I was somewhat surprised at your argument as to why a meat-eating diet kept you in strength, for, if you put yourself out of the question, your reason will teach you that a meat diet is not of as much advantage as you suppose. You know how you would answer a tobacco devotee if he urged, as a plea for the use of tobacco, the arguments you have advanced as a reason why you should continue the use of the flesh of dead animals as food.

The weakness you experience without the use of meat is one of the strongest arguments I could present to you as a reason why you should discontinue its use. Those who eat meat feel stimulated after eating this food, and they suppose they are made stronger. After one discontinues the use of meat, he may for a time feel a weakness, but when his system is cleansed from the effect of this diet, he no longer feels the weakness, and will cease to wish for that which he has pleaded for as essential to his strength.

[Faintness experienced by E. G. White when on heavy meat diet—Appendix I:4, 5, 10]
[Struggle of E. G. White in changing from meat diet—Appendix I:4, 5]

Provide Substitutes

(1905) M.H. 316, 317

708. When flesh is discarded, its place should be supplied with a variety of grains, nuts, vegetables, and fruits, that will be both nourishing and appetizing. This is especially necessary in the case of those who are weak, or who are

taxed with continuous labor. In some countries, where poverty abounds, flesh is the cheapest food. Under these circumstances, the change will be made with greater difficulty; but it can be effected. We should, however, consider the situation of the people and the power of lifelong habit, and should be careful not to urge even right ideas unduly. None should be urged to make the change abruptly. The place of meat should be supplied with wholesome foods that are inexpensive. In this matter very much depends on the cook. With care and skill, dishes may be prepared that will be both nutritious and appetizing, and will, to a great degree, take the place of flesh food.

In all cases, educate the conscience, enlist the will, supply good, wholesome food, and the change will be readily made, and the demand for flesh will soon cease.

Letter 60a, 1896

709. The proper cooking of foods is a most important accomplishment. Especially where meat is not made a principal article of food is good cooking an essential requirement. Something must be prepared to take the place of meat, and these substitutes for meat must be well prepared, so that meat will not be desired.

[Make changes understandingly—320, 380]
[Adequate diet needed when leaving off meat—320]
[God will give skill in preparing health foods to take the place of flesh meats—376, 400, 401, 404]
[Diet of fruits, grains, nuts, and vegetables to replace meat—472, 483, 484, 513]

Illogical Excuses

(1870) 2T 486, 487

710. When Satan takes possession of the mind, how soon the light and instruction that the Lord has graciously given, fade away, and have no force! How many frame excuses and make necessities which have no existence, to bear them up in their course of wrong, in setting aside the light and trampling it underfoot. I speak with assurance. The greatest objection to health reform is that this people do not live it out; and yet they will gravely say they cannot live the health reform and preserve their strength.

We find in every such instance a good reason why they cannot live out the health reform. They do not live it out, and have never followed it strictly, therefore they cannot be benefited by it. Some fall into the error that because they discard meat, they have no need to supply its place with the best fruits and vegetables, prepared in their most natural state, free from grease and spices. If they would only skillfully arrange the bounties with which the Creator has surrounded them, parents and children with a clear conscience unitedly engaging in the work, they would enjoy simple food, and would then be able to speak understandingly of health reform. Those who have not been converted to health reform, and have never fully adopted it, are not judges of its benefits. Those who digress occasionally to gratify the taste in eating a fattened turkey or other flesh meats, pervert their appetites, and are not the ones to judge the benefits of the system of health reform. They are controlled by taste, not by principle.

Earnest Appeals for Reform

MS 133, 1902

711. Many parents act as if they were bereft of reason. They are in a state of lethargy, palsied by the indulgence of perverted appetite and debasing passion. Our ministers, who know the truth, should arouse the people from their paralyzed condition, and lead them to put away those things that create an appetite for flesh meat. If they neglect to reform, they will lose spiritual power, and become more and more debased by sinful indulgence. Habits that disgust the heavenly universe, habits that degrade human beings lower than the beasts, are practiced in many homes. Let all those who know the truth, say, "Flee fleshly lusts that war against the soul."

Let not any of our ministers set an evil example in the eating of flesh meat. Let them and their families live up to the light of health reform. Let not our ministers animalize their own nature and the nature of their children. Children whose desires have not been restrained, are tempted not only to indulge in the common habits of intemperance, but to give loose rein to their lower passions, and to disregard

purity and virtue. These are led on by Satan not only to
corrupt their own bodies, but to whisper their evil communications to others. If parents are blinded by sin, they
will often fail of discerning these things.

To parents who are living in the cities, the Lord is
sending the warning cry, Gather your children into your
own houses; gather them away from those who are disregarding the commandments of God, who are teaching and
practicing evil. Get out of the cities as fast as possible.

Parents can secure small homes in the country, with
land for cultivation, where they can have orchards and
where they can raise vegetables and small fruits to take
the place of flesh meat, which is so corrupting to the life-
blood coursing through the veins.

Strength to Resist Through Fasting and Prayer

Letter 73, 1896

712. If our appetites clamor for the flesh of dead animals, it is a necessity to fast and pray for the Lord to give
His grace to deny fleshly lusts which war against the soul.

[Fasting beneficial in changing from a diet of flesh meat and
rich foods—312]

When Prayer for Healing Is Inconsistent

Letter 200, 1903

713. There are those among Seventh-day Adventists
who will not heed the light given them in regard to this
matter. They make flesh meat a part of their diet. Disease
comes upon them. Sick and suffering as a result of their
own wrong course, they ask for the prayers of the servants
of God. But how can the Lord work in their behalf when
they are not willing to do His will, when they refuse to heed
His instruction in regard to health reform?

For thirty years the light on health reform has been
coming to the people of God, but many have made it a subject of jest. They have continued to use tea, coffee, spices,
and flesh meat. Their bodies are full of disease. How can
we, I ask, present such ones to the Lord for healing?

(Written 1884) E. from U.T. 2

714. Hot biscuits and flesh meats are entirely out of harmony with health reform principles. If we would allow reason to take the place of impulse and love of sensual indulgence, we should not taste of the flesh of dead animals. What is more repulsive to the sense of smell than a shop where flesh meats are kept for sale? The smell of the raw flesh is offensive to all whose senses have not been depraved by culture of the unnatural appetites. What more unpleasant sight to a reflective mind than the beasts slain to be devoured? If the light God has given in regard to health reform is disregarded, He will not work a miracle to keep in health those who pursue a course to make themselves sick.

Leaders in Reform

Letter 48, 1902

715. While we do not make the use of flesh meat a test, while we do not want to force any one to give up its use, yet it is our duty to request that no minister of the conference shall make light of or oppose the message of reform on this point. If, in the face of the light God has given concerning the effect of meat eating on the system, you will still continue to eat meat, you must bear the consequences. But do not take a position before the people that will permit them to think that it is not necessary to call for a reform in regard to meat eating; because the Lord is calling for a reform. The Lord has given us the work of proclaiming the message of health reform, and if you cannot step forward in the ranks of those who are giving this message you are not to make this prominent. In counterworking the efforts of your fellow laborers, who are teaching health reform, you are out of order, working on the wrong side.

[Work of health reform will go forward; beware of opposing it—42]

Pacific Union Recorder, Oct. 9, 1902

716. As God's messengers, shall we not bear a decided testimony against the indulgence of perverted appetite? ... God has provided an abundance of fruits and grains, which may be healthfully prepared and used in proper quantities.

Why, then, do men continue to choose flesh meats? Can we possibly have confidence in ministers who at tables where flesh is served join with others in eating it? . . .

"Ye shall diligently keep the commandments of the Lord your God." Every one who transgresses the laws of health will surely be visited with God's displeasure. Oh, how much of the Holy Spirit we might have day by day, if we would walk circumspectly, denying self, and practicing the virtues of Christ's character.

MS 113, 1901

717. Let our ministers and canvassers step under the banners of strict temperance. Never be ashamed to say, "No, thank you; I do not eat meat. I have conscientious scruples against eating the flesh of dead animals." If tea is offered, refuse it, giving your reason for so doing. Explain that it is harmful, and though stimulating for a time, the stimulus soon wears off, and a corresponding depression is felt.

Letter 135, 1902

718. Concerning flesh meat we can all say, Let it alone. And all should bear clear testimony against tea and coffee, never using them. They are narcotics, injurious alike to the brain and to the other organs of the body. The time has not yet come when I can say that the use of milk and eggs should be wholly discontinued. Milk and eggs should not be classed with flesh meats. In some ailments the use of eggs is very beneficial.

Let the members of our churches deny every selfish appetite. Every penny expended for tea, coffee, and flesh meat is worse than wasted; for these things hinder the best development of the physical, mental, and spiritual powers.

[Flesh meat not served in White home or used by E. G. White —Appendix I:4, 5, 8, 10, 14, 15, 16, 17, 18, 21, 23]

[Flesh meat banished from E. G. White table—Appendix I:12, 13]

A Summary

(1909) 9T 156-160

719. If we could be benefited by indulging the desire for flesh foods, I would not make this appeal to you; but I know

we cannot. Flesh foods are injurious to the physical well-being, and we should learn to do without them. Those who are in a position where it is possible to secure a vegetarian diet, but who choose to follow their own preferences in this matter, eating and drinking as they please, will gradually grow careless of the instruction the Lord has given regarding other phases of the present truth, and will lose their perception of what is truth; they will surely reap as they have sown.

I have been instructed that the students in our schools are not to be served with flesh foods or with food preparations that are known to be unhealthful. Nothing that will serve to encourage a desire for stimulants should be placed on the tables. I appeal to old and young and to middle-aged. Deny your appetite of those things that are doing you injury. Serve the Lord by sacrifice.

Let the children have an intelligent part in this work. We are all members of the Lord's family, and the Lord would have His children, young and old, determine to deny appetite, and to save the means needed for the building of meetinghouses and the support of missionaries.

I am instructed to say to parents: Place yourselves, soul and spirit, on the Lord's side of this question. We need ever to bear in mind that in these days of probation we are on trial before the Lord of the universe. Will you not give up indulgences that are doing you injury? Words of profession are cheap; let your acts of self-denial testify that you will be obedient to the demands that God makes of His peculiar people. Then put into the treasury a portion of the means you save by your acts of self-denial, and there will be that with which to carry on the work of God.

There are many who feel that they cannot get along without flesh foods; but if these would place themselves on the Lord's side, resolutely resolved to walk in the way of His guidance, they would receive strength and wisdom as did Daniel and his fellows. They would find that the Lord would give them sound judgment. Many would be surprised to see how much could be saved for the cause of God by acts of self-denial. The small sums saved by deeds of sacrifice will do more for the upbuilding of the cause of God than larger gifts will accomplish that have not called for denial of self.

Seventh-day Adventists are handling momentous truths. More than forty years ago * the Lord gave us special light on health reform, but how are we walking in that light? How many have refused to live in harmony with the counsels of God! As a people we should make advancement proportionate to the light received. It is our duty to understand and respect the principles of health reform. On the subject of temperance we should be in advance of all other people; and yet there are among us well-instructed members of the church, and even ministers of the gospel, who have little respect for the light that God has given upon this subject. They eat as they please, and work as they please. . . .

We do not mark out any precise line to be followed in diet; but we do say that in countries where there are fruits, grains, and nuts in abundance, flesh food is not the right food for God's people. I have been instructed that flesh food has a tendency to animalize the nature, to rob men and women of that love and sympathy which they should feel for every one, and to give the lower passions control over the higher powers of the being. If meat eating were ever healthful, it is not safe now. Cancers, tumors, and pulmonary diseases are largely caused by meat eating.

We are not to make the use of flesh food a test of fellowship, but we should consider the influence that professed believers who use flesh foods have over others. As God's messengers, shall we not say to the people, "Whether therefore ye eat, or drink, or whatsoever ye do, do all to the glory of God'? 1 Cor. 10:31. Shall we not bear a decided testimony against the indulgence of perverted appetite? Will any who are ministers of the gospel, proclaiming the most solemn truth ever given to mortals, set an example in returning to the fleshpots of Egypt? Will those who are supported by the tithe from God's storehouse permit themselves by self-indulgence to poison the life-giving current flowing through their veins? Will they disregard the light and

* Written in 1909.

warnings that God has given them? The health of the body is to be regarded as essential for growth in grace and the acquirement of an even temper. If the stomach is not properly cared for, the formation of an upright, moral character will be hindered. The brain and nerves are in sympathy with the stomach. Erroneous eating and drinking result in erroneous thinking and acting.

All are now being tested and proved. We have been baptized into Christ, and if we will act our part by separating from everything that would drag us down and make us what we ought not to be, there will be given us strength to grow up into Christ, who is our living head, and we shall see the salvation of God.

PROGRESSIVE DIETETIC REFORM IN SEVENTH-DAY ADVENTIST INSTITUTIONS

[NOTE: It is a matter of historical record that Seventh-day Adventist health institutions in their early days served flesh meat in a greater or lesser degree to patients and helpers. The reform in this phase of healthful living was progressive. In the older institutions, after a long struggle, flesh meat was eventually discarded from all tables. In the case of the Battle Creek Sanitarium this step was taken in 1898, largely in response to counsel from Mrs. White's pen appearing in this chapter (722). At the St. Helena Sanitarium the change took place in 1903. By this time education in the matter of a nonflesh diet had spread widely, and flesh was left out of the dietary of the guests with less difficulty than if it had been excluded at an earlier date. It was a joy to the managers of the older institutions to know that in the new plants opened at about this time, flesh food was not served to the patients.

The counsel on the subject of flesh meat is not complete without the picture of the struggle for its nonuse in our institutions as brought to view in several communications from Mrs. White, and the instruction urging a progressive reform in diet. It is essential that the reader keep these facts and the time of writing of the several statements in mind as he gives study to this phase of the flesh-meat question.—COMPILERS.]

Appeals for a Nonflesh Diet in Our Early Medical Institutions (1884)

Letter 3, 1884

720. I have arisen this morning at four o'clock to write you a few lines. I have been thinking much of late how the

institution over which you preside could be made all God would have it, and I have a few thoughts to suggest.

We are health reformers, seeking to come back, as far as possible, to the Lord's original plan of temperance. Temperance does not consist merely in abstaining from intoxicating liquors and tobacco; it extends farther than this. It must regulate what we eat.

You are all acquainted with the light upon the subject of health reform. But when I visit the Retreat, I see that there is a very marked departure from health reform on the matter of meat eating, and I am convinced that there must be a change, and at once. Your diet is largely composed of meat. God is not leading in this direction; the enemy is seeking to establish the diet question upon a wrong basis by leading those in charge of the institution to accommodate the diet to the appetite of the patients.

When the Lord led the children of Israel from Egypt, He purposed to establish them in Canaan a pure, happy, healthy people. Let us study the plan of God, and see how this was accomplished. He restricted their diet. To a large degree, He took flesh food from them. But they hankered after the fleshpots of Egypt, and God gave them flesh, and with it the sure result.

The Health Retreat was established at a great cost to treat the sick without drugs. It should be conducted on hygienic principles. Drug medication should be worked away from as fast as possible, until entirely discarded. Education should be given on proper diet, dress, and exercise. Not only should our own people be educated, but those who have not received the light upon health reform should be taught how to live healthfully, according to God's order. But if we have no standard in this respect ourselves, what is the need of going to such large expense to establish a health institute? Where does the reform come in?

I cannot admit that we are moving in God's order. We must have a different order of things, or give up the name Health Retreat; for it is wholly inappropriate. The Lord has shown me that the Health Institute must not be molded to meet the appetite or any person's ideas. I am aware that the excuse for the meat eating allowed in the institution has been that the pleasure seekers who come are not pleased with any other diet. Then let them go where they can obtain the diet they wish. When the institution cannot be conducted, even for guests, according to right principles, then let it drop the name it has assumed. But the excuse that has been urged does not now exist; for outside patronage is very small.

A positive injury is done to the system by continuous meat eating. There is no excuse for it but a depraved, perverted appetite. You may ask, Would you do away entirely with meat eating? I answer, It will eventually come to this, but we are not prepared for this step just now. Meat eating will eventually be done away. The flesh of animals will no longer compose a part of our diet; and we shall look upon a butcher's shop with disgust. . . .

We are built up from that which we eat. Shall we strengthen the animal passions by eating animal food? In the place of educating the taste to love this gross diet, it is high time that we were educating ourselves to subsist upon fruits, grains, and vegetables. This is the work of all who are connected with our institutions. Use less and less meat, until it is not used at all. If meat is discarded, if the taste is not educated in that direction, if a liking for fruits and grains is encouraged, it will soon be as God in the beginning designed it should be. No meat will be used by His people.

When meat is not used as it has been, you will learn a more correct way of cooking, and will be able to supply the place of meat with something else. Many healthful dishes can be prepared which are free from grease and from the flesh of dead animals. A variety of simple dishes, perfectly healthful and nourishing, may be provided, aside from meat. Hearty men must have plenty of vegetables, fruits, and grains. Occasionally some meat may have to be given to outsiders who have so educated their taste that they think that unless they have meat, they cannot keep up their strength. But they will have greater powers of endurance if they abstain from meat than if they subsist largely upon it.

The principal objection with physicians and helpers at the Health Retreat to discarding a meat diet is that they want meat, and then plead they must have meat. Therefore, they encourage its use. But God does not want those who come to the Health Retreat educated to live on a flesh diet. By parlor talks and by example, educate in the other direction. This will call for great skill in the preparation of wholesome food. More labor will be required, but nevertheless, it must gradually be done. Use less meat. Let those who do the cooking and those who bear the responsibility educate their own tastes and habits of eating in accordance with the laws of health.

We have been going back to Egypt rather than on to Canaan. Shall we not reverse the order of things? Shall we not have plain, wholesome food on our tables? Shall we not dispense with hot biscuits, which only cause dyspepsia? Those who elevate the standard as nearly as they can to the order of God, according to the light God has given them through His word and the testimonies of His Spirit, will not change their course of action to meet the wishes of their friends or relatives, be they one or two or a host, who are living contrary to God's wise arrangement. If we move from principle in these things, if we observe strict rules of diet, if as Christians we educate our tastes after God's plan, we shall exert an influence which will meet the mind of God. The question is, "Are we willing to be true health reformers?"

It is essential that continuous sameness in diet be avoided. The appetite will be much better if changes in the food are made. Be uniform. Do not have several kinds of food on the table at one meal, and no variety the next. Study economy in this line. Let people complain if they will. Let them find fault if there is not enough to suit them. The Israelites always complained of Moses and of God. It is your duty to maintain the standard of health reform. More can be accomplished for sick people by regulating their diet than by all the baths that can be given them.

Let the same amount of money expended for meat be used to purchase fruit. Show the people a right way of living. Had this been done from the first at the institution t ———, the Lord would have been pleased, and would have approved the effort. . . .

Care and skill should be used in the preparation of food. I hope that Doctor ——— will fill the position assigned her, that she will counsel with the cook, so that the food placed on the tables at the Health Retreat may be in accordance with health reform. Because one is inclined to indulge his appetite, he must not argue that his is the way to live; he must not by his course of action seek to mold the institution to suit his tastes and practices. Those who bear the responsibility of the institution should frequently counsel together. They should move in perfect harmony.

Do not, I beg of you, argue that meat eating must be right, because this one or that one, who is a slave to appetite, has said that he could not live at the Health Retreat without meat. Subsisting on the flesh of dead animals is a gross way of living, and as a people, we should be working a change, a reform, teaching the people that there are healthful preparations of food that will give them more strength, and better preserve their health, than meat.

The sin of this age is gluttony in eating and drinking. Indulgence of appetite is the god which many worship. Those who are connected with the Health Institute should set a right example in these things. They should move conscientiously in the fear of God, and not be controlled by a perverted taste. They should be thoroughly enlightened in regard to the principles of health reform, and under all circumstances should stand under its banner.

I hope, Doctor ———, that you will learn more and more how to cook healthfully. Provide an abundance of good, wholesome food. Do not practice economy in this direction. Restrict your meat bills, but have plenty of good fruit and vegetables, and then you will enjoy seeing the hearty appetites with which all will partake of your preparations. Never feel that good, hygienic food that is eaten is lost. It will make blood and muscle, and give strength for daily duties.

[Cooking of flesh food not to be taught in our schools—817]
[Meat-eating physicians not to be employed in our sanitariums—433]

Letter 2, 1884

721. I have been thinking much of the Health Institut
at ———. Many thoughts crowd into my mind, and I wis⟩
to express some of them to you.

I have been calling to mind the light God has given m⟨
and through me to you, on health reform. Have you care
fully and prayerfully sought to understand the will of Go⟩
in these matters? The excuse has been, that the outsider
would have a meat diet, but even if they had some meat,
know that with care and skill, dishes could be prepared t⟨
take the place of meat in a large degree, and in a short tim⟨
they could be educated to let the flesh of dead animals alon⟨
But if one performs the cooking whose main dependence i⟩
meat, she can and will encourage meat eating, and the de
praved appetite will frame every excuse for this kind of die⟨

When I saw how matters were going,—that if ——— ha⟩
not meat to cook, she knew not what to provide as a substi
tute, and that meat was the principal article of diet,—I fe⟨
that there must be a change at once. There may be consump
tives who demand meat, but let them have it in their ow⟨
rooms, and do not tempt the already-perverted appetite c
those who should not eat it. . . . You may think you cann⟨
work without meat. I thought so once, but I know that i⟩
His original plan, God did not provide for the flesh of dea⟨
animals to compose the diet for man. It is a gross, perverte⟨
taste that will accept such food. . . . Then the fact that me⟨
is largely diseased, should lead us to make strenuous effort
to discontinue its use entirely. My position now is to le⟨
meat altogether alone. It will be hard for some to do thi⟩
as hard as for the rum drinker to forsake his dram; but the⟨
will be better for the change.

Meeting the Issue Squarely

Letter 59, 1898

722. The sanitarium is doing good work. We have jus⟨
come to the point of the vexed meat question. Should n⟨
those who come to the sanitarium have meat on their table⟩
and be instructed to leave it off gradually? . . . Years ago th⟨

ght was given me that the position should not be taken posi-
ively to discard all meat, because in some cases it was better
han the desserts, and dishes composed of sweets. These are
ure to create disturbances. It is the variety and mixture of
eat, vegetables, fruit, wines, tea, coffee, sweet cakes, and
ch pies that ruin the stomach, and place human beings in
 position where they become invalids with all the disagree-
ble effects of sickness upon the disposition. . . .

I present the word of the Lord God of Israel. Because
f transgression, the curse of God has come upon the earth
self, and upon the cattle, and upon all flesh. Human beings
re suffering the result of their own course of action in
eparting from the commandments of God. The beasts also
uffer under the curse.

Meat eating should not come into the prescription for
ny invalids from any physicians from among those who
nderstand these things. Disease in cattle is making meat
ating a dangerous matter. The Lord's curse is upon the
arth, upon man, upon beasts, upon the fish in the sea; and
s transgression becomes almost universal, the curse will be
ermitted to become as broad and as deep as the transgres-
ion. Disease is contracted by the use of meat. The dis-
ased flesh of these dead carcasses is sold in the market
laces, and disease among men is the sure result.

The Lord would bring His people into a position where
ey will not touch or taste the flesh of dead animals. Then
t not these things be prescribed by any physicians who
ave a knowledge of the truth for this time. There is no
fety in the eating of the flesh of dead animals, and in a
ort time the milk of the cows will also be excluded from
e diet of God's commandment-keeping people. In a short
me it will not be safe to use anything that comes from the
nimal creation. Those who take God at His word, and
bey His commandments with the whole heart, will be
essed. He will be their shield of protection. But the Lord
ill not be trifled with. Distrust, disobedience, alienation
om God's will and way, will place the sinner in a position
here the Lord cannot give him His divine favor. . . .

Again I will refer to the diet question. We cannot now do as we have ventured to do in the past in regard to meat eating. It has always been a curse to the human family, but now it is made particularly so in the curse which God has pronounced upon the herds of the field, because of man's transgression and sin. The disease upon animals is becoming more and more common, and our only safety now is in leaving meat entirely alone. The most aggravated diseases are now prevalent, and the very last thing that physicians who are enlightened should do, is to advise patients to eat meat. It is in eating meat so largely in this country that men and women are becoming demoralized, their blood corrupted and disease planted in the system. Because of meat eating many die, and they do not understand the cause. If the truth were known, it would bear testimony it was the flesh of animals that have passed through death. The thought of feeding on dead flesh is repulsive, but there is something beside this. In eating meat we partake of diseased dead flesh, and this sows its seed of corruption in the human organism.

I write to you, my brother, that the giving of prescriptions for the eating of the flesh of animals shall no more be practiced in our sanitarium. There is no excuse for this. There is no safety in the afterinfluence and results upon the human mind. Let us be health reformers in every sense of the term. Let us make known in our institutions that there is no longer a meat table, even for the boarders; and then the education given upon the discarding of a meat diet will be not only saying but doing. If patronage is less, so let it be. The principles will be of far greater value when they are understood, when it is known that the life of no living thing shall be taken to sustain the life of the Christian.

A Second Letter Meeting the Issue

Letter 84, 1898

723. I received your letter, and will explain as best I can in reference to the meat. The words you mention were in a letter to ———— and some others at the time Sister ———— was at the Health Retreat [720]. I had these letters hunted

up. Some letters were copied and some were not. I told them to give dates to the time of the statements made. At that time the meat diet was being prescribed and used very largely. The light given me was that meat in a healthy condition was not to be cut off all at once, but talks were to be given in the parlor in regard to the use of dead flesh of any kind; that fruits, grains, and vegetables, properly prepared, were all the system required to keep it in health; but that they must first show that we have no need to use meat, where there was an abundance of fruit, as in California. But at the Health Retreat they were not prepared to make abrupt moves, after using meat so abundantly as they had done. It would be necessary for them to use meat very sparingly at first and finally discontinue it entirely. But there must be only one table called the patients' meat-eating table. The other tables were to be free from this article. . . .

I labored most earnestly to have all meat discarded, but this difficult question must be handled discreetly and not rashly, after meat had been used three times a day. The patients must be educated from a health standpoint.

This is all I can remember on that point. Increased light has been coming, for us to consider. The animal creation is diseased, and it is difficult to determine the amount of disease in the human family that is the result of meat eating. We read constantly in the daily papers about the inspection of meat. Butcher shops are continually being cleaned out; the meat being sold is condemned as unfit for use.

The light has come to me for many years that meat eating is not good for health or morals. And yet it seems so strange that I have to meet this meat-eating question again and again. I had a very close and decided talk with the physicians in the Health Home. They had considered the matter, and Brother and Sister ——— were brought into very strait places. Meat was being prescribed for patients. . . . Sabbath, while at the Australian Union Conference, held at Stanmore, I felt urged by the Spirit of the Lord, to take up the case of the Health Home established at Summer Hill, which is only a few stations from Stanmore.

I presented the advantages to be obtained in this sanitar ium. I showed that meat was never to be placed on the table as an article of food, that the life and health of thousand were being sacrificed at the altars where dead flesh was being offered for consumption. I never gave a more earnest and decided appeal. I said, We are thankful that we have an institution here where the flesh of dead animals is not pre scribed for any patients. Let it be said that not one morsel of meat has been placed on the tables, either for physicians managers, helpers, or patients. I said, We have confidence in our physicians that this question will be treated from a health standpoint; for dead carcasses should always be looked upon as not fit to compose the diet of Christians.

I did not varnish the matter one particle. I said that should those in our health home bring the flesh of dead ani mals upon the table, they would merit the displeasure of God. They would defile the temple of God, and they would need the words spoken to them, Whoso defileth the temple of God, him will God destroy. The light that God has given me is that the curse of God is on the earth, the sea, the cattle on the animals. There will soon be no safety in the posses sion of flocks or herds. The earth is decaying under the curse of God.

Remaining True to Our Principles

MS 3a, 1903

724. Lately the number of patients at the sanitarium ha decreased, owing to an array of circumstances that could no be helped. One reason for the lack of patronage is, I think the stand that those at the head of the institution have taken against serving flesh meat to the patients. Ever since the opening of the sanitarium, meat has been served in the din ing room. We felt that the time had come to take a decided stand against this practice. We knew that it was not pleas ing to God for flesh meat to be placed before the patients

Now no tea, coffee, or flesh meat is served in the institu tion. We are determined to live out the principles of health reform, to walk in the way of truth and righteousness. We shall not, for fear of losing patronage, be half-and-half re ormers. We have taken our position, and by God's help ve shall stand by it. The food provided for the patients s wholesome and palatable. The diet is composed of fruits nd grains and nuts. Here in California there is an abundance of fruit of all kinds.

If patients come who are so dependent on a diet of flesh meat that they think that [they] cannot live without it, we hall try to make them look at the matter from an intelligent oint of view. And if they will not do this, if they are letermined to use that which destroys health, we shall not efuse to provide it for them, if they are willing to eat it in heir rooms and willing to risk the consequences. But they must take upon themselves the responsibility of their action. Ve shall not sanction their course. We dare not dishonor ur stewardship by sanctioning the use of that which taints he blood and brings disease. We should be unfaithful to ur Master if we did that which we know He does not pprove.

This is the stand that we have taken. We are resolved o be true to the principles of health reform, and may God elp us, is my prayer.

Plans must be set in operation that will bring an increase f patronage. But would it be right for us, for the sake of btaining more patients, to return to the serving of flesh meat? Shall we give the sick that which has made them ick, that which will keep them sick if they continue to use it s food? Shall we not rather take our stand as those who re resolved to carry out the principles of health reform?

[Tea, coffee, and meat served in patients' rooms—437]

MS 73, 1908

725. There are some in our institutions who claim to believe the principles of health reform, and yet who indulge in he use of flesh meats and other foods which they know to e injurious to health. I say to such in the name of the Lord, Do not accept positions in our institutions while you efuse to live the principles for which our institutions stand; or by doing this, you make doubly hard the work of teachers nd leaders who are striving to carry the work on right

lines. Clear the King's highway. Cease to block the way
of the message He sends.

I have been shown that the principles that were given
us in the early days of the message are to be regarded as
just as important by our people today as they were then.
There are some who have never followed the light given us
on the question of diet. It is time now to take the light
from under the bushel, and let it shine forth in clear, bright
rays.

[Not to be served in our sanitariums—424, 431, 432]
[Not to be served to helpers—432, 444]
[Excessive use of sweet foods as harmful as the use of
undiseased flesh meat—533, 556, 722]

Beverages

Quotations in Section XXIV

Beverages

PART I—WATER DRINKING
Pure Water a Blessing

(1905) M.H. 237

726. IN health and in sickness, pure water is one of Heaven's choicest blessings. Its proper use promotes health. It is the beverage which God provided to quench the thirst of animals and man. Drunk freely, it helps to supply the necessities of the system, and assists nature to resist disease.

Health Reformer, January, 1871

727. I should eat sparingly, thus relieving my system of unnecessary burden, and should encourage cheerfulness, and give myself the benefits of proper exercise in the open air. I should bathe frequently, and drink freely of pure, soft water.

Use of Water in Sickness

Letter 35, 1890

728. Water can be used in many ways to relieve suffering. Drafts of clear, hot water taken before eating (half quart, more or less), will never do any harm, but will rather be productive of good.

(1866) H. to L., ch. 4, p. 56

729. Thousands have died for want of pure water and pure air, who might have lived. . . . These blessings they need in order to become well. If they would become enlightened, and let medicine alone, and accustom themselves to outdoor exercise, and to air in their houses, summer and winter, and use soft water for drinking and bathing purposes, they would be comparatively well and happy instead of dragging out a miserable existence.

In Fever Cases

(1866) H. to L., ch. 3, pp. 62, 63

730. If, in their fevered state, water had been given them to drink freely, and applications had also been made externally, long days and nights of suffering would have been saved, and many precious lives spared. But thousands have

died with raging fevers consuming them, until the fuel which fed the fever was burned up, the vitals consumed, and have died in the greatest agony, without being permitted to have water to allay their burning thirst. Water, which is allowed a senseless building to put out the raging elements, is not allowed human beings to put out the fire which is consuming the vitals.

A Right and Wrong Use of Water

R. & H., July 29, 1884

731. Many make a mistake in drinking cold water with their meals. Taken with meals, water diminishes the flow of the salivary glands; and the colder the water, the greater the injury to the stomach. Ice water or ice lemonade, drunk with meals, will arrest digestion until the system has imparted sufficient warmth to the stomach to enable it to take up its work again. Hot drinks are debilitating; and besides, those who indulge in their use become slaves to the habit. Food should not be washed down; no drink is needed with meals. Eat slowly, and allow the saliva to mingle with the food. The more liquid there is taken into the stomach with the meals, the more difficult it is for the food to digest; for the liquid must first be absorbed. Do not eat largely of salt; give up bottled pickles; keep fiery spiced food out of your stomach; eat fruit with your meals, and the irritation which calls for so much drink will cease to exist. But if anything is needed to quench thirst, pure water, drunk some little time before or after the meal, is all that nature requires. Never take tea, coffee, beer, wine, or any spirituous liquors. Water is the best liquid possible to cleanse the tissues.

[More about drinking with meals—165, 166]
[One of God's medicines—451, 452, 454]

PART II—TEA AND COFFEE

The Stimulating Effects of Tea and Coffee

R. H., Feb. 21, 1888

732. The stimulating diet and drink of this day are not conducive to the best state of health. Tea, coffee, and to-

bacco are all stimulating, and contain poisons. They are not only unnecessary, but harmful, and should be discarded if we would add to knowledge temperance.

(1868) 2T 64, 65

733. Tea is poisonous to the system. Christians should let it alone. The influence of coffee is in a degree the same as tea, but the effect upon the system is still worse. Its influence is exciting, and just in the degree that it elevates above par, it will exhaust and bring prostration below par. Tea and coffee drinkers carry the marks upon their faces. The skin becomes sallow, and assumes a lifeless appearance. The glow of health is not seen upon the countenance.

MS 22, 1887

734. Diseases of every stripe and type have been brought upon human beings by the use of tea and coffee and the narcotics, opium and tobacco. These hurtful indulgences must be given up, not only one but all; for all are hurtful, and ruinous to the physical, mental, and moral powers, and should be discontinued from a health standpoint.

[Sowing seeds of death—655]

R. & H., July 29, 1884

735. Never take tea, coffee, beer, wine, or any spirituous liquors. Water is the best liquid possible to cleanse the tissues.

(1890) C.T.B.H. 34-36

736. Tea, coffee, and tobacco, as well as alcoholic drinks, are different degrees in the scale of artificial stimulants.

The effect of tea and coffee, as heretofore shown, tends in the same direction as that of wine and cider, liquor and tobacco. . . .

Coffee is a hurtful indulgence. It temporarily excites the mind to unwonted action, but the aftereffect is exhaustion, prostration, paralysis of the mental, moral, and physical powers. The mind becomes enervated, and unless through determined effort the habit is overcome, the activity of the brain is permanently lessened. All these nerve irritants are wearing away the life forces, and the restlessness caused by shattered nerves, the impatience, the mental feebleness, become a warring element, antagonizing to spiritual progress. Then should not those who advocate temperance and reform be awake to counteract the evils of these injurious drinks? In some cases it is as difficult to break up the tea-and-coffee habit as it is for the inebriate to discontinue the use of liquor. The money expended for tea and coffee is worse than wasted. They do the user only harm, and that continually. Those who use tea, coffee, opium, and alcohol, may sometimes live to an old age, but this fact is no argument in favor of the use of these stimulants. What these persons might have accomplished, but failed to do because of their intemperate habits, the great day of God alone will reveal.

Those who resort to tea and coffee for stimulation to labor, will feel the evil effects of this course in trembling nerves and lack of self-control. Tired nerves need rest and quiet. Nature needs time to recuperate her exhausted energies. But if her forces are goaded on by the use of stimulants, there is, whenever this process is repeated, a lessening of real force. For a time more may be accomplished under the unnatural stimulus, but gradually it becomes more difficult to rouse the energies to the desired point, and at last exhausted nature can no longer respond.

HARMFUL EFFECTS ATTRIBUTED TO OTHER CAUSES

The habit of drinking tea and coffee is a greater evil than is often suspected. Many who have accustomed themselves to the use of stimulating drinks, suffer from headache and nervous prostration, and lose much time on account of sickness. They imagine they cannot live without the stimulus, and are ignorant of its effect upon health. What makes it the more dangerous is, that its evil effects are so often attributed to other causes.

EFFECTS ON MIND AND MORALS

Through the use of stimulants, the whole system suffers. The nerves are unbalanced, the liver is morbid in its action, the quality and circulation of the blood are affected, and the skin becomes inactive and sallow. The mind, too, is injured. The immediate influence of these stimulants is to excite the brain to undue activity, only to leave it weaker and less capable of exertion. The aftereffect is prostration, not only mental and physical, but moral. As a result we see nervous men and women, of unsound judgment and unbalanced mind. They often manifest a hasty, impatient, accusing spirit, viewing the faults of others as through a magnifying glass, and utterly unable to discern their own defects.

When these tea and coffee users meet together for social entertainment, the effects of their pernicious habit are manifest. All partake freely of the favorite beverages, and as the stimulating influence is felt, their tongues are loosened, and they begin the wicked work of talking against others. Their words are not few or well chosen. The tidbits of gossip are passed around, too often the poison of scandal as well. These thoughtless gossipers forget that they have a witness. An unseen Watcher is writing their words in the books of heaven. All these unkind criticisms, these exaggerated reports, these envious feelings, expressed under the excitement of the cup of tea, Jesus registers as against Himself. "Inasmuch as ye have done it unto one of the least of these My brethren, ye have done it unto Me."

We are already suffering because of the wrong habits of our fathers, and yet how many take a course in every way worse than theirs! Opium, tea, coffee, tobacco, and liquor are rapidly extinguishing the spark of vitality still left in the race. Every year millions of gallons of intoxicating liquors are drunk, and millions of dollars are spent for tobacco. And the slaves of appetite, while constantly spending their earnings in sensual indulgence, rob their children of food and clothing and the advantages of education. There can never be a right state of society while these evils exist.

Create Nervous Excitement, Not Strength

(1879) 4T 365

737. You are highly nervous and excitable. Tea has an influence to excite the nerves, and coffee benumbs the brain;

both are highly injurious. You should be careful of your diet. Eat the most wholesome, nourishing food, and keep yourself in a calm state of mind, where you will not become so excited and fly into a passion.

(1905) M.H. 326, 327

738. Tea acts as a stimulant, and, to a certain extent, produces intoxication. The action of coffee and many other popular drinks is similar. The first effect is exhilarating. The nerves of the stomach are excited; these convey irritation to the brain, and this in turn is aroused to impart increased action to the heart, and short-lived energy to the entire system. Fatigue is forgotten, the strength seems to be increased. The intellect is aroused, the imagination becomes more vivid.

Because of these results, many suppose that their tea or coffee is doing them great good. But this is a mistake. Tea and coffee do not nourish the system. Their effect is produced before there has been time for digestion and assimilation, and what seems to be strength is only nervous excitement. When the influence of the stimulant is gone, the unnatural force abates, and the result is a corresponding degree of languor and debility.

The continued use of these nerve irritants is followed by headache, wakefulness, palpitation of the heart, indigestion, trembling, and many other evils, for they wear away the life forces. Tired nerves need rest and quiet instead of stimulation and overwork. Nature needs time to recuperate her exhausted energies. When her forces are goaded on by the use of stimulants, more will be accomplished for a time; but as the system becomes debilitated by their constant use, it gradually becomes more difficult to rouse the energies to the desired point. The demand for stimulants becomes more difficult to control, until the will is overborne, and there seems to be no power to deny the unnatural craving. Stronger and still stronger stimulants are called for, until exhausted nature can no longer respond.

[Tea and coffee ruin the stomach—722]

No Food Value

Letter 69, 1896

739. The health is in no way improved by the use of those things which stimulate for a time, but afterward cause a reaction which leaves the system lower than before. Tea and coffee whip up the flagging energies for the time being, but when their immediate influence has gone, a feeling of depression is the result. These beverages have no nourishment whatever in themselves. The milk and sugar it contains constitute all the nourishment afforded by a cup of tea or coffee.

Spiritual Perception Blunted

(1864) Sp. Gifts IV, 128, 129

740. Tea and coffee are stimulating. Their effects are similar to those of tobacco; but they affect in a lesser degree. Those who use these slow poisons, like the tobacco user, think they cannot live without them, because they feel so very bad when they do not have these idols. . . . Those who indulge a perverted appetite, do it to the injury of health and intellect. They cannot appreciate the value of spiritual things. Their sensibilities are blunted, and sin does not appear very sinful, and truth is not regarded of greater value than earthly treasure.

MS 44, 1896

741. Tea and coffee drinking is a sin, an injurious indulgence, which, like other evils, injures the soul. These darling idols create an excitement, a morbid action of the nervous system; and after the immediate influence of the stimulants is gone, it lets down below par just to that degree that its stimulating properties elevated above par.

(1861) 1T 222

742. Those who use tobacco, tea, and coffee should lay aside those idols, and put their cost into the treasury of the Lord. Some have never made a sacrifice for the cause of God, and are asleep as to what God requires of them. Some of the very poorest will have the greatest struggle to deny themselves of these stimulants. This individual sacrifice is

not required because the cause of God is suffering for means. But every heart will be tested, every character developed. It is principle that God's people must act upon. The living principle must be carried out in the life.

Cravings Interfere With Spiritual Worship

R. & H., Jan. 25, 1881

743. Tea and coffee, as well as tobacco, have an injurious effect upon the system. Tea is intoxicating; though less in degree, its effect is the same in character as that of spirituous liquors. Coffee has a greater tendency to becloud the intellect and benumb the energies. It is not so powerful as tobacco, but is similar in its effects. The arguments brought against tobacco may also be urged against the use of tea and coffee.

Those who are in the habit of using tea, coffee, tobacco, opium, or spirituous liquors, cannot worship God when they are deprived of the accustomed indulgence. Let them, while deprived of these stimulants, engage in the worship of God, and divine grace would be powerless to animate, enliven, or spiritualize their prayers or their testimonies. These professed Christians should consider the means of their enjoyment. Is it from above, or from beneath?

The Stupefied Transgressor Not Guiltless

(1890) C.T.B.H. 79, 80

744. Satan sees that he cannot have so great power over minds when the appetite is kept under control as when it is indulged, and he is constantly working to lead men to indulgence. Under the influence of unhealthful food, the conscience becomes stupefied, the mind is darkened, and its susceptibility to impressions is impaired. But the guilt of the transgressor is not lessened because the conscience has been violated till it has become insensible.

Since a healthy state of mind depends upon the normal condition of the vital forces, what care should be exercised that neither stimulants nor narcotics be used! Yet we see that a large number of those who profess to be Christians are using tobacco. They deplore the evils of intemperance;

yet while speaking against the use of liquors, these very men will eject the juice of tobacco. There must be change of sentiment with reference to tobacco using before the root of the evil will be reached. We press the subject still closer. Tea and coffee are fostering the appetite for stronger stimulants. And then we come still closer home, to the preparation of food, and ask, Is temperance practiced in all things? are the reforms which are essential to health and happiness carried out here?

Every true Christian will have control of his appetites and passions. Unless he is free from the bondage of appetite, he cannot be a true, obedient servant of Christ. The indulgence of appetite and passion blunts the effect of truth upon the heart.

A Losing Battle With Appetite

(1875) 3T 487, 488

745. Intemperance commences at our tables, in the use of unhealthful food. After a time, through continued indulgence, the digestive organs become weakened, and the food taken does not satisfy the appetite. Unhealthy conditions are established, and there is a craving for more stimulating food. Tea, coffee, and flesh meats produce an immediate effect. Under the influence of these poisons, the nervous system is excited, and, in some cases, for the time being, the intellect seems to be invigorated and the imagination to be more vivid. Because these stimulants produce for the time being such agreeable results, many conclude that they really need them, and continue their use. But there is always a reaction. The nervous system, having been unduly excited, borrowed power for present use from its future resources of strength. All this temporary invigoration of the system is followed by depression. In proportion as these stimulants temporarily invigorate the system, will be the letting down of the power of the excited organs after the stimulus has lost its force. The appetite is educated to crave something stronger, which will have a tendency to keep up and increase the agreeable excitement, until indulgence becomes habit, and there is a continual craving for stronger stimulus, as to-

bacco, wines, and liquors. The more the appetite is indulged, the more frequent will be its demands, and the more difficult of control. The more debilitated the system becomes, and the less able to do without unnatural stimulus, the more the passion for these things increases, until the will is overborne, and there seems to be no power to deny the unnatural craving for these indulgences.

THE ONLY SAFE COURSE

The only safe course is to touch not, taste not, handle not, tea, coffee, wines, tobacco, opium, and alcoholic drinks. The necessity for the men of this generation to call to their aid the power of the will, strengthened by the grace of God, in order to withstand the temptations of Satan, and resist the least indulgence of perverted appetite, is twice as great as it was several generations ago.

The Conflict Between Truth and Self-indulgence

(1864) Sp. Gifts IV, 36, 37

746. The facts relative to Korah and his company, who rebelled against Moses and Aaron, and against Jehovah, are recorded for a warning to God's people, especially those who live upon the earth near the close of time. Satan has led persons to imitate the example of Korah, Dathan, and Abiram, in raising insurrection among the people of God. Those who permit themselves to rise in opposition to the plain testimony, become self-deceived, and have really thought that those upon whom God laid the burden of His work were exalted above the people of God, and that their counsels and reproofs were uncalled for. They have risen in opposition to the plain testimony which God would have them bear in rebuking the wrongs among God's people. The testimonies borne against hurtful indulgences, as tea, coffee, snuff, and tobacco, have irritated a certain class, because it would destroy their idols. Many for a while were undecided whether to make an entire sacrifice of all these hurtful things, or reject the plain testimonies borne, and yield to the clamors of appetite. They occupied an unsettled position. There was a conflict between their convictions of truth and their

self-indulgences. Their state of indecision made them weak, and with many, appetite prevailed. Their sense of sacred things was perverted by the use of these slow poisons; and they at length fully decided, let the consequence be what it might, they would not deny self. This fearful decision at once raised a wall of separation between them and those who were cleansing themselves, as God has commanded, from all filthiness of the flesh and of the spirit, and were perfecting holiness in the fear of the Lord. The straight testimonies borne were in their way, and caused them great uneasiness, and they found relief in warring against them, and striving to make themselves and others believe that they were untrue. They said the people were all right, but it was reproving testimonies which made the trouble. And when the rebellious unfurl their banner, all the disaffected rally around the standard, and all the spiritually defective, the lame, the halt, and the blind, unite their influence to scatter and sow discord.

The Roots of Intemperance

(1905) M.H. 335

747. Great efforts are made to put down intemperance; but there is much effort that is not directed to the right point. The advocates of temperance reform should be awake to the evils resulting from the use of unwholesome food, condiments, tea, and coffee. We bid all temperance workers Godspeed; but we invite them to look more deeply into the cause of the evil they war against, and to be sure that they are consistent in reform.

It must be kept before the people that the right balance of the mental and moral powers depends in a great degree on the right condition of the physical system. All narcotics and unnatural stimulants that enfeeble and degrade the physical nature tend to lower the tone of the intellect and morals. Intemperance lies at the foundation of the moral depravity of the world. By the indulgence of perverted appetite, man loses his power to resist temptation.

Temperance reformers have a work to do in educating the people in these lines. Teach them that health, character, and even life, are endangered by the use of stimulants, which excite the exhausted energies to unnatural, spasmodic action.

PERSEVERE, AND NATURE WILL RALLY

In relation to tea, coffee, tobacco, and alcoholic drinks, the only safe course is to touch not, taste not, handle not. The tendency of tea, coffee, and similar drinks is in the same direction as that of alcoholic liquor and tobacco, and in some cases the habit is as difficult to break as it is for the drunkard to give up intoxicants. Those who attempt to leave off these stimulants will for a time feel a loss, and will suffer without them. But by persistence they will overcome the craving, and cease to feel the lack. Nature may require a little time to recover from the abuse she has suffered; but give her a chance, and she will again rally, and perform her work nobly and well.

(1875) 3T 569

748. Satan is corrupting minds and destroying souls through his subtle temptations. Will our people see and feel the sin of indulging perverted appetite? Will they discard tea, coffee, flesh meats, and all stimulating food, and devote the means expended for those hurtful indulgences to spreading the truth? . . . What power can the tobacco devotee have to stay the progress of intemperance? There must be a revolution in our world upon the subject of tobacco before the ax is laid at the root of the tree. We press the subject still closer. Tea and coffee are fostering the appetite which is developing for stronger stimulants, as tobacco and liquor.

Letter 135, 1902

749. Concerning flesh meat we can all say, Let it alone. And all should bear a clear testimony against tea and coffee, never using them. They are narcotics, injurious alike to the brain and to the other organs of the body. . . .

Let the members of our churches deny every selfish appetite. Every penny expended for tea, coffee, and flesh meat is worse than wasted; for these things hinder the best development of the physical, mental, and spiritual powers.

A Suggestion of Satan

(1867) 1T 548, 549

750. Some think that they cannot reform, that health would be sacrificed should they attempt to leave the use of tea, tobacco, and flesh meats. This is the suggestion of Satan. It is these hurtful stimulants that are surely undermining the constitution and preparing the system for acute diseases, by impairing nature's fine machinery and battering down her fortifications erected against disease and premature decay. . . .

The use of unnatural stimulants is destructive to health, and has a benumbing influence upon the brain, making it impossible to appreciate eternal things. Those who cherish these idols cannot rightly value the salvation which Christ has wrought out for them by a life of self-denial, continual suffering, and reproach, and by finally yielding His own sinless life to save perishing man from death.

[The effect of tea and coffee upon children—354, 360]
[Tea and coffee in our sanitariums—420, 424, 437, 438]
[Tea, coffee, and flesh foods unnecessary—805]
[Refusal of tea and coffee, etc., proves workers to be practical health reformers—227, 717]
[Results of partaking of tea and coffee at dinners and suppers —233]
[Those with cravings for tea and coffee to be enlightened—779]
[Making a covenant with God to give up tea, coffee, etc. —41]
[Tea and coffee not used by E. G. White—Appendix I:18, 23]
[Tea occasionally used by E. G. White as medicine—Appendix I:18]

PART III—CEREAL SUBSTITUTES FOR TEA AND COFFEE

Letter 200, 1902

751. Neither tea nor coffee should be served. Caramel cereal, made as nicely as possible, should be served in the place of these health-destroying beverages.

(1905) M.H. 321

752. Under some circumstances persons may require a third meal. This should, however, if taken at all, be very light, and of food most easily digested. Crackers—the Eng-

lish biscuit—or zwieback, and fruit, or cereal coffee, are the foods best suited for the evening meal.

Letter 73a, 1896

753. I use a little boiled milk in my simple homemade coffee.

Immoderate Use of Hot and Injurious Drinks

Letter 14, 1901

754. Hot drinks are not required, except as a medicine. The stomach is greatly injured by a large quantity of hot food and hot drink. Thus the throat and digestive organs, and through them the other organs of the body, are enfeebled.

PART IV—CIDER

(1885) 5T 354-361

755. We are living in an age of intemperance, and catering to the appetite of the ciderbibber is an offense against God. With others, you have engaged in this work because you have not followed the light. Had you stood in the light, you would not, you could not, have done this. Every one of you who has acted a part in this work will come under the condemnation of God, unless you make an entire change in your business. You need to be in earnest. You need to commence the work at once to clear your souls from condemnation. . . .

After you had taken a decided stand in opposition to active participation in the work of the temperance societies, you might still have retained an influence over others for good, had you acted conscientiously in accordance with the holy faith which you profess, but by engaging in the manufacture of cider, you have hurt your influence very much; and what is worse, you have brought reproach upon the truth, and your own souls have been injured. You have been building up a barrier between yourselves and the temperance cause. Your course led unbelievers to question your principles. You are not making straight paths for your feet; and the lame are halting and stumbling over you to perdition.

I cannot see how, in the light of the law of God, Christians can conscientiously engage in the raising of hops or in the manufacture of wine or cider for the market. All these articles may be put to a good use, and prove a blessing; or they may be put to a wrong use, and prove a temptation and a curse. Cider and wine may be canned when fresh, and kept sweet a long time; and if used in an unfermented state, they will not dethrone reason. . . .

MODERATE DRINKING THE HIGHWAY TO DRUNKENNESS

Persons may become just as really intoxicated on wine and cider as on stronger drinks, and the worst kind of inebriation is produced by these so-called milder drinks. The passions are more perverse; the transformation of character is greater, more determined and obstinate. A few quarts of cider or wine may awaken a taste for stronger drinks, and in many cases those who have become confirmed drunkards have thus laid the foundation of the drinking habit. For some persons it is by no means safe to have wine or cider in the house. They have inherited an appetite for stimulants, which Satan is continually soliciting them to indulge. If they yield to his temptations, they do not stop; appetite clamors for indulgence, and is gratified to their ruin. The brain is benumbed and clouded; reason no longer holds the reins, but they are laid on the neck of lust. Licentiousness, adultery, and vices of almost every type, are committed as the result of indulging the appetite for wine and cider. A professor of religion who loves these stimulants, and accustoms himself to their use, never grows in grace. He becomes gross and sensual; the animal passions control the higher powers of the mind, and virtue is not cherished.

Moderate drinking is the school in which men are receiving an education for the drunkard's career. So gradually does Satan lead away from the strongholds of temperance, so insidiously do the harmless wine and cider exert their influence upon the taste, that the highway to drunkenness is entered upon all unsuspectingly. The taste for stimulants is cultivated; the nervous system is disordered; Satan keeps the mind in a fever of unrest, and the poor victim, imagining himself perfectly secure, goes on and on, until every barrier is broken down, every principle sacrificed. The strongest resolutions are undermined; and eternal interests are not strong enough to keep the debased appetite under the control of reason.

Some are never really drunk, but are always under the influence of cider or fermented wine. They are feverish, unbalanced in mind, not really delirious, but in fully as bad a condition; for all the noble powers of the mind are perverted. A tendency to disease of various kinds, as dropsy, liver complaint, trembling nerves, and a determination of blood to the head, results from the habitual use of sour cider. By its use many bring upon themselves permanent disease. Some die of consumption or fall under the power of apoplexy from this cause alone. Some suffer from dyspepsia. Every vital function is deadened and the physicians tell them that they have liver complaint, when if they would break open the cider barrel, and never replace it, their abused life forces would recover their vigor.

Cider drinking leads to the use of stronger drinks. The stomach loses its natural vigor, and something stronger is needed to arouse it to action. . . . We see the power that appetite for strong drink has over men; we see how many of all professions and of heavy responsibilities—men of exalted station, of eminent talents, of great attainments, of fine feelings, of strong nerves, and of good reasoning powers—sacrifice everything for the indulgence of appetite, until they are reduced to the level of the brutes; and in very many cases their downward course commenced with the use of wine or cider.

OUR EXAMPLE TO BE ON THE SIDE OF REFORM

When intelligent men and women who are professedly Christians, plead that there is no harm in making wine or cider for the market, because when unfermented it will not intoxicate, I feel sad at heart. I know there is another side to this subject that they refuse to look upon; for selfishness has closed their eyes to the terrible evils that may result from the use of these stimulants. . . .

As a people, we profess to be reformers, to be light bearers in the world, to be faithful sentinels for God, guarding every avenue whereby Satan could come in with his temptations to pervert the appetite. Our example and influence must be a power on the side of reform. We must abstain from any practice which will blunt the conscience or encourage temptation. We must open no door that will give Satan access to the mind of one human being formed in the image of God. If all would be vigilant and faithful in guarding the little openings made by the moderate use of the so-called harmless wine and cider, the highway to drunkenness would be closed up. What is needed in every community is firm purpose, and a will to touch not, taste not, handle not; then the temperance reformation will be strong, permanent, and thorough. . . .

The world's Redeemer, who knows well the state of society in the last days, represents eating and drinking as the sins that condemn this age. He tells us that as it was in the days of Noah, so shall it be when the Son of man is revealed. "They were eating and drinking, marrying and giving in marriage, until that day that Noah entered into the ark, and knew not until the flood came, and took them all away." Just such a state of things will exist in the last days, and those who believe these warnings will use the utmost caution not to take a course that will bring them under condemnation.

Brethren, let us look at this matter in the light of the Scriptures, and exert a decided influence on the side of temperance in all things. Apples and grapes are God's gifts; they may be put to excellent use as healthful articles of food, or they may be abused by being put to a wrong use. Already God is blighting the grapevine and the apple crop because of men's sinful practices. We stand before the world as reformers; let us give no occasion for infidels or unbelievers to reproach our faith. Said Christ, "Ye are the salt of the earth," "the light of the world." Let us show that our hearts and consciences are under the transforming influence of divine grace, and that our lives are governed by the pure principles of the law of God, even though these principles may require the sacrifice of temporal interests.

Under the Microscope

(1905) M.H. 332, 333

756. Persons who have inherited an appetite for unnatural stimulants should by no means have wine, beer, or cider in their sight or within their reach; for this keeps the temptation constantly before them. Regarding sweet cider as harmless, many have no scruples in purchasing it freely. But it remains sweet for a short time only; then fermentation begins. The sharp taste which it then acquires makes it all the more acceptable to many palates, and the user is loath to admit that it has become hard, or fermented.

There is danger to health in the use of even sweet cider as ordinarily produced. If people could see what the microscope reveals in regard to the cider they buy, few would be willing to drink it. Often those who manufacture cider for the market are not careful as to the condition of the fruit used, and the juice of wormy and decayed apples is expressed. Those who would not think of using the poisonous, rotten apples in any other way, will drink the cider made from them, and call it a luxury; but the microscope shows that even when fresh from the press, this pleasant beverage is wholly unfit for use.

Intoxication is just as really produced by wine, beer, and cider, as by stronger drinks. The use of these drinks awakens the taste for those that are stronger, and thus the liquor habit is established. Moderate drinking is the school in which men are educated for the drunkard's career. Yet so insidious is the work of these milder stimulants, that the highway to drunkenness is entered before the victim suspects his danger.

PART V—FRUIT JUICE

Sweet Grape Juice

MS 126, 1903

757. The pure juice of the grape, free from fermentation, is a wholesome drink. But many of the alcoholic drinks which are now so largely consumed contain death-dealing potions. Those who partake of them are often mad-

dened, bereft of their reason. Under their deadly influence men commit crimes of violence and often murder.

Beneficial to Health

Letter 72, 1896

758. Make fruit the article of diet to be placed on your table, which shall constitute the bill of fare. The juices of fruit, mingled with bread, will be highly enjoyed. Good, ripe, undecayed fruit is a thing we should thank the Lord for, because it is beneficial to health.

[Taking a raw egg in unfermented wine—324]

[Use of lemon juice by E. G. White in seasoning for greens —522]

Teaching Health Principles

Quotations in Section XXV

Teaching Health Principles

PART I—INSTRUCTION TO BE GIVEN ON HEALTH TOPICS

The Need of Health Education

(1905) M.H. 125, 126

759. EDUCATION in health principles was never more needed than now. Notwithstanding the wonderful progress in so many lines relating to the comforts and conveniences of life, even to sanitary matters and to the treatment of disease, the decline in physical vigor and power of endurance is alarming. It demands the attention of all who have at heart the well-being of their fellow men.

Our artificial civilization is encouraging evils destructive of sound principles. Custom and fashion are at war with nature. The practices they enjoin, and the indulgences they foster, are steadily lessening both physical and mental strength, and bringing upon the race an intolerable burden. Intemperance and crime, disease and wretchedness, are everywhere.

Many transgress the laws of health through ignorance, and they need instruction. But the greater number know better than they do. They need to be impressed with the importance of making their knowledge a guide of life.

(1905) M.H. 146

760. There is great need of instruction in regard to dietetic reform. Wrong habits of eating and the use of unhealthful food are in no small degree responsible for the intemperance and crime and wretchedness that curse the world.

[Medical Missionary, November-December, 1892] C.H. 505

761. If we would elevate the moral standard in any country where we may be called to go, we must begin by correcting their physical habits. Virtue of character depends upon the right action of the powers of the mind and body.

Many Will Be Enlightened

(1900) 6T 378, 379

762. The Lord has presented before me that many, many will be rescued from physical, mental, and moral degeneracy through the practical influence of health reform. Health talks will be given, publications will be multiplied. The principles of health reform will be received with favor; and many will be enlightened. The influences that are associated with health reform will commend it to the judgment of all who want light; and they will advance step by step to receive the special truths for this time. Thus truth and righteousness will meet together. . . .

The gospel and the medical missionary work are to advance together. The gospel is to be bound up with the principles of true health reform. Christianity is to be brought into the practical life. Earnest, thorough reformatory work is to be done. True Bible religion is an outflowing of the love of God for fallen man. God's people are to advance in straightforward lines to impress the hearts of those who are seeking for truth, who desire to act their part aright in this intensely earnest age. We are to present the principles of health reform before the people, doing all in our power to lead men and women to see the necessity of these principles and to practice them.

Pioneer Efforts in Teaching Health Reform Principles

MS 27, 1906

763. When the State fair was held in Battle Creek [1864], our people took with them onto the grounds three or four cooking stoves, and demonstrated how good meals might be prepared without the use of flesh meat. We were told that we set the best table on the ground. Whenever large gatherings are held, it is your privilege to devise plans whereby you can provide those who attend with wholesome food, and you are to make your efforts educational.

The Lord gave us favor with the people, and we had many wonderful opportunities to demonstrate what could be done

hrough the principles of health reform to restore to health
hose whose cases had been pronounced hopeless. . . .

We should put forth greater efforts to teach the people
he truths of health reform. At every camp meeting an effort
hould be made to demonstrate what can be done in provid-
ng an appetizing, wholesome diet from grains, fruits, nuts,
nd vegetables. In every place where new companies are
rought into the truth, instruction should be given in the
cience of preparing wholesome food. Workers should be
hosen who can labor from house to house in an educational
ampaign.

The Medical Tent on the Campground

(1900) 6T 112, 113

764. As we near the close of time, we must rise higher
nd still higher upon the question of health reform and
Christian temperance, presenting it in a more positive and
ecided manner. We must strive continually to educate the
eople, not only by our words, but by our practice. Precept
nd practice combined have a telling influence.

At the camp meeting, instruction on health topics should
e given to the people. At our meetings in Australia, lec-
ures on health subjects were given daily, and a deep interest
as aroused. A tent for the use of physicians and nurses
as on the ground, medical advice was given freely, and was
ought by many. Thousands of people attended the lectures,
nd at the close of the camp meeting the people were not
atisfied to let the matter drop with what they had already
earned. In several cities where camp meetings were held,
ome of the leading citizens urged that a branch sanitarium
e established, promising their cooperation.

By Example as Well as Precept

(1900) 6T 112

765. The large gatherings of our people afford an excel-
nt opportunity of illustrating the principles of health re-
orm. Some years ago at these gatherings much was said in
egard to health reform and the benefits of a vegetarian diet;

but at the same time flesh meats were furnished at the table
in the dining tent, and various unhealthful articles of food
were sold at the provision stand.   Faith without work is
dead; and the instruction upon health reform, denied by
practice, did not make the deepest impression.   At later
camp meetings those in charge have educated by practice
as well as by precept.   No meat has been furnished at the
dining tent, but fruits, grains, and vegetables have been supplied in abundance.   As visitors ask questions in regard to
the absence of meat, the reason is plainly stated, that flesh
is not the most healthful food.

[Sale of candies, ice cream, and other knickknacks on the
campground—529, 530]

In Our Sanitariums

Letter 79, 1905

766. The light given me was that a sanitarium should
be established, and that in it drug medication should be discarded, and simple, rational methods of treatment employed
for the healing of disease.   In this institution people were
to be taught how to dress, breathe, and eat properly,—how
to prevent sickness by proper habits of living.

[See also 458]

Letter 233, 1905

767. Our sanitariums are to be the means of enlightening
those who come to them for treatment.   The patients are to
be shown how they can live upon a diet of grains, fruits,
nuts, and other products of the soil.   I have been instructed
that lectures should be regularly given in our sanitariums
on health topics.   People are to be taught to discard those
articles of food that weaken the health and strength of the
beings for whom Christ gave His life.   The injurious effect
of tea and coffee are to be shown.   The patients are to be
taught how they can dispense with those articles of diet that
injure the digestive organs. . . . Let the patients be shown
the necessity of practicing the principles of health reform
if they would regain their health.   Let the sick be shown
how to get well by being temperate in eating and by taking
regular exercise in the open air. . . . By the work of our
sanitariums, suffering is to be relieved and health restored

People are to be taught how, by carefulness in eating and drinking, they may keep well. . . . Abstinence from flesh meat will benefit those who abstain. The diet question is a subject of living interest. . . . Our sanitariums are established for a special purpose, to teach people that we do not live to eat, but that we eat to live.

Educate Patients in Home Nursing

Letter 204, 1906

768. Keep the patients out of doors as much as possible, and give them cheering, happy talks in the parlor, with simple reading and Bible lessons, easy to be understood, which will be an encouragement to the soul. Talk on health reform, and do not you, my brother, become burden bearer in so many lines that you cannot teach the simple lessons of health reform. Those who go from the sanitarium should go so well instructed that they can teach others the methods of treating their families.

There is danger of spending far too much money on machinery and appliances which the patients can never use in their home lessons. They should rather be taught how to regulate the diet, so that the living machinery of the whole being will work in harmony.

Temperance Instruction to Be Given

Letter 145, 1904

769. In our medical institutions clear instruction should be given in regard to temperance. The patients should be shown the evil of intoxicating liquor, and the blessing of total abstinence. They should be asked to discard the things that have ruined their health, and the place of these things should be supplied with an abundance of fruit. Oranges, lemons, prunes, peaches, and many other varieties can be obtained; for the Lord's world is productive, if painstaking effort is put forth.

(1905) M.H. 176, 177

770. Those who are struggling against the power of appetite should be instructed in the principles of healthful living. They should be shown that violation of the laws of health, by creating diseased conditions and unnatural crav-

ings, lays the foundation of the liquor habit. Only by living in obedience to the principles of health can they hope to be freed from the craving for unnatural stimulants. While they depend upon divine strength to break the bonds of appetite, they are to cooperate with God by obedience to His laws, both moral and physical.

Comprehensive Nature of Reform Required

MS 1, 1888

771. What is the special work that we are called upon to do in our health institutions? Instead of giving, by precept and example, an education in the indulgence of perverted appetite, educate away from these things. Lift the standard of reform in every line. The apostle Paul lifts up his voice, "I beseech you, therefore, brethren, by the mercies of God, that ye present your bodies a living sacrifice, holy, acceptable unto God, which is your reasonable service. And be not conformed to this world: but be ye transformed by the renewing of your mind, that ye may prove what is that good and acceptable, and perfect, will of God."

Our health institutions are established to present the living principles of a clean, pure, healthful diet. The knowledge must be imparted in regard to self-denial, self-control. Jesus, who made man and redeemed man, is to be held up before all who shall come to our institutions. The knowledge of the way of life, peace, health, must be given line upon line, precept upon precept, that men and women may see the need of reform. They must be led to renounce the debasing customs and practices which existed in Sodom and in the antediluvian world, which God destroyed because of their iniquity (Matt. 24:37-39.) . . .

All who shall visit our health institutions are to be educated. The plan of redemption should be brought before all, high and low, rich and poor. Carefully prepared instruction is to be given, that indulgence in fashionable intemperance in eating and drinking may be seen as the cause of disease and suffering and of evil practices that follow as a result.

[How to bring about reforms in diet—426]

Leaves From the Tree of Life

(1909) 9T 168

772. I have been instructed that we are not to delay to do the work that needs to be done in health reform lines. Through this work we are to reach souls in the highways and byways. I have been given special light that in our sanitariums many souls will receive and obey present truth. In these institutions men and women are to be taught how to care for their own bodies, and at the same time how to become sound in the faith. They are to be taught what is meant by eating the flesh and drinking the blood of the Son of God. Said Christ, "The words that I speak unto you, they are spirit, and they are life." John 6:63.

Our sanitariums are to be schools in which instruction shall be given in medical missionary lines. They are to bring to sin-sick souls the leaves of the tree of life, which will restore to them peace and hope and faith in Christ Jesus.

Preparation for Prayer for Healing

(1905) M.H. 227, 228

773. It is labor lost to teach people to look to God as a healer of their infirmities, unless they are taught also to lay aside unhealthful practices. In order to receive His blessing in answer to prayer, they must cease to do evil and learn to do well. Their surroundings must be sanitary, their habits of life correct. They must live in harmony with the laws of God, both natural and spiritual.

The Physician's Responsibility to Enlighten His Patients

MS 22, 1887

774. The health institutions for the sick will be the best places to educate the suffering ones to live in accordance with nature's laws, and cease their health-destroying practices in wrong habits in diet, in dress, that are in accordance with the world's habits and customs, which are not at all after God's order. They are doing a good work to enlighten our world. . . .

There is now positive need even with physicians, reformers in the line of treatment of disease, that greater painstaking effort be made to carry forward and upward the work for themselves, and to interestedly instruct those who look to them for medical skill to ascertain the cause of their infirmities. They should call their attention in a special manner to the laws which God has established, which cannot be violated with impunity. They dwell much on the working of disease, but do not, as a general rule, arouse the attention to the laws which must be sacredly and intelligently obeyed to prevent disease. Especially if the physician has not been correct in his dietetic practices, if his own appetite has not been restricted to a plain, wholesome diet, in a large measure discarding the use of the flesh of dead animals,—he loves meat, —he has educated and cultivated a taste for unhealthful food. His ideas are narrow, and he will as soon educate and discipline the taste and the appetite of his patients to love the things that he loves, as to give them the sound principles of health reform. He will prescribe for sick patients flesh meat, when it is the very worst diet that they can have; it stimulates, but does not give strength. They do not inquire into their former habits of eating and drinking, and take special notice of their erroneous habits which have been for many years laying the foundation of disease.

Conscientious physicians should be prepared to enlighten those who are ignorant, and should with wisdom make out their prescriptions, prohibiting those things in their diet which they know to be erroneous. They should plainly state the things which they regard as detrimental to the laws of health, and leave these suffering ones to work conscientiously to do those things for themselves which they can do, and thus place themselves in right relation to the laws of life and health.

[Duty of physicians and helpers to educate their own tastes —720]

[The physician's responsibility to educate by pen and voice in healthful cookery—382]

[Patients at Health Retreat to be educated away from a flesh diet—720]

A Solemn Charge

(1902) 7T 74, 75

775. When a physician sees that a patient is suffering from an ailment caused by improper eating and drinking, yet

neglects to tell him of this, and to point out the need of reform, he is doing a fellow being an injury. Drunkards, maniacs, those who are given over to licentiousness,—all appeal to the physician to declare clearly and distinctly that suffering is the result of sin. We have received great light on health reform. Why, then, are we not more decidedly in earnest in striving to counteract the causes that produce disease? Seeing the continual conflict with pain, laboring constantly to alleviate suffering, how can our physicians hold their peace? Can they refrain from lifting the voice in warning? Are they benevolent and merciful if they do not teach strict temperance as a remedy for disease?

Moral Courage Required by Diet Reformers

[C.T.B.H. 121] (1890) C.H. 451, 452

776. A great amount of good can be done by enlightening all to whom we have access, as to the best means, not only of curing the sick, but of preventing disease and suffering. The physician who endeavors to enlighten his patients as to the nature and causes of their maladies and to teach them how to avoid disease, may have uphill work; but if he is a conscientious reformer, he will talk plainly of the ruinous effects of self-indulgence in eating, drinking, and dressing, of the overtaxation of the vital forces that has brought his patients where they are. He will not increase the evil by administering drugs till exhausted nature gives up the struggle, but will teach the patients how to form correct habits, and to aid nature in her work of restoration by a wise use of her own simple remedies.

In all our health institutions, it should be made a special feature of the work to give instruction in regard to the laws of health. The principles of health reform should be carefully and thoroughly set before all, both patients and helpers. This work requires moral courage; for while many will profit by such efforts, others will be offended. But the true disciple of Christ, he whose mind is in harmony with the mind of God, while constantly learning, will be teaching as well, leading the minds of others upward, away from the prevailing errors of the world.

Cooperation of Sanitariums and Schools

Letter 82, 1908

777. Clear light has been given that our educational institutions should be connected with our sanitariums wherever this is possible. The work of the two institutions is to blend. I am thankful that we have a school at Loma Linda. The educational talent of competent physicians is a necessity to the schools where medical missionary evangelists are to be trained for service. The students in the school are to be taught to be strict health reformers. The instruction given in regard to disease and its causes, and how to prevent disease, and the training given in the treatment of the sick, will prove an invaluable education, and one that the students in all our schools should have.

This blending of our schools and sanitariums will prove an advantage in many ways. Through the instruction given by the sanitarium, students will learn how to avoid forming careless, intemperate habits in eating.

In Evangelistic Work and City Missions

(1909) 9T 112

778. As a people we have been given the work of making known the principles of health reform. There are some who think that the question of diet is not of sufficient importance to be included in their evangelistic work. But such make a great mistake. God's word declares, "Whether therefore ye eat, or drink, or whatsoever ye do, do all to the glory of God." I Cor. 10:31. The subject of temperance in all its bearings, has an important place in the work of salvation.

In connection with our city missions there should be suitable rooms where those in whom an interest has been awakened can be gathered for instruction. This necessary work is not to be carried on in such a meager way that an unfavorable impression will be made on the minds of the people. All that is done should bear favorable witness to the Author of truth, and should properly represent the sacredness and importance of the truths of the third angel's message.

[C.T.B.H. 117] (1890) C.H. 449, 450

779. In all our missions, women of intelligence should have charge of the domestic arrangements,—women who know how to prepare food nicely and healthfully. The table should be abundantly supplied with food of the best quality. If any have a perverted taste that craves tea, coffee, condiments, and unhealthful dishes, enlighten them. Seek to arouse the conscience. Set before them the principles of the Bible upon hygiene.

Let Ministers Teach Reform Principles

[C.T.B.H. 117] (1890) C.H. 449

780. We should educate ourselves, not only to live in harmony with the laws of health, but to teach others the better way. Many, even of those who profess to believe the special truths for this time, are lamentably ignorant with regard to health and temperance. They need to be educated, line upon line, precept upon precept. The subject must be kept fresh before them. This matter must not be passed over as nonessential; for nearly every family needs to be stirred up on the question. The conscience must be aroused to the duty of practicing the principles of true reform. God requires that His people shall be temperate in all things. Unless they practice true temperance, they will not, they cannot, be susceptible to the sanctifying influence of the truth.

Our ministers should become intelligent upon this question. They should not ignore it, nor be turned aside by those who call them extremists. Let them find out what constitutes true health reform, and teach its principles, both by precept and by a quiet, consistent example. At our large gatherings, instruction should be given upon health and temperance. Seek to arouse the intellect and the conscience. Bring into service all the talent at command, and follow up the work with publications upon the subject. "Educate, educate, educate," is the message that has been impressed upon me.

(1900) 6T 112

781. As we near the close of time, we must rise higher and still higher upon the question of health reform and

Christian temperance, presenting it in a more positive and decided manner. We must strive continually to educate the people, not only by our words, but by our practice. Precept and practice combined have a telling influence.

Appeal to Ministers, Conference Presidents, and Other Leaders

(1900) 6T 376-378

782. Our ministers should become intelligent on health reform. They need to become acquainted with physiology and hygiene; they should understand the laws that govern physical life, and their bearing upon the health of mind and soul.

Thousands upon thousands know little of the wonderful body God has given them or of the care it should receive; and they consider it of more importance to study subjects of far less consequence. The ministers have a work to do here. When they take a right position on this subject, much will be gained. In their own lives and homes they should obey the laws of life, practicing right principles and living healthfully. Then they will be able to speak correctly on this subject, leading the people higher and still higher in the work of reform. Living in the light themselves, they can bear a message of great value to those who are in need of just such a testimony.

There are precious blessings and a rich experience to be gained if ministers will combine the presentation of the health question with all their labors in the churches. The people must have the light on health reform. This work has been neglected, and many are ready to die because they need the light which they ought to have and must have before they will give up selfish indulgence.

The presidents of our conferences need to realize that it is high time they were placing themselves on the right side of this question. Ministers and teachers are to give to others the light they have received. Their work in every line is needed. God will help them; He will strengthen His servants who stand firmly, and will not be swayed from truth and righteousness in order to accommodate self-indulgence.

The work of educating in medical missionary lines is an advance step of great importance in awakening man to his moral responsibilities. Had the ministers taken hold of this work in its various departments in accordance with the light which God has given, there would have been a most decided reformation in eating, drinking, and dressing. But some have stood directly in the way of the advance of health reform. They have held the people back by their indifferent or condemnatory remarks, or by pleasantries and jokes. They themselves and a large number of others have been sufferers unto death, but all have not yet learned wisdom.

It has been only by the most aggressive warfare that any advancement has been made. The people have been unwilling to deny self, unwilling to yield the mind and will to the will of God; and in their own sufferings, and in their influence on others, they have realized the sure result of such a course.

The church is making history. Every day is a battle and a march. On every side we are beset by invisible foes, and we either conquer through the grace given us by God or we are conquered. I urge that those who are taking a neutral position in regard to health reform be converted. This light is precious, and the Lord gives me the message to urge that all who bear responsibilities in any line in the work of God take heed that truth is in the ascendancy in the heart and life. Only thus can any meet the temptations they are sure to encounter in the world.

FAILURE TO PRACTICE HEALTH REFORM DISQUALIFIES FOR THE MINISTRY

Why do some of our ministering brethren manifest so little interest in health reform? It is because instruction on temperance in all things is opposed to their practice of self-indulgence. In some places this has been the great stumbling block in the way of our bringing the people to investigate and practice and teach health reform. No man should be set apart as a teacher of the people while his own teaching or example contradicts the testimony God has given His servants to bear in regard to diet, for this will bring confusion. His disregard of health reform unfits him to stand as the Lord's messenger.

The light that the Lord has given on this subject in His word is plain, and men will be tested and tried in many ways to see if they will heed it. Every church, every family, needs to be instructed in regard to Christian temperance. All should know how to eat and drink in order to preserve health. We are amid the closing scenes of this world's history; and there should be harmonious action in the ranks of Sabbathkeepers. Those who stand aloof from the great work of instructing the people upon this question, do not follow where the Great Physician leads the way. "If any man will come after Me," Christ said, "let him deny himself, and take up his cross, and follow Me." Matt. 16:24.

Health Education in the Home

(1905) M.H. 386

783. Parents should live more for their children, and less for society. Study health subjects, and put your knowledge to a practical use. Teach your children to reason from cause to effect. Teach them that if they desire health and happiness, they must obey the laws of nature. Though you may not see so rapid improvement as you desire, be not discouraged, but patiently and perseveringly continue your work.

Teach your children from the cradle to practice self-denial and self-control. Teach them to enjoy the beauties of nature, and in useful employments to exercise systematically all the powers of body and mind. Bring them up to have sound constitutions and good morals, to have sunny dispositions and sweet tempers. Impress upon their tender minds the truth that God does not design that we should live for present gratification merely, but for our ultimate good. Teach them that to yield to temptation is weak and wicked; to resist, noble and manly. These lessons will be as seed sown in good soil, and they will bear fruit that will make your hearts glad.

God's Work Hindered by Selfish Indulgence

(1900) 6T 370, 371

784. There is a message regarding health reform to be borne in every church. There is a work to be done in every school. Neither principal nor teachers should be entrusted with the education of the youth until they have a practical knowledge of this subject. Some have felt at liberty to criticize and question and find fault with health reform principles of which they know little by experience. They should stand shoulder to shoulder, heart to heart, with those who are working in right lines.

The subject of health reform has been presented in the churches; but the light has not been heartily received. The selfish, health-destroying indulgences of men and women have counteracted the influence of the message that is to prepare a people for the great day of God. If the churches expect strength, they must live the truth which God has given them. If the members of our churches disregard the light on this subject, they will reap the sure result in both spiritual and physical degeneracy. And the influence of these older church members will leaven those newly come to the faith. The Lord does not now work to bring many souls into the truth, because of the church members who have never been converted, and those who were once converted, but who have backslidden. What influence would these unconsecrated members have on new converts? Would they not make of no effect the God-given message which His people are to bear?

Every Member to Impart Truth

(1902) 7T 62

785. We have come to a time when every member of the church should take hold of medical missionary work. The world is a lazar house filled with victims of both physical and spiritual disease. Everywhere people are perishing for lack of a knowledge of the truths that have been committed to us. The members of the church are in need of an awakening, that they may realize their responsibility to impart

these truths. Those who have been enlightened by the truth are to be light bearers to the world. To hide our light at this time is to make a terrible mistake. The message to God's people today is, "Arise, shine; for thy light is come, and the glory of the Lord is risen upon thee."

On every hand we see those who have had much light and knowledge deliberately choosing evil in the place of good. Making no attempt to reform, they are growing worse and worse. But the people of God are not to walk in darkness. They are to walk in the light, for they are reformers.

Establish New Centers

(1904) 8T 148

786. It is the positive duty of God's people to go into the regions beyond. Let forces be set at work to clear new ground, to establish new centers of influence wherever an opening can be found. Rally workers who possess true missionary zeal, and let them go forth to diffuse light and knowledge far and near. Let them take the living principles of health reform into the communities that to a large degree are ignorant of these principles. Let classes be formed, and instruction be given regarding the treatment of disease.

(1909) 9T 36, 37

787. There is a wide field of service for women as well as for men. The efficient cook, the seamstress, the nurse—the help of all is needed. Let the members of poor households be taught how to cook, how to make and mend their own clothing, how to nurse the sick, how to care properly for the home. Even the children should be taught to do some little errand of love and mercy for those less fortunate than themselves.

Educators, Go Forward

(1909) 9T 112, 113

788. The work of health reform is the Lord's means for lessening suffering in our world and for purifying His church. Teach the people that they can act as God's helping hand, by cooperating with the Master Worker in restoring physical and spiritual health. This work bears the signature

of Heaven, and will open doors for the entrance of other precious truths. There is room for all to labor who will take hold of this work intelligently.

Keep the work of health reform to the front, is the message I am instructed to bear. Show so plainly its value that a widespread need for it will be felt. Abstinence from all hurtful food and drink is the fruit of true religion. He who is thoroughly converted will abandon every injurious habit and appetite. By total abstinence he will overcome his desire for health-destroying indulgences.

I am instructed to say to health reform educators, Go forward. The world needs every jot of the influence you can exert to press back the tide of moral woe. Let those who teach the third angel's message stand true to their colors.

PART II—HOW TO PRESENT THE PRINCIPLES OF HEALTH REFORM

Keep in View the Great Object of Reform

(1905) M.H. 146, 147

789. There is great need of instruction in regard to dietetic reform. Wrong habits of eating and the use of unhealthful food are in no small degree responsible for the intemperance and crime and wretchedness that curse the world.

In teaching health principles, keep before the mind the great object of reform,—that its purpose is to secure the highest development of body and mind and soul. Show that the laws of nature, being the laws of God, are designed for our good; that obedience to them promotes happiness in this life, and aids in the preparation for the life to come.

Lead the people to study the manifestation of God's love and wisdom in the works of nature. Lead them to study that marvelous organism, the human system, and the laws by which it is governed. Those who perceive the evidences of God's love, who understand something of the wisdom and beneficence of His laws, and the results of obedience, will come to regard their duties and obligations from an altogether different point of view. Instead of looking upon an observance of the laws of health as a matter of sacrifice or self-denial, they will regard it, as it really is, as an inestimable blessing.

Every gospel worker should feel that the giving of instruction in the principles of healthful living, is a part of his appointed work. Of this work there is great need, and the world is open for it.

(1905) M.H. 130

790. The requirements of God must be brought home to the conscience. Men and women must be awakened to the duty of self-mastery, the need of purity, freedom from every depraving appetite and defiling habit. They need to be impressed with the fact that all their powers of mind and body are the gift of God, and are to be preserved in the best possible condition for His service.

Follow the Saviour's Methods

(1905) M.H. 143, 144

791. Christ's method alone will give true success in reaching the people. The Saviour mingled with men as one who desired their good. He showed His sympathy for them, ministered to their needs, and won their confidence. Then He bade them, "Follow Me."

There is need of coming close to the people by personal effort. If less time were given to sermonizing, and more time were spent in personal ministry, greater results would be seen. The poor are to be relieved, the sick cared for, the sorrowing and bereaved comforted, the ignorant instructed, the inexperienced counseled. We are to weep with those that weep, and rejoice with those that rejoice. Accompanied by the power of persuasion, the power of prayer, the power of the love of God, this work will not, cannot, be without fruit.

We should ever remember that the object of the medical missionary work is to point sin-sick men and women to the Man of Calvary, who taketh away the sin of the world. By beholding Him, they will be changed into His likeness. We are to encourage the sick and suffering to look to Jesus and live. Let the workers keep Christ, the Great Physician, constantly before those to whom disease of the body and soul has brought discouragement. Point them to the One who can heal both physical and spiritual disease. Tell them of the One who is touched with the feeling of their infirmities. Encourage them to place themselves in the care of Him who gave His life to make it possible for them to have life eternal. Talk of His love; tell of His power to save.

Use Tact and Courtesy

(1905) M.H. 156, 157

792. In all your work remember that you are bound up with Christ, a part of the great plan of redemption. The love of Christ, in a healing, life-giving current, is to flow through your life. As you seek to draw others within the circle of His love, let the purity of your language, the unselfishness of your service, the joyfulness of your demeanor, bear witness to the power of His grace. Give to the world so pure and righteous a representation of Him, that men shall behold Him in His beauty.

It is of little use to try to reform others by attacking what we may regard as wrong habits. Such effort often results in more harm than good. In His talk with the Samaritan woman, instead of disparaging Jacob's well, Christ presented something better. "If thou knewest the gift of God," He said, "and who it is that saith to thee, Give Me to drink; thou wouldst have asked of Him, and He would have given thee living water." He turned the conversation to the treasure He had to bestow, offering the woman something better than she possessed, even living water, the joy and hope of the gospel.

This is an illustration of the way in which we are to work. We must offer men something better than that which they possess, even the peace of Christ, which passeth all understanding. We must tell them of God's holy law, the transcript of His character, and an expression of that which He wishes them to become. . . .

Of all the people in the world, reformers should be the most unselfish, the most kind, the most courteous. In their lives should be seen the true goodness of unselfish deeds. The worker who manifests a lack of courtesy, who shows impatience at the ignorance or waywardness of others, who speaks hastily or acts thoughtlessly, may close the door to hearts so that he can never reach them.

Diet Reform to Be Progressive

(1902) 7T 132-136

793. From the beginning of the health reform work, we have found it necessary to educate, educate, educate. God desires us to continue this work of educating the people. . . .

In teaching health reform, as in all other gospel work, we are to meet the people where they are. Until we can teach them how to prepare health reform foods that are palatable, nourishing, and yet inexpensive, we are not at liberty to present the most advanced propositions regarding health reform diet.

Let the diet reform be progressive. Let the people be taught how to prepare food without the use of milk or butter. Tell them that the time will soon come when there will be no safety in using eggs, milk, cream, or butter, because disease in animals is increasing in proportion to the increase of wickedness among men. The time is near when, because of the iniquity of the fallen race, the whole animal creation will groan under the diseases that curse our earth.

God will give His people ability and tact to prepare wholesome food without these things. Let our people discard all unwholesome recipes. Let them learn how to live healthfully, teaching to others what they have learned. Let them impart this knowledge as they would Bible instruction. Let them teach the people to preserve the health and increase the strength by avoiding the large amount of cooking that has filled the world with chronic invalids. By precept and example make it plain that the food which God gave Adam in his sinless state is the best for man's use as he seeks to regain that sinless state.

Those who teach the principles of health reform should be intelligent in regard to disease and its causes, understanding that every action of the human agent should be in perfect harmony with the laws of life. The light God has given on health reform is for our salvation and the salvation of the world. Men and women should be informed in regard to the human habitation, fitted up by our Creator as His dwelling place, and over which He desires us to be faithful stewards. "For ye are the temple of the living God; as God hath said, I will dwell in them, and walk in them; and I will be their God, and they shall be My people." 2 Cor. 6:16.

Hold up the principles of health reform, and let the Lord lead the honest in heart. Present the principles of temperance in their most attractive form. Circulate the books that give instruction in regard to healthful living.

THE INFLUENCE OF OUR HEALTH PUBLICATIONS

The people are in sad need of the light shining from the pages of our health books and journals. God desires to use these books and journals as mediums through which flashes of light shall arrest the attention of the people, and cause them to heed the warning of the message of the third angel. Our health journals are instrumentalities in the field to do a special work in disseminating the light that the inhabitants of the world must have in this day of God's preparation. They wield an untold influence in the interests of health and temperance and social-purity reform, and will accomplish great good in presenting these subjects in a proper manner and in their true light to the people.

Tracts on Health Reform

R. & H., Nov. 4, 1875

794. There should be more earnest efforts made to enlighten the people upon the great subject of health reform. Tracts of four, eight, twelve, sixteen, and more pages, con-

taining pointed, well-written articles on this great question, should be scattered like the leaves of autumn.

[Sanitarium patients to be taught in parlor lectures—426]
[Sanitarium patients to be taught correct diet by properly furnished table—442, 443]
[Sanitarium patients to be taught temperance—474]

Handle the Flesh Meat Question Wisely

Letter 102, 1896

795. In this country [Australia] there is an organized vegetarian society, but its numbers are comparatively few. Among the people in general, meat is largely used by all classes. It is the cheapest article of food; and even where poverty abounds, meat is usually found upon the table. Therefore there is the more need of handling wisely the question of meat eating. In regard to this matter there should be no rash movements. We should consider the situation of the people, and the power of lifelong habits and practices, and should be careful not to urge our ideas upon others, as if this question were a test, and those who eat largely of meat were the greatest sinners.

All should have the light on this question, but let it be carefully presented. Habits that have been thought right for a lifetime are not to be changed by harsh or hasty measures. We should educate the people at our camp meetings and other large gatherings. While the principles of health reform should be presented, let the teaching be backed by example. Let no meat be found at our restaurants or dining tents, but let its place be supplied with fruits, grains, and vegetables. We must practice what we teach. When sitting at a table where meat is provided, we are not to make a raid upon those who use it, but we should let it alone ourselves, and when asked our reasons for doing this, we should in a kindly manner explain why we do not use it.

A Time to Keep Silent

Letter 76, 1895

796. I have never felt that it was my duty to say that no one should taste of meat under any circumstances. To say

this when the people have been educated to live on flesh to so great an extent, would be carrying matters to extremes. I have never felt that it was my duty to make sweeping assertions. What I have said I have said under a sense of duty, but I have been guarded in my statements, because I did not want to give occasion for any one to be conscience for another. . . .

I have been passing through an experience in this country that is similar to the experience I had in new fields in America. I have seen families whose circumstances would not permit them to furnish their table with healthful food. Unbelieving neighbors have sent them in portions of meat from animals recently killed. They have made soup of the meat, and supplied their large families of children with meals of bread and soup. It was not my duty, nor did I think it was the duty of any one else, to lecture them upon the evils of meat eating. I feel sincere pity for families who have newly come to the faith, and who are so pressed with poverty that they know not from whence their next meal is coming. It is not my duty to discourse to them on healthful eating. There is a time to speak, and a time to keep silent. The opportunity furnished by circumstances of this order is an opportunity to speak words that will encourage and bless, rather than condemn and reprove. Those who have lived upon a meat diet all their life do not see the evil of continuing the practice, and they must be treated tenderly.

(1909) 9T 163

797. While working against gluttony and intemperance, we must recognize the condition to which the human family is subjected. God has made provision for those who live in the different countries of the world. Those who desire to be co-workers with God must consider carefully before they specify just what foods should and should not be eaten. We are to be brought into connection with the masses. Should health reform in its most extreme form be taught to those whose circumstances forbid its adoption, more harm than good would be done. As I preach the gospel to the poor, I am instructed to tell them to eat that food which is most nourishing. I cannot say to them: "You must not eat eggs,

or milk or cream. You must use no butter in the preparation of food." The gospel must be preached to the poor, but the time has not yet come to prescribe the strictest diet.

A Wrong Method of Working

(1890) C.T.B.H. 119, 120

798. Do not catch hold of isolated ideas and make them a test, criticizing others whose practice may not agree with your opinion; but study the subject broadly and deeply, and seek to bring your own ideas and practices into perfect harmony with the principles of true Christian temperance.

There are many who try to correct the lives of others by attacking what they regard as wrong habits. They go to those whom they think in error, and point out their defects, but do not seek to direct the mind to true principles. Such a course often comes far short of securing the desired results. When we make it evident that we are trying to correct others, we too often arouse their combativeness, and do more harm than good. And there is the danger to the reprover also. He who takes it upon himself to correct others, is likely to cultivate a habit of faultfinding, and soon his whole interest will be in picking flaws and finding defects. Do not watch others, to pick at their faults, or expose their errors. Educate them to better habits by the power of your own example.

Let it ever be kept before the mind that the great object of hygienic reform is to secure the highest possible development of mind and soul and body. All the laws of nature—which are the laws of God—are designed for our good. Obedience to them will promote our happiness in this life, and will aid us in a preparation for the life to come.

There is something better to talk about than the faults and weaknesses of others. Talk of God and His wonderful works. Study into the manifestations of His love and wisdom in all the works of nature.

Teach by Example

(1900) 6T 336

799. In your association with unbelievers, do not allow yourselves to be swerved from right principles. If you sit at

their table, eat temperately, and only of food that will not confuse the mind. Keep clear of intemperance. You cannot afford to weaken your mental or physical powers, lest you become unable to discern spiritual things. Keep your mind in such a condition that God can impress it with the precious truths of His word. . . . Do not watch others in order to point out their faults or errors. Teach by example. Let your self-denial and your victory over appetite be an illustration of obedience to right principles. Let your life bear witness to the sanctifying, ennobling influence of truth.

Present Temperance in Its Most Attractive Form

Letter 135, 1902

800. The Lord desires every minister, every physician, every church member, to be careful not to urge those who are ignorant of our faith to make sudden changes in diet, thus bringing them to a premature test. Hold up the principles of health reform, and let the Lord lead the honest in heart. They will hear and believe. The Lord does not require His messengers to present the beautiful truths of health reform in a way that will prejudice the minds of others. Let no one place stumbling blocks before those who are walking in the dark paths of ignorance. Even in praising a good thing, it is well not to be too enthusiastic, lest you turn out of the way those who come to hear. Present the principles of temperance in their most attractive form.

We must not move presumptuously. The laborers who enter new territory to raise up churches must not create difficulties by attempting to make prominent the question of diet. They should be careful not to draw the lines too closely. Impediments would thus be thrown on the pathway of others. Do not drive the people. Lead them. Preach the word as it is in Christ Jesus. . . . Workers must put forth resolute, persevering effort, remembering that everything cannot be learned at once. They must have a fixed determination patiently to teach the people.

MS 1a 1890

801. Do you not remember that we have an individual accountability? We do not make articles of diet a test question, but we do try to educate the intellect, and to arouse the moral sensibility to take hold of health reform in an intelligent manner, as Paul presents it in Romans 13:8-14; 1 Corinthians 9:24-27; 1 Timothy 3:8-12.

Meet the People Where They Are

Letter 363, 1907

802. On one occasion Sara [McEnterfer] was called to a family at Dora Creek, where every member of the household was sick. The father belonged to a highly respectable family, but he had taken to drink, and his wife and children were in great want. At this time of sickness there was nothing in the house suitable to eat. And they refused to eat anything that we took them. They had been accustomed to having meat. We felt that something must be done. I said to Sara, Take chickens from my place, and prepare them some broth. So Sara treated them for their illness, and fed them with this broth. They soon recovered.

Now this is the course we pursued. We did not say to the people, You must not eat meat. Although we did not use flesh foods ourselves, when we thought it essential for that family in their time of sickness, we gave them what we felt they needed. There are occasions when we must meet the people where they are.

The father of this family was an intelligent man. When the family was well again, we opened to them the Scriptures, and this man was converted, and accepted the truth. He threw away his pipe and gave up the use of drink, and from that time, as long as he lived, he neither smoked nor drank. As soon as it was possible, we took him on our farm, and gave him work on the land. While we were away attending meetings in Newcastle, this man died. Thorough treatment was given him by some of our workers, but the long-abused body could not respond to their efforts. But he died a Christian and a commandment keeper.

Meeting Extreme Views—A Historical Statement*

(1870) 3T 18-21

803. When we returned from Kansas in the autumn of 1870, Brother B was at home sick with fever. . . . His case was critical. . . .

There was no period of rest for us, however much we needed it. The *Review,* the *Reformer,* and the *Instructor* must be edited. [Their editors were all sick at this time.] . . . My husband commenced his labor and I helped him what I could. . . .

The *Reformer* was about dead. Brother B had urged the extreme positions of Doctor Trall. This had influenced the doctor to come out in the *Reformer* stronger than he otherwise would have done, in discarding milk, sugar, and salt. The position to entirely discontinue the use of these things may be right in its order; but the time had not come to take a general stand upon these points. And those who do take their position, and advocate the entire disuse of milk, butter, and sugar, should have their own tables free from these things. Brother B, even while taking his stand in the *Reformer* with Doctor Trall in regard to the injurious effects of salt, milk, and sugar, did not practice the things he taught. Upon his own table these things were used daily.

Many of our people had lost their interest in the *Reformer,* and letters were daily received with this discouraging request, "Please discontinue my *Reformer.*" . . . We could not raise an interest anywhere in the West to obtain subscribers for the *Health Reformer.* We saw that the writers in the *Reformer* were going away from the people, and leaving them behind. If we take positions that conscientious Christians, who are indeed reformers, cannot adopt, how can we expect to benefit the class whom we can reach only from a health standpoint.

---

* For a collateral statement by James White, see Appendix II.

PATIENCE, CAUTION, AND CONSISTENCY NECESSARY
IN REFORM MOVEMENTS

We must go no faster than we can take those with us whose consciences and intellects are convinced of the truths we advocate. We must meet the people where they are. Some of us have been many years in arriving at our present position in health reform. It is slow work to obtain a reform in diet. We have powerful appetites to meet; for the world is given to gluttony. If we should allow the people as much time as we have required to come up to the present advanced state in reform, we would be very patient with them, and allow them to advance step by step, as we have done, until their feet are firmly established upon the health reform platform. But we should be very cautious not to advance too fast, lest we be obliged to retrace our steps. In reforms, we would better come one step short of the mark than to go one step beyond it. And if there is error at all, let it be on the side next to the people.

Above all things, we should not with our pens advocate positions that we do not put to a practical test in our own families, upon our own tables. This is a dissimulation, a species of hypocrisy. In Michigan we can get along better without salt, sugar, and milk, than can many who are situated in the Far West or in the Far East, where there is a scarcity of fruit. . . . We know that a free use of these things is positively injurious to health, and in many cases we think that if they were not used at all, a much better state of health would be enjoyed.

But at present our burden is not upon these things. The people are so far behind that we see it is all they can bear to have us draw the line upon their injurious indulgences and stimulating narcotics. We bear positive testimony against tobacco, spirituous liquors, snuff, tea, coffee, flesh meats, butter, spices, rich cakes, mince pies, a large amount of salt, and all exciting substances used as articles of food.

If we come to persons who have not been enlightened in regard to health reform, and present our strongest positions at first, there is danger of their becoming discouraged as they see how much they have to give up, so that they will make no effort to reform. We must lead the people along patiently and gradually, remembering the hole of the pit whence we were digged.

PART III—COOKING SCHOOLS

A Work of Utmost Importance

(1902) 7T 55

804. Wherever medical missionary work is carried on in our large cities, cooking schools should be held; and wherever a strong educational missionary work is in progress, a hygienic restaurant of some sort should be established, which shall give a practical illustration of the proper selection and the healthful preparation of foods.

(1909) 9T 112

805. Cooking schools are to be held. The people are to be taught how to prepare wholesome food. They are to be shown the need of discarding unhealthful foods. But we should never advocate a starvation diet. It is possible to have a wholesome, nutritious diet without the use of tea, coffee, and flesh food. The work of teaching the people how to prepare a dietary that is at once wholesome and appetizing, is of the utmost importance.

(1902) 7T 126

806. Some, after adopting a vegetarian diet, return to the use of flesh meat. This is foolish, indeed, and reveals a lack of knowledge of how to provide proper food in the place of meat.

Cooking schools, conducted by wise instructors, are to be held in America and in other lands. Everything that we can do should be done to show the people the value of the reform diet.

(1905) M.H. 320, 321

807. The diet reform should be progressive. As disease in animals increases, the use of milk and eggs will become more and more unsafe. An effort should be made to supply their place with other things that are healthful and inexpen-

sive. The people everywhere should be taught how to cook without milk and eggs so far as possible, and yet have their food wholesome and palatable.

(1890) C.T.B.H. 119

808. Those who can avail themselves of the advantages of properly conducted, hygienic cooking schools, will find it a great benefit, both in their own practice and in teaching others.

In Every Church, Church School, and Mission Field

(1905) M.H. 149

809. Every church should be a training school for Christian workers. Its members should be taught how to give Bible readings, how to conduct and teach Sabbath school classes, how best to help the poor and to care for the sick, how to work for the unconverted. There should be schools of health, cooking schools, and classes in various lines of Christian help work. There should not only be teaching, but actual work under experienced instructors.

MS 79, 1900

810. Every hygienic restaurant should be a school for the workers connected with it. In the cities this line of work may be done on a much larger scale than in smaller places. But in every place where there is a church and a church school, instruction should be given in regard to the preparation of simple health foods for the use of those who wish to live in accordance with the principles of health reform. And in all our missionary fields a similar work can be done.

The work of combining fruits, seeds, grains, and roots into wholesome foods, is the Lord's work. In every place where a church has been established, let the church members walk humbly before God. Let them seek to enlighten the people with health reform principles.

Their Rightful Place

(1900) 6T 44, 45

811. As far as possible, our camp meeting should be wholly devoted to spiritual interests. . . . Business matters should be attended to by those specially appointed for this

work. And as far as possible they should be brought before the people at some other time than the camp meeting. Instruction in canvassing, in Sabbath school work, and in the details of tract and missionary work, should be given in the home churches, or in meetings specially appointed. The same principle applies to cooking schools. While these are all right in their place, they should not occupy the time of our camp meetings.

A Reforming Agency

(1902) 7T 113, 114

812. Cooking schools are to be established in many places. This work may begin in a humble way, but as intelligent cooks do their best to enlighten others, the Lord will give them skill and understanding. The word of the Lord is, "Forbid them not; for I will reveal Myself to them as their Instructor." He will work with those who carry out His plans, teaching the people how to bring about a reformation in their diet by the preparation of healthful, inexpensive foods. Thus the poor will be encouraged to adopt the principles of health reform; they will be helped to become industrious and self-reliant.

It has been presented to me that men and women of capability were being taught of God how to prepare wholesome, palatable foods in an acceptable manner. Many of these were young, and there were also those of mature age. I have been instructed to encourage the conducting of cooking schools in all places where medical missionary work is being done. Every inducement to lead the people to reform must be held out before them. Let as much light as possible shine upon them. Teach them to make every improvement that they can in the preparation of food, and encourage them to impart to others that which they learn.

Shall we not do all in our power to advance the work in all of our large cities? Thousands upon thousands who live near us need help in various ways. Let the ministers of the gospel remember that the Lord Jesus Christ said to His disciples: "Ye are the light of the world. A city that is set on a hill cannot be hid." "Ye are the salt of the earth; but if the salt have lost his savor, wherewith shall it be salted?" Matt. 5:14, 13.

Teaching From House to House

R. & H., June 6, 1912

813. Because the avenues to the soul have been closed by the tyrant Prejudice, many are ignorant of the principles of healthful living. Good service can be done by teaching the people how to prepare healthful food. This line of work is as essential as any that can be taken up. More cooking schools should be established, and some should labor from house to house, giving instruction in the art of cooking wholesome foods. Many, many will be rescued from physical, mental, and moral degeneracy through the influence of health reform. These principles will commend themselves to those who are seeking for light; and such will advance from this to receive the full truth for this time.

God wants His people to receive to impart. As impartial, unselfish witnesses, they are to give to others what the Lord has given them. And as you enter into this work, and by whatever means in your power seek to reach hearts, be sure to work in a way that will remove prejudice instead of creating it. Make the life of Christ your constant study, and labor as He did, following His example.

Teaching Diet Reform at Holiday Gatherings and Special Entertainments

Letter 166, 1903

814. When the light of health reform first came to us, we used, on holiday occasions, to take cooking stoves to the grounds where the people were assembled, and right there bake unleavened bread,—gems and rolls. And I think that the result of our efforts was good, though, of course, we had not the health food preparations that we now have. At that time we were just beginning to learn how to live without using flesh meat.

Sometimes we gave entertainments, and we took great care that all that we prepared for the table was palatable and

icely served. In fruit season, we would get blueberries and
ispberries fresh from the bushes, and strawberries fresh
om the vines. We made the table fare an object lesson
hich showed those present that our diet, even though it
as in accordance with the principles of health reform, was
ir from being a meager one.

Sometimes a short temperance lecture was given in con-
ection with these entertainments, and thus people became
cquainted with our principles of living. As far as we know,
ll were pleased and all were enlightened. We always had
>mething to say about the necessity of providing wholesome
>od and of preparing it simply, and yet making it so pala-
ible and appetizing that those eating it would be satisfied.

The world is full of the temptation to indulge appetite,
nd words of warning, earnest and right to the point, have
iade wonderful changes in families and in individuals.

he Opportunities and Dangers of Our Restaurants

MS 27, 1906

815. Light was also given that in the cities there would be
>pportunity to do a work similar to that which we did on the
iattle Creek fairgrounds. In harmony with this light, hy-
ienic restaurants have been established. But there is grave
anger that our restaurant workers will become so imbued
ith the spirit of commercialism that they will fail to impart
ie light which the people need. Our restaurants bring us
a contact with many people, but if we allow our minds to be
ngrossed with the thought of financial profit, we shall fail
> fulfill the purpose of God. He would have us take advan-
ige of every opportunity to present the truth that is to save
ien and women from eternal death.

I have tried to ascertain how many souls have been con-
erted to the truth as a result of the restaurant work here
1 ———. Some may have been saved, but many more
ight be converted to God if every effort were made to
>nduct the work in God's order, and to let light shine into
ie pathway of others.

I would say to the workers connected with the restau-rant, Do not continue to work as you have been working. Seek to make the restaurant a means of communicating to others the light of present truth. For this purpose only have our restaurants been established. . . .

The workers in the ———— restaurant and the members of the ———— church need to be thoroughly converted. To every one has been given the talent of intellect. Have you received power to prevail with God? "As many as received Him, to them gave He power to become the sons of God, even to them that believe on His name."

Tact and Discretion Required in Educators

(1909) 9T 161

816. Greater efforts should be put forth to educate the people in the principles of health reform. Cooking schools should be established, and house-to-house instruction should be given in the art of cooking wholesome food. Old and young should learn how to cook more simply. Wherever the truth is presented, the people are to be taught how to prepare food in a simple, yet appetizing way. They are to be shown that a nourishing diet can be provided without the use of flesh foods. . . .

Much tact and discretion should be employed in pre-paring nourishing food to take the place of that which has formerly constituted the diet of those who are learning to be health reformers. Faith in God, earnestness of purpose, and a willingness to help one another, will be required. A diet lacking in the proper elements of nutrition, brings reproach upon the cause of health reform. We are mortal, and must supply ourselves with food that will give proper nourishment to the body.

Cooking Classes in All Our Schools

(1913) C.T. 312, 313

817. In all our schools there should be those who are fitted to teach cooking. Classes for instruction in this subject should be held. Those who are receiving a training for

ervice suffer a great loss when they do not gain a knowledge of how to prepare food so that it is both wholesome nd palatable.

The science of cooking is not a small matter. The skillful preparation of food is one of the most essential arts. It hould be regarded as among the most valuable of all the rts, because it is so closely connected with the life. Both physical and mental strength depend to a great degree upon he food we eat; therefore the one who prepares the food ccupies an important and elevated position.

Both young men and young women should be taught how o cook economically, and to dispense with everything in the ine of flesh food. Let no encouragement be given to the reparation of dishes which are composed in any degree of lesh food; for this is pointing to the darkness and ignorance f Egypt, rather than to the purity of health reform.

Women especially should learn how to cook. What part f the education of a girl is so important as this? Whatever nay be her circumstances in life, here is knowledge that she nay put to practical use. It is a branch of education which as a most direct influence upon health and happiness. There is practical religion in a loaf of good bread.

(1900) 6T 182

818. Many young people will come to school who desire training in industrial lines. The industrial instruction hould include the keeping of accounts, carpentry, and verything that is comprehended in farming. Preparation hould also be made for teaching blacksmithing, painting, hoemaking, cooking, baking, laundering, mending, typevriting, and printing. Every power at our command is to e brought into this training work, that students may go ut equipped for the duties of practical life.

MS 95, 1901

819. Connected with our sanitariums and schools there hould be cooking schools, where instruction is given on the roper preparation of food. In all our schools there should e those who are fitted to educate the students, both men nd women, in the art of cooking. Women especially should earn how to cook.

820. The students in our schools should be taught how t
cook. Let tact and skill be brought into this branch of edu
cation. With all deceivableness of unrighteousness, Sata
is working to turn the feet of the youth into paths of tempta
tion that lead to ruin. We must strengthen and help the
to withstand the temptations that are to be met on ever
side regarding the indulgence of appetite. To teach the
the science of healthful living is to do missionary wor
for the Master.

(1903) Ed. 218

821. Manual training is deserving of far more attentio
than it has received. Schools should be established that, i
addition to the highest mental and moral culture, shall pr
vide the best possible facilities for physical development an
industrial training. Instruction should be given in agricul
ture, manufactures,—covering as many as possible of th
most useful trades,—also in household economy, healthfu
cookery, sewing, hygienic dressmaking, the treatment of th
sick, and kindred lines.

Faithfulness in Common Duties

(1903) Ed. 216

822. Many of the branches of study that consume the stu
dent's time are not essential to usefulness or happiness; bu
it is essential for every youth to have a thorough acquaint
ance with everyday duties. If need be, a young woman ca
dispense with a knowledge of French and algebra, or eve
of the piano; but it is indispensable that she learn to mak
good bread, to fashion neatly fitting garments, and to per
form efficiently the many duties that pertain to homemaking

To the health and happiness of the whole family nothin
is more vital than skill and intelligence on the part of th
cook. By ill-prepared, unwholesome food she may hinde
and even ruin both the adult's usefulness and the child'
development. Or by providing food adapted to the needs o
the body, and at the same time inviting and palatable, sh
can accomplish as much in the right as otherwise she accom

plishes in the wrong direction. So in many ways, life's happiness is bound up with faithfulness in common duties.

Since both men and women have a part in homemaking, boys as well as girls should gain a knowledge of household duties. To make a bed and put a room in order, to wash dishes, to prepare a meal, to wash and repair his own clothing, is a training that need not make any boy less manly; it will make him happier and more useful.

[Every woman should become mistress of the culinary art—385]

[Important and elevated position of the cook—371]

[Cooking demonstrations to be given at camp meetings—763, 764]

[People to be taught to use local products—376, 407]

Appendix

Quotations in Appendix

Appendix

APPENDIX I

PERSONAL EXPERIENCE OF ELLEN G. WHITE AS A HEALTH REFORMER

[In reading the statements from Mrs. White's pen regarding her dietetic practices, the thoughtful student will recognize the following principles:

First: "The diet reform should be progressive."—*M.H. 320.* The light was not given in its fullness at the first. It was bestowed with increasing force from time to time as people were prepared to understand and act upon it, and it was fitted to the general practices and customs of eating at the time the instruction was given.

Second: "We do not mark out any precise line to be followed in diet."—*9T 159.* Repeated warnings were given against certain specific injurious foods. But in the main, general principles were laid down, and detailed application of these broad principles must sometimes be determined by experimentation, and by the best scientific conclusions available.

Third: "I make myself a criterion for no one else."—*Letter 45, 1903.* Having by intelligent experimentation adopted certain rules for herself, Mrs. White at times described the dietetic regimen of her own home, but not as a rule by which others must be rigidly governed.—COMPILERS.]

The First Health Reform Vision

R. & H., Oct. 8, 1867

1. IT was at the house of Brother A. Hilliard, at Otsego, Michigan, June 6, 1863, that the great subject of health reform was opened before me in vision.

Revealed as Progressive Work

[General Conference Bulletin, April 12, 1901] C.H. 531

2. In the light given me so long ago (1863), I was shown that intemperance would prevail in the world to an alarming extent, and that every one of the people of God must take an elevated stand in regard to reformation in habits and practices. . . . The Lord presented a general plan before me. I was shown that God would give to His commandment-keeping people a reform diet, and that as they received this,

their disease and suffering would be greatly lessened. was shown that this work would progress.

[To steadily progress toward the ideal diet—651]
[A caution against advancing too fast—803]

A Personal Acceptance of the Message

MS 50, 1904

3. I accepted the light on health reform as it came to me It has been a great blessing to me. I have better health today notwithstanding I am seventy-six years old, than I had in my younger days. I thank God for the principles of health reform.

After One Year's Trial—Benefits Received

(1864) Sp. Gifts IV, 153, 154

4. I have thought for years that I was dependent upon a meat diet for strength. I have eaten three meals a day until within a few months. It has been very difficult for me to go from one meal to another without suffering from faintness at the stomach, and dizziness of the head. Eating would remove these feelings. I seldom allowed myself to eat anything between my regular meals, and have made it a practice to often retire without supper. But I have suffered greatly for want of food from breakfast to dinner, and have frequently fainted. Eating meat removed for the time these faint feelings. I therefore decided that meat was indispensable in my case.

But since the Lord presented before me, in June, 1863, the subject of meat eating in relation to health, I have left the use of meat. For a while it was rather difficult to bring my appetite to bread, for which, formerly, I had but little relish. But by persevering, I have been able to do this. I have lived for nearly one year without meat. For about six months most of the bread upon our table has been unleavened cakes, made of unbolted wheat meal and water, and a very little salt. We use fruits and vegetables liberally. I have lived for eight months upon two meals a day.

I have applied myself to writing the most of the time for above a year. For eight months have been confined closely to writing. My brain has been constantly taxed, and I have had but little exercise. Yet my health has never been better than for the past six months. My former faint and dizzy feelings have left me. I have been troubled every spring with loss of appetite. The last spring I had no trouble in this respect.

Our plain food, eaten twice a day, is enjoyed with a keen relish. We have no meat, cake, or any rich food upon our table. We use no lard, but in its place, milk, cream, and some butter. We have our food prepared with but little salt, and have dispensed with spices of all kinds. We breakfast at seven, and take our dinner at one. It is seldom I have a faint feeling. My appetite is satisfied. My food is eaten with a greater relish than ever before.

[Some salt essential to blood—571, 572]

The Battle for Victory

(1870) 2T 371, 372

5. I have not changed my course a particle since I adopted the health reform. I have not taken one step back since the light from heaven upon this subject first shone upon my pathway. I broke away from everything at once, —from meat and butter, and from three meals,—and that while engaged in exhaustive brain labor, writing from early morning till sundown. I came down to two meals a day without changing my labor.

I have been a great sufferer from disease, having had five shocks of paralysis. I have been with my left arm bound to my side for months, because the pain in my heart was so great. When making these changes in my diet, I refused to yield to taste, and let that govern me. Shall that stand in the way of my securing greater strength, that I may therewith glorify my Lord? Shall that stand in my way for a moment? Never!

I suffered keen hunger, I was a great meat eater. But when faint, I placed my arms across my stomach, and said, "I will not taste a morsel. I will eat simple food, or I will not eat at all." Bread was distasteful to me. I could seldom eat a piece as large as a dollar. Some things in the reform I could get along with very well; but when I came to the bread, I was especially set against it. When I made these changes, I had a special battle to fight. The first two or three meals, I could not eat. I said to my stomach, "You may wait until you can eat bread." In a little while I could eat bread, and graham bread, too. This I could not eat before; but now it tastes good, and I have had no loss of appetite.

ACTED ON PRINCIPLE

When writing "Spiritual Gifts," Volumes III and IV [1863-64], I would become exhausted by excessive labor. I then saw that I must change my course of life, and by resting a few days I came out all right again. I left off these things from principle. I took my stand on health reform from principle. And since that time, brethren, you have not heard me advance an extreme view of health reform that I have had to take back. I have advanced nothing but what I stand to today. I recommend to you a healthful, nourishing diet.

I do not regard it a great privation to discontinue the use of those things which leave a bad smell in the breath and a bad taste in the mouth. Is it self-denial to leave these things, and get into a condition where everything is as sweet as honey; where no bad taste is left in the mouth; and no feeling of goneness in the stomach? These I used to have much of the time. I have fainted away with my child in my arms again and again. I have none of this now; and shall I call this a privation, when I can stand before you as I do this day? There is not one woman in a hundred that could endure the amount of labor that I do. I moved out from principle, not from impulse. I moved because I believed Heaven would approve of the course I was taking to bring myself into the very best condition of health, that I might glorify God in my body and spirit, which are His.

A Battle Against the Vinegar Habit

Letter 70, 1911

6. I have just read your letter. You seem to have an earnest desire to work out your salvation with fear and trembling. I encourage you to do this. I counsel you to discard everything that would cause you to do halfway work in

seeking the kingdom of God and His righteousness. Put away every indulgence that would hinder you in the work of overcoming. Ask for the prayers of those who can comprehend your need of help.

There was a time when I was in a situation similar in some respects to yours. I had indulged the desire for vinegar. But I resolved with the help of God to overcome this appetite. I fought the temptation, determined not to be mastered by this habit.

For weeks I was very sick; but I kept saying over and over, The Lord knows all about it. If I die, I die; but I will not yield to this desire. The struggle continued, and I was sorely afflicted for many weeks. All thought that it was impossible for me to live. You may be sure we sought the Lord very earnestly. The most fervent prayers were offered for my recovery. I continued to resist the desire for vinegar, and at last I conquered. Now I have no inclination to taste anything of the kind. This experience has been of great value to me in many ways. I obtained a complete victory.

I relate this experience to you for your help and encouragement. I have faith, my sister, that you can come through this trial, and reveal that God is the helper of His children in every time of need. If you determine to conquer this habit, and will fight it perseveringly, you can obtain an experience of the highest value. When you set your will resolutely to break off this indulgence, you will have the help you need from God. Try it, my sister.

As long as you acknowledge this habit by indulging it, Satan will retain his hold on your will, and bring it into obedience to himself. But if you will determine to overcome, the Lord will heal you, and will give you strength to resist every temptation. Ever remember that Christ is your Saviour and Keeper.

A Spare, but Adequate Diet

(1870) 2T 373, 374

7. I eat enough to satisfy the wants of nature; but when I get up from the table, my appetite is just as good as when I sat down. And when the next meal comes, I am ready to

take my portion, and no more. Should I eat a double amount now and then because it tastes good, how could I bow down and ask God to help me in my work of writing, when I could not get an idea on account of my gluttony? Could I ask God to take care of that unreasonable load upon my stomach? That would be dishonoring Him. That would be asking to consume upon my lust. Now I eat just what I think is right, and then I can ask Him to give me strength to perform the work that He has given me to do. And I have known that Heaven has heard and answered my prayer, when I have offered this petition.

A Well-supplied Table

(1870) 2T 487

8. I have a well-set table on all occasions. I make no change for visitors, whether believers or unbelievers. I intend never to be surprised by an unreadiness to entertain at my table from one to half a dozen extra who may chance to come in. I have enough simple, healthful food ready to satisfy hunger and nourish the system. If any want more than this, they are at liberty to find it elsewhere. No butter or flesh meats of any kind come on my table. Cake is seldom found there. I generally have an ample supply of fruits, good bread, and vegetables. Our table is always well patronized, and all who partake of the food do well, and improve upon it. All sit down with no epicurean appetite, and eat with a relish the bounties supplied by our Creator.

[Food sweetened as required; no sugar on table—532]

On the Cars

Health Reformer, December, 1870

9. While parents and children were eating of their dainties, my husband and myself partook of our simple repast, at our usual hour, at 1 P.M., of graham bread without butter, and a generous supply of fruit. We ate our meal with a keen relish, and with thankful hearts that we were not obliged to carry a popular grocery with us to provide for a capricious appetite. We ate heartily, and felt no sense of

hunger until the next morning. The boy with his oranges, nuts, popcorn, and candies, found us poor customers.

[In 1873, a little milk and some sugar—532]

Encountering Difficulties and Resultant Compromises

Letter 83, 1901

10. Over thirty years ago I was often in great weakness. Many prayers were offered in my behalf. It was thought that flesh meat would give me vitality, and this was, therefore, my principal article of diet. But instead of gaining strength, I grew weaker and weaker. I often fainted from exhaustion. Light came to me, showing me the injury men and women were doing to the mental, moral, and physical faculties by the use of flesh meat. I was shown that the whole human structure is affected by this diet, that by it man strengthens the animal propensities and the appetite for liquor.

I at once cut meat out of my bill of fare. After that I was at times placed where I was compelled to eat a little meat.

[At times compelled to eat a little meat when other food was not available—699]

[NOTE.—From the time of her girlhood, Mrs. White was burdened with writing and public ministry, and was therefore obliged to place the responsibilities of the domestic work in her home largely upon housekeepers and cooks. She was not always able to secure the services of those trained in hygienic cookery. So there were times in her own home when various compromises had to be made between the ideal standards, and the knowledge, experience, and standards of a new cook. Then, too, much of the time while traveling, she was dependent for her food upon those whom she was visiting. Although able to subsist upon a spare diet, it sometimes seemed necessary to eat some meat, which she knew was not the best food and which was not of her own choosing.—COMPILERS.]

Lament for Want of a Cook—1892

Letter 19c, 1892

11. I am suffering more now for want of some one who is experienced in the cooking line,—to prepare things I can eat. ... Food is prepared in such a way that it is not appetizing, but is having the tendency to dry up the desire for food. I would pay a higher price for a cook than for any other part of my work.

Final Pledge for Teetotal Nonflesh Diet

Letter 76, 1895

12. Since the camp meeting at Brighton (January, 1894) I have absolutely banished meat from my table. It is an understanding that whether I am at home or abroad, nothing of this kind is to be used in my family, or come upon my table. I have had much representation before my mind in the night season on this subject.

MS 25, 1894

13. We have plenty of good milk, fruit, and bread. I have already consecrated my table. I have freed it from all flesh meats. It is better for physical and mental soundness to refrain from living upon the flesh of animals. As far as possible we are to come back to God's original plan. From henceforth my table shall be free from the flesh of dead animals, and devoid of those things in desserts which take much time and strength to prepare. We may use fruit freely, and in different ways, and run no risk of incurring the diseases that are incurred by using the flesh of diseased animals. We should bring our appetite under control, so that we shall enjoy plain, wholesome food, and have an abundance of it, that none may suffer hunger.

One Year After the Advance Step

Letter 76, 1895

14. We have a large family, and besides have many guests, but neither meat nor butter is placed upon our table. We use the cream from the milk of the cows which we feed ourselves. We purchase butter for cooking purposes from dairies where the cows are in healthy condition, and have good pasture.

Two Years After the Advance Step

Letter 73a, 1896

15. I have a large family which often numbers sixteen. In it there are men who work at the plow and who fell trees. These have most vigorous exercise, but not a particle of the flesh of animals is placed on our table. Meat has not been

used by us since the Brighton camp meeting. It was not my purpose to have it on my table at any time, but urgent pleas were made that such a one was unable to eat this or that, and that his stomach could take care of meat better than it could anything else. Thus I was enticed to place it on my table. . . .

All who come to my table are welcome, but I place before them no meat. Grains, vegetables, and fresh and canned fruit constitute our table fare. At present we have plenty of the best oranges, and plenty of lemons. This is the only fresh fruit we can get at this season of the year. . . .

I have written this to give you some idea of how we live. I never enjoyed better health than I do at the present time, and never did more writing. I rise at three in the morning, and do not sleep during the day. I am often up at one o'clock, and when my mind is especially burdened, I rise at twelve o'clock to write out matter that has been urged upon my mind. I praise the Lord with heart and soul and voice for His great mercy toward me.

Moderate Use of Nut Foods

Letter 73, 1899

16. We eat no meat or butter, and use very little milk in cooking. There is no fresh fruit at this season. We have a good yield of tomatoes, but our family think much of the nuts prepared in a variety of ways. We use one fifth as much as the recipe specifies.

[Tomatoes especially good—523]

An Adequate Diet—but No Meat

MS 82, 1901

17. When I was at Cooranbong, many that were great meat eaters came into my family, and when they would sit at my table, where not a particle of meat was served, they would say, "Well, if you have food like this, I could do without meat." I think that our food satisfies our family. I tell our family, "Whatever you do, do not get a poverty-stricken diet. Place enough on the table to nourish the system. You must do this. You must invent and invent and study all the

time, and get up the very best dishes you can, so as not to have a poverty-stricken diet."

Tea and Coffee

Letter 12, 1888

18. I have not bought a penny's worth of tea for years. Knowing its influence, I would not dare to use it, except in cases of severe vomiting when I take it as a medicine, but not as a beverage. . . .

I am not guilty of drinking any tea except red-clover-top tea, and if I liked wine, tea, and coffee, I would not use these health-destroying narcotics, for I prize health and I prize a healthful example in all these things. I want to be a pattern of temperance and of good works to others.

[Statement regarding diet in 1902—522]

Simple Food

Letter 150, 1903

19. My health is good. My appetite is excellent. I find that the simpler my food, and the fewer varieties I eat, the stronger I am.

Following the Light in 1903

Letter 45, 1903

20. In our family we have breakfast at half past six o'clock, and dinner at half past one. We have no supper. We would change our times of eating a little, were it not for the fact that these are the most convenient hours for some of the members of the family.

I eat but two meals a day, and still follow the light given me thirty-five years ago. I use no meat. As for myself, I have settled the butter question. I do not use it. This question should easily be settled in every place where the purest article cannot be obtained. We have two good milch cows, a Jersey and a Holstein. We use cream, and all are satisfied with this.

Letter 62, 1903

21. I am seventy-five years old; but I do as much writing as I ever did. My digestion is good, and my brain is clear.

Our fare is simple and wholesome. We have on our table no butter, no meat, no cheese, no greasy mixtures of food. For some months a young man who was an unbeliever, and who had eaten meat all his life, boarded with us. We made no change in our diet on his account; and while he stayed with us he gained about twenty pounds. The food which we provided for him was far better for him than that to which he had been accustomed. All who sit at my table express themselves as being well satisfied with the food provided.

The Family Not Bound With Rigid Rules

Letter 127, 1904

22. I eat the most simple food, prepared in the most simple way. For months my principal diet has been vermicelli and canned tomatoes, cooked together. This I eat with zwieback. Then I have also stewed fruit of some kind and sometimes lemon pie. Dried corn, cooked with milk or a little cream, is another dish that I sometimes use.

But the other members of my family do not eat the same things that I do. I do not hold myself up as a criterion for them. I leave each one to follow his own ideas as to what is best for him. I bind no one else's conscience by my own. One person cannot be a criterion for another in the matter of eating. It is impossible to make one rule for all to follow. There are those in my family who are very fond of beans, while to me beans are poison. Butter is never placed on my table, but if the members of my family choose to use a little butter away from the table, they are at liberty to do so. Our table is set twice a day, but if there are those who desire something to eat in the evening, there is no rule that forbids them from getting it. No one complains or goes from our table dissatisfied. A variety of food that is simple, wholesome, and palatable, is always provided.

A Statement for Those Who Question Mrs. White's Manner of Eating

Letter 50, 1908

23. It is reported by some that I have not lived up to the principles of health reform, as I have advocated them with

my pen. But I can say that so far as my knowledge goes, I have not departed from those principles. Those who have eaten at my table know that I have not placed flesh meats before them. . . .

It is many years since I have had meat on my table at home. We never use tea or coffee. Occasionally I have used red-clover-blossom tea for a warm drink, but few of my family drink any fluid at our meals. The table is provided with cream instead of butter, even though we have company present. I have not used butter for many years.

Yet we do not have an impoverished diet. We have an abundance of dried and canned fruit. If our own fruit crop is short, we buy some in the market. Sister Gray sends me the seedless grapes, and these stewed make a very appetizing dish. We raise our own loganberries, and use them freely. Strawberries do not grow well in this locality, but from our neighbors we purchase blackberries, raspberries, apples, and pears. We have also an abundance of tomatoes. We also raise a fine variety of sweet corn, and dry a large amount for use during the winter months. Near by us is a food factory, where we can supply ourselves with the grain preparations.

[Use of dried corn and peas—524]

We endeavor to use good judgment in determining what combinations of food best agree with us. It is our duty to act wisely in regard to our habits of eating, to be temperate, and to learn to reason from cause to effect. If we will do our part, then the Lord will do His part in preserving our brain-nerve power.

For more than forty years I have eaten but two meals a day. And if I have a specially important work to do, I limit the quantity of food that I take. I regard it as my duty to refuse to place in my stomach any food that I have reason to believe will create disorder. My mind must be sanctified to God, and I must guard carefully against any habit that would tend to lessen my powers of intellect.

I am now in my eighty-first year, and I can bear testimony that we do not, as a family, hunger for the fleshpots of

Egypt. I have known something of the benefits to be received by living up to the principles of health reform. I consider it a privilege as well as a duty to be a health reformer.

Yet I am sorry that there are many of our people who do not strictly follow the light on health reform. Those who in their habit transgress the principles of health, and do not heed the light that the Lord has given them, will surely suffer the consequences.

I write you these details, that you may know how to answer any who may question my manner of eating. . . .

I consider that one reason why I have been able to do so much work both in speaking and in writing, is because I am strictly temperate in my eating. If several varieties of food are placed before me, I endeavor to choose only those that I know will agree. Thus I am enabled to preserve clear mental faculties. I refuse to place in my stomach knowingly anything that will set up fermentation. This is the duty of all health reformers. We must reason from cause to effect. It is our duty to be temperate in all things.

General Principles of Reform

MS 29, 1897

24. I have had great light from the Lord upon the subject of health reform. I did not seek this light; I did not study to obtain it; it was given to me by the Lord to give to others. I present these matters before the people, dwelling upon general principles, and sometimes, if questions are asked me at the table to which I have been invited, I answer according to the truth. But I have never made a raid upon any one in regard to the table or its contents. I would not consider such a course at all courteous or proper.

Tolerance of Others

Letter 45, 1903

25. I make myself a criterion for no one else. There are things that I cannot eat without suffering great distress. I

try to learn that which is best for me, and then saying nothing to any one, I partake of the things that I can eat, which often are simply two or three varieties that will not create a disturbance in the stomach.

Letter 19a, 1891

26. There is a wide difference in constitutions and temperaments, and the demands of the system differ greatly in different persons. What would be food for one, might be poison for another; so precise rules cannot be laid down to fit every case. I cannot eat beans, for they are poison to me; but for me to say that for this reason no one must eat them would be simply ridiculous. I cannot eat a spoonful of milk gravy, or milk toast, without suffering in consequence; but other members of my family can eat these things, and realize no such effect; therefore I take that which suits my stomach best, and they do the same. We have no words, no contention; all moves along harmoniously in my large family, for I do not attempt to dictate what they shall or shall not eat.

"I Have Been a Faithful Health Reformer"

(1909) 9T 158, 159

27. When the message of health reform first came to me, I was weak and feeble, subject to frequent fainting spells. I was pleading with God for help, and He opened before me the great subject of health reform. He instructed me that those who are keeping His commandments must be brought into sacred relation to Himself, and that by temperance in eating and drinking they must keep mind and body in the most favorable condition for service. This light has been a great blessing to me. I took my stand as a health reformer, knowing that the Lord would strengthen me. I have better health today, notwithstanding my age, than I had in my younger days.

It is reported by some that I have not followed the principles of health reform as I have advocated them with my pen; but I can say that I have been a faithful health reformer. Those who have been members of my family know that this is true.

APPENDIX II

A STATEMENT BY JAMES WHITE RELATING TO THE TEACHING OF HEALTH REFORM

[In reporting the Kansas camp meeting of 1870, Elder James White made the following statement regarding the progressive light that had been received on health reform, the dangers of injudicious methods of teaching the subjects, and Mrs. White's relation to certain extreme positions that were then being advocated by some. As a historical statement it illuminates some of her teaching recorded at that time.—COMPILERS.]

R. & H., Nov. 8, 1870

MRS. WHITE has spoken on the health question in a manner to give entire satisfaction. Her remarks were clear and forcible, yet prudent, so that she carried the feelings of the entire congregation with her. On this subject she always avoids extremes, and is careful to take only those positions where she is quite sure not to excite prejudices.

The people are easily excited and prejudiced upon the subject of health reform, if those who handle it are unfortunate in the selection of the occasion, or in the style in which they present it, especially if they stand before the people in the light of extremists. Some delicate questions, such as "solitary vice," should seldom, if ever, be discussed, only in suitable publications upon the subject. There is not one in ten of our preachers who are suitably informed, and properly guarded, to handle the health question in its several branches before the people. And the amount of harm done to the cause of present truth by the injudicious course of those who have introduced the subject of health reform at the wrong time and place, and in a wrong manner, can hardly be estimated.

"I have yet many things to say unto you," said Jesus, "but ye cannot bear them now." Jesus knew how to lead along the minds of His disciples. The Lord also knew how to introduce to His waiting people the great subject of health reform, step by step, as they could bear it, and make a good use of it, without souring the public mind. It was twenty-two years ago the present autumn, that our minds were called to the injurious effects of tobacco, tea, and coffee, through the testimony of Mrs. White. God has wonderfully blessed the effort to put these things away from us, so that we as a denomination can rejoice in victory, with very few exceptions, over these pernicious indulgences of appetite. . . .

When we had gained a good victory over these things, and when the Lord saw that we were able to bear it, light was given relative to food and dress. And the cause of health reform among our people moved steadily forward, and great changes were made, especially in regard to the use of swine's flesh, up to a certain point, when, in consequence of our sickness, Mrs. White ceased to speak and write upon the subject of health reform. From that point may be dated the commencement of our misfortunes and mistakes as a people relative to this subject.

And since we have become active again, Mrs. White oftener feels called upon to speak upon the subject of health reform because of existing extremes of health reformers, than from any other reason. The fact that all, or nearly all, of the existing extremes upon health reform among our people are supposed to receive her unqualified sanction, is the reason why she feels called upon to speak her real sentiments. The people must, and will in due time, know her position upon this subject.

In reference to the use of tobacco, tea, coffee, flesh meats, also to dress, there is a general agreement. But at present she is not prepared to take the extreme position relative to salt, sugar, and milk. If there were no other reasons for moving carefully in reference to these things of so common and abundant use, there is a sufficient one in the fact that the minds of many are not prepared, even to receive the facts relative to these things. The complete overthrow of individuals, and the almost destruction of some of our churches, can be clearly traced to some extreme positions upon diet, injudiciously given in the *Review* some time since. The results have been bad. While some have rejected the subject of health reform, because badly handled, others, prompt and conscientious, have carried out the most extreme positions, greatly detrimental to their health, and consequently to the cause of health reform.

In this state of things, however discouraging, Mrs. White feels called upon to resume her work in this field of labor, and in so doing, will let her views be fully understood. It may be well here to state, however, that while she does not regard milk, taken in large quantities, as customarily eaten with bread, the best article of food, her mind, as yet, has only been called to the importance of the best and most healthy condition possible of the cow, whose milk is used as an article of food. She cannot unite in circulating publications broadcast which take an extreme position on the important question of milk, with her present light upon the subject. Such works may be well enough with well-informed health reformers, and may be a proper guide in the cooking department of our Health Institute at Battle Creek, after its tables shall be cleared of the habitual use of milk. And such works may have a greater influence among our people when our ministers, who are ardent health reformers, shall leave the free use of cow's milk.

Here is our weakness upon this subject. Our publications, which go out to the untaught and those very susceptible to prejudices, are in advance, upon some of these points, of the practices of those among us who represent the health reform. Mrs. White pleads to have this matter so reversed that our publications shall speak out only those sentiments upon which those standing at the head of the reform are agreed, and then in a style not to prejudice, and put good men and good women beyond our influence. Let the united practices of health reformers take the advance, and then let our publications follow, and speak out well-matured sentiments as the untaught can bear them.

Mrs. White thinks that a change from the simplest kinds of flesh meats, to an abundant use of sugar, is going from "bad to worse." She would recommend a very sparing use of both sugar and salt. The appetite can, and should, be brought to a very moderate use of both. In the case of salt, food with so reduced an amount that it would taste insipid to the one accustomed to the use of much salt, after a few weeks of very temperate use, will be painfully salty to the taste.

While tobacco, tea, and coffee may be left at once, one at a time, however, by those who are so unfortunate as to be slaves to all, changes in diet should be made carefully, one at a time. And while she would say this to those who are in danger of making changes too rapidly, she would also say to the tardy, Be sure and not forget to change. The plainest facts possible demand a change from the common habits of life, but let them not be made so fast as to injure the health and constitution.

Index

God's people will discontinue
82, 380, 381

imparts nature of animals 390

increases liability to disease 386

in emergency conditions 394, 395, 407, 410

injures physical health 403, 413

irritates and excites nerves 396, 397

is unnatural 380

largely prevented Israel from reaching God's standard 374, 375

made antediluvians cruel and depraved 147, 373

many die of diseases wholly due to 385, 392

moral evils of, not less than physical 383

never best, now doubly objectionable 384

not to be made a test of fellowship 383, 401, 404

permitted in Canaan, under restrictions 374

positive testimony against 468

produces cancer, tumors, pulmonary diseases 384, 388, 389, 404

robs men of love and sympathy 383

strengthens animal propensities 382-384, 389, 390, 397, 399
See also Animalism

weakens, intellect 382, 384
spiritual nature 382, 383
See also Meat

Flour, wheat, unbolted 124, 320
See also Bread

Food, cold 86, 106
combinations of 109-113
for patients 282
harmful, fruit and vegetables 112, 395
meat, vegetables, fruit, wines, tea, coffee, sweet cakes 411

rich and complicated foods 113

salads with oil and vinegar 345

sugar and milk 113, 196, 328, 330, 331

sweet cake with milk or cream 335

dry, preferable to liquid 108

spiced, See Spices

study effects of various 93

temporal, think less of, and more of spiritual 90

to correspond with climate, season of year, and occupation 94, 364

to be, appetizing 92, 201, 203, 207, 282, 289, 354, 355
nourishing, well cooked 91
warm but not hot 86, 106

varieties of 109-113
not to be carried to excess 275
to be shunned when visiting 168, 169

Foods, rich 331, 332

Food Sales should not tempt to self-indulgence 329

Fruit 87, 96, 201, 240, 296, 309-312, 333, 352, 408, 420, 436, 437
canned or dried 85, 309, 311, 312, 335
cultivation of, by sanitarium 312
diet of 189, 305, 310
juices of 437

Fruits and Grains 64, 355, 402

Fruits and Vegetables 200, 312, 315, 321, 394, 409
danger in eating decayed 309
See also Food, combinations of

Fruits, Grains, Nuts, and Vegetables 81, 92, 310, 313, 315, 363, 396, 397

Fruits, Nuts, and Grains 93, 95, 269, 271

Fruits, Vegetables, and Grains 81, 92, 124, 267, 296, 322, 381, 407

G

H